Limnology in Developing Countries

Volume 1

Limnology in Developing Countries

Vol. 1

Edited by

B. GOPAL

School of Environmental Sciences
Jawaharlal Nehru University, New Delhi 110067

and

R.G. WETZEL

Department of Biological Sciences
University of Alabama, Tuscaloosa, AL 35487-0206

1995

SIL
International Association for Limnology

First published 1995

Disclaimer

The international boundaries of different countries shown in the maps in this book serve merely the purpose of indicating the geographical area covered by the author(s). These are neither accurate nor have any political significance whatsoever. The International Association for Limnology neither approves them nor is responsible for any error.

ISBN: 81-86047-14-X

Published for the

INTERNATIONAL ASSOCIATION OF THEORETICAL AND APPLIED LIMNOLOGY (SIL)

by

INTERNATIONAL SCIENTIFIC PUBLICATIONS
(Publication wing of the Science and Environmental Education Society)
50-B, Pocket C, Siddhartha Extension
New Delhi 110014, India

This book is printed on neutral paper made in India.

Printed in India

New United Process, A-26 Naraina Industrial Area Phase II, New Delhi 110028

CONTENTS

CONTENTS

PREFACE

Fresh water is one of the most important natural resources crucial for the survival of all living beings. It is even more important for humans as they depend on it also for food production, industrial growth, hydropower generation and waste disposal as well as for cultural requirements. Limnology, the science which deals with the freshwater environments - their physico-chemical characteristics, their biota and the ecosystem processes therein - is therefore universal in its significance.

Although people in all parts of the world have been aware of the quality and biotic resources of their lakes and rivers, limnology emerged as a science in Europe. It matured and flourished in Europe and North America where institutes of limnology were established in many countries. Early in this century, scientists from these countries led expeditions to different tropical countries of Asia, Africa and South America. Despite a continued interest in the tropics, the development of limnology as a science in the developing countries, majority of which lie in the tropical belt, has in general lagged far behind. Whereas major research effort in some countries has been contributed by scientists from the developed countries, and in others, such as Brazil, considerable advancement has been achieved by individuals within the region, in most of the third world countries, the subject has not received adequate attention. Among many other factors, the lack of trained manpower and necessary infrastructure have been chiefly responsible for the uneven growth of limnology in the tropics. An international course on Limnology, conducted since 1970 by the Limnology Institute of the Austrian Academy of Sciences in Vienna (Austria), with the cooperation of UNESCO, has contributed significantly by training more than 250 scientists from many tropical/developing countries. However, few of them have been able to continue active research in the field and a large number of these trained people have shifted to other disciplines for lack of facilities and opportunities.

The International Association for Theoretical and Applied Limnology (SIL), as the oldest professional association founded in 1922, has over the past three decades made much effort to promote the growth of limnology in the tropical regions. The issue of promoting limnology in developing countries was discussed first at a workshop during the 1980 SIL Congress in Japan where participants from 12 countries presented overviews of the subject in their respective areas (Mori and Ikusima 1980). Later, a working group on Tropical Limnology was established in order to improve communication with the researchers in developing countries. At the 23rd Congress in Hamilton (New Zealand) in 1987, "recognising the urgent need for promoting Limnology in developing countries, particularly in the tropics", the SIL resolved "to foster exchanges between developed and developing countries for training and research; to collaborate with other national and international organizations in the tropics; and to change the status of the working group on Tropical limnology to that of a Committee on Limnology in Developing Countries, working directly under the responsibility of the Executive Board of SIL". At the same time, SIL set up a Tonolli Memorial Fund to provide financial support for training in limnology to the researchers from developing countries.

The Committee which was duly constituted at the 24th Congress in Munich (Germany) in 1989, quickly identified the need for a Directory of limnologists and institutions in the developing countries and for an assessment of the state of limnology in different countries, as two major areas requiring immediate attention. A number of scientists in most of the developing countries were contacted for preparing the state-of-the-art reviews of the studies conducted in their respective countries. The Committee provided the authors with a general framework for the reviews and asked them to specifically include information on the status of conservation, management policies, training and research facilities, and scientific organisations, and to identify important gaps in knowledge and specific needs and priorities. The international conference on Conservation and Management of Tropical Inland Waters, held with the support from SIL and UNESCO, among others, provided an early opportunity to discuss some of these reviews (see Dudgeon and Lam 1994). Since then good progress, albeit slow, has been made in this direction.

This volume, the first in a series to be published by SIL, includes reviews of limnology in seven countries namely, Ghana, Tunisia, Sri Lanka, Bangladesh, Papua New Guinea, Malaysia and Pakistan. We encouraged the authors to collaborate with colleagues in different fields of both pure and applied limnology in their country in order to cover all aspects. Although all but one of the reviews were finally prepared by a single author, we believe that these reviews adequately reflect the current state of limnology in these countries and that the references included there would help in obtaining more detailed information about other studies. As expected beforehand, great variability has emerged in the treatment of the status of limnology in each of the countries evaluated in this volume. This variability is of course partly related to the marked differences in inland water resources and limnological programs among the countries. In some countries like Pakistan, information about the water resources alone is not readily available and very little effort, if any, has been made to study water quality and the biota. Writing styles differ markedly as well among authors and editors accepted some individuality from authors. In the end we found information particularly useful and informative, and welcomed the collation of widely disparate and often obscure literature. Further reviews of the state of limnology in several other countries are in different stages of preparation and several additional volumes are planned to be published in the next few years. We hope that these reviews would stimulate further research in the respective countries and promote cooperation among scientists and institutions from both developed and developing countries.

The publication of this volume has been possible due to the active interest and cooperation of the members of the SIL Committee, and the efforts put in by the authors. We are grateful to all of them. We also wish to acknowledge the help of several reviewers who offered comments on the earlier drafts of these manuscripts. On behalf of the SIL Committee and on our own we also thank the SIL for providing funds for the publication of this volume.

Mori, S. and Ikusima, I. (Editors) 1980. Proceedings of the First Workshop on the Promotion of Limnology in the Developing Countries. Organising Committee of XXI SIL Congress, Kyoto, Japan. 172 pages.

Dudgeon, D. and Lam, P.K.S. (Editors) 1994. Inland Waters of Tropical Asia and Australia: Conservation and Management. Mitteilungen der Internationale Vereinigung für theoretische und angewandte Limnologie 24. E. Schweizerbart'sche Verlagsbuchhandlung, Stuttgart. 386 pages.

B. GOPAL AND R.G. WETZEL

Gopal, B. and Wetzel, R.G. (Editors) **Limnology in Developing Countries**: 1-39

Limnological Research and Training in Ghana:
The Past, Present and Perspectives for Future Development

Emmanuel Frempong
Department of Biological Sciences, University of Science and Technology, Kumasi, Ghana

ABSTRACT

The present work is concerned primarily with the development of limnological research in Ghana. There are considerable gaps in our knowledge of aquatic systems in the country and attempts have been made to draw attention to the many deficiencies that exist.

This paper is also intended to provide an overview of the physico-chemical and biological features of the inland water resources. It is expected that the work will help research institutions and limnologists to identify and intensify research in such areas which require urgent attention in order to improve on our present knowledge of the aquatic ecosytems. Appropriate references to guide the reader to more detailed information on the various subjects have been provided.

There is definitely insufficient information on the aquatic ecosystems to provide an acceptable basis for effective planning and utilization of all the potential water resources.

INTRODUCTION

Interest in the aquatic resources of the country began almost 90 years ago when Gunther (1902) started documentation of the fishes based on collections of specimen made by R.B.N. Walker from 1898-1900. The contribution of other collectors and the publication on the fish and fisheries of the Gold Coast by Irvine (1947) provide an indication of the area of concentration of the pioneer workers. Early work on the mineral composition of some inland waters was published by Dunn (1947).

The beginnings of intensive limnological research, to a great extent, date back to May 1964, with the creation of the Volta Lake which is backed up behind the Akosombo dam. A summary of the scientific research activities during the period 1963 to 1980 has been given by Frempong (1980).

The recognition by the University of Ghana, Legon in 1963 of the urgent need for background studies just before the closure of the Akosombo dam and the beginning of lake formation led to the establishment of the Volta Basin Research Project (Lawson 1963). The objective was to carry out limnological as well as sociological and archaeological observations. A detailed review of the hydrobiological changes in the lake was made by Ewer (1966) and Lawson et al. (1969). Other work has been published by Viner (1970a,b) and Biswas (1970a,b, 1972a,b).

The scope of aquatic research on the Volta Lake as well as on other inland water bodies was extended in 1965, by the setting up of the Institute of Aquatic Biology at Accra by the Government of Ghana. Comprehensive records of the invertebrate and fish fauna of the rivers in the Volta basin are available at the Institute. In ad1xtion research on aquatic weeds, phytoplankton, parasites and vectors of human and veterinary diseases and aquaculture are in progress (IAB 1990).

The establishment in January 1968, of the Volta Lake Research and Development Project, a joint UNDP/Ghana Government project, led to further limnological research by the Institute of Aquatic Biology, University of Ghana, and the Fisheries Department of the Ministry of Agriculture (Obeng 1969). Other research activities centred on fish processing and marketing, resettlement and public health. Hydrobiological work up to 1968 may be found in a bibliography by Brooks (1969) and in Ackerman et al. (1973). Accounts of various investigations carried out from 1969 to 1979 are given by Entz (1969a), Hall et al. (1969), Pierce (1971), Owusu (1972), Obeng (1973), Odei (1973), Okali and Hall (1974a, b), Biswas (1978) and Allen and Gaudet (1978). Much of the early limnological work was thus focussed on the Volta Lake.

During the period of intensive research on the Volta Lake very limited work was carried out on some of the smaller reservoirs and other aquatic habitats e.g., Barekese reservoir (Frempong and Nijjhar 1973), Nungua reservoir (Thomas and Ratcliffe 1973), Weija and Owabi reservoirs and river systems (IAB 1977) and Bosumtwi Lake (Whyte 1975, Talbot and Delibrias 1977).

There are many other aquatic habitats in the country including fish ponds, ornamental ponds, irrigation ditches, floodplain pools, rice paddy fields and over the rainy season several temporary pools, ponds and lakelets. The physico-chemical conditions and hydrobiological features of such habitats have received little or no attention by limnologists. The only available information may be found widely scattered in unpublished student project reports or theses.

Over the last decade, 1980-1990, little consideration has been given to limnological work in the country. The lack of concentration on research activities was related mainly to the harsh economic climate during the early parts of the decade. Research projects received little or no funding, the rehabilitation of research equipment and facilities was discontinued leading to further reduction in research output and finally the closure and dismantling in 1986 of one of the research establishments, the Volta Lake Research and Development Project.

It is hoped that with the gradual improvement in the national economy more attention would be given to limnological research which is vital to the effective harnessing of the potentialities of our inland water resources and thus to the economic development of the nation.

Location

Ghana lies almost in the centre of the countries along the Gulf of Guinea. Its southern coast extends between 4.5° North Latitude at Cape Three Points and 6.5° North in the extreme east. From the coast, the country extends inland to 11.5° North Latitude covering a distance of some 672 km from south to north. The distance across the widest part from east to west measures about 536 km between Longitude 1.5° East and Longitude 3.5° West. The country has a surface area of 238,539 km².

Geology and Physiography

Ghana falls within the Precambrian Guinea Shield of West Africa. The main Precambrian rock units existing in Ghana are the metamorphosed and folded Precambrian Birimian, Tarkwaian and Dahomeyan systems, Togo series and the Buem Formation (Figure 1).

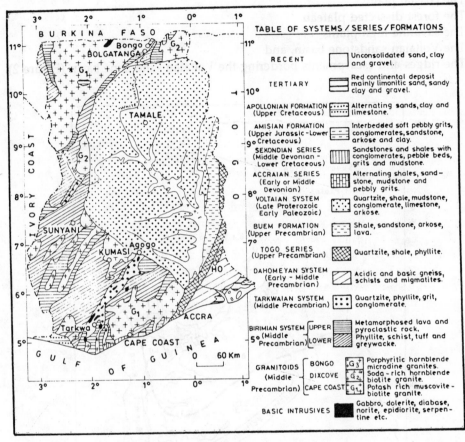

Figure 1. Geological formations in Ghana

The Precambrian rocks are overlain by Late Proterozoic to Paleozoic rocks of the Voltaian system. This system consists of sandstones, shales, mudstones, conglomerates, limestones and tillites.

Rock units which are younger than the Voltaian system and occur at several places along the coast include the Early or Middle Devonian Accraian Series; Middle Devonian - Lower Cretaceous Sekondian Series; Upper Jurassic to Lower Cretaceous Amisian Formation; Upper Cretaceous Apollonian Formation; Tertiary to Recent unconsolidated, marine, coastal, lagoonal, fluviatile sediments and deposits.

The geological units of Ghana can be divided into five main groups:
1. Tertiary to Recent deposits,
2. The Coastal Basins which range in age from the Ordovician to Recent,
3. The Voltaian Basin bordered in the east by the Buem Formation and the Togo Series,

4. The Dahomeyan System which outcrops in the southeast, and
5. The Birimian System which covers a large area of the country and which infolds the Tarkwaian System.

The following five physiographic regions may be distinguished:
1. The coastal plain
2. The forest dissected plateau
3. The savanna high plains
4. The Voltaian sandstone basin, and
5. The ridges and escarpments bordering the Voltaian sandstone basin (Figure 2).

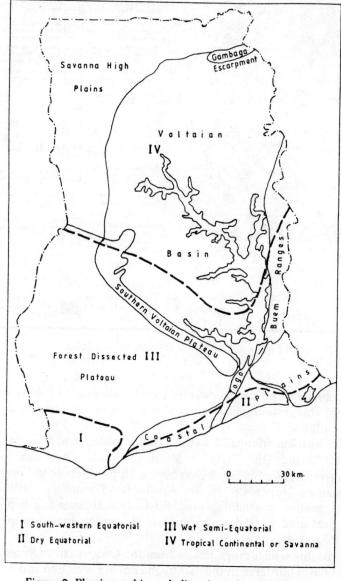

Figure 2. Physiographic and climatic regions of Ghana

Dickson and Benneh (1970) give further information on the geology and physiography of Ghana and a good summary is provided by Kesse (1985).

Climate

There are four main climatic regions in the country: South-western equatorial, dry equatorial, wet semi-equatorial and tropical continental or interior savanna (Figure 2).

In the south there are two rainy seasons (March-June and September-November) with a relatively dry interseason. In the north, there is a single rainy season (May-October) with hot dry season from November to March. The annual rainfall decreases northwards from over 2030 mm to 1010 mm (Figure 3). The interaction of moist south-west monsoon, dry north eastern trade winds and high equatorial easterlies are responsible for these climatic variations.

The general features of the climate of Ghana are given by Dickson and Benneh (1970), and the main aspects are summarized by Welcomme (1979).

AQUATIC HABITATS

There are a variety of aquatic habitats in the country. These include a natural lake, man-made reservoirs, rivers and streams as well as other waterbodies.

(i) Natural Lakes

The only natural lake in Ghana is Lake Bosumtwi, which lies in a deep circular crater surrounded by very steep hills. The main source of lake water is rainwater flowing inwards from the crater rim down the steep slopes. This is supplemented by water from streams (see Figure 4).

(ii) Man-made Lakes (Reservoirs)

In the past 30 years, the rising demand not only for electrical power related to rapid urbanization and industrialization, but also for water conservation has led to the construction of dams and other related storage works. The damming of the River Volta and the closure of the dam at Akosombo on 8 May 1964, resulted in the formation of Lake Volta, the largest man-made lake in Africa (see Table 1). This relatively shallow lake (mean depth - 19 m) may be divided into four regions (John 1986). These are:
- the main north-south water body;
- the major "arms" marking what were formerly the lower reaches of the River Volta and its tributaries;
- the shallow littoral areas originally cleared in some places of trees; and
- the 24 km long gorge area where the lake narrows at its southernmost end.

The lake was primarily built for the generation of electrical power but associated with this the opportunity for the development of inland fisheries, an irrigation scheme for agriculture and water transport and communication.

Most of the other reservoirs are comparatively small and serve either as reservoirs for the supply of potable water e.g., Barekese and Weija reservoirs or for the storage

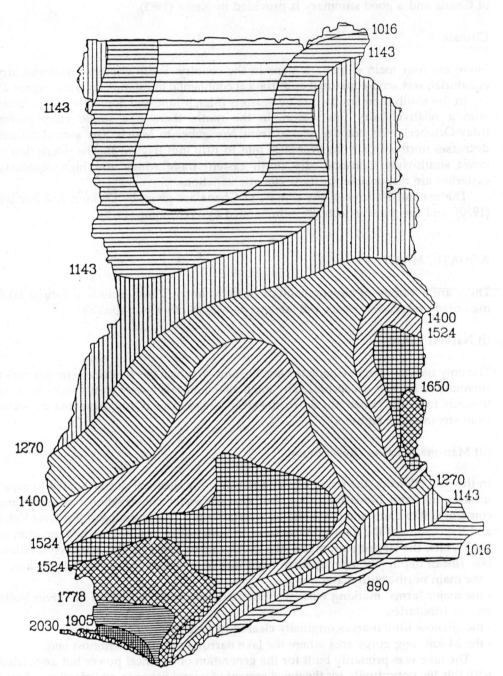

Figure 3. Average annual rainfall (mm) in Ghana (from FAO 1991).

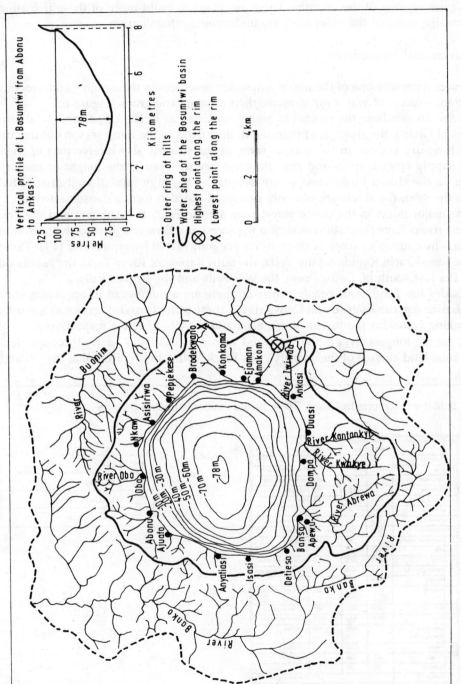

Figure 4. The drainage system of the Bosumtwi basin and surrounding countryside.
A vertical profile of the lake is also shown. (after Whyte 1975)

of water during the dry season for the purposes of irrigation and for watering of livestock (see Figure 5). A number of irrigation dams exist primarily in the Northern and Upper regions of the country. There are plans to build more of these irrigation dams whilst some of the older ones are undergoing rehabilitation.

(iii) Rivers and Floodplains

The rivers represent one of the major renewable resources in the country and serve as important sources of water for humans, their animals and crops (Figure 6).

In the areas where the rainfall is highly seasonal, as in the Upper and Northern regions of Ghana, the rivers are intermittent; they flood in the rainy season but dry up in the long dry season. In these areas some of the streams also receive part of their water supply from springs and may thus not dry up even at the height of the dry season. In the closed forest zone where because of the high rainfall well distributed within the year, the rivers are not only perennial but also form a dense network.

The major rivers in the closed forest zone are the Tano, the Ankobra and the Pra; all these rivers have their sources within the forest and flow roughly north-south into the sea. The courses of some of these rivers are punctuated by rapids and falls. There are the Kete-Krachi Rapids on the Volta, the Sutri Rapids of River Tano, the rapids on River Pra just south of Twifu Praso, the Boti Falls and the Begoro Falls.

Besides the Tano, Ankobra and the Pra, there are a number of minor rivers with small basins e.g. the Ayensu and Densu rivers; these provide useful service as a source of drinking water for the towns of Winneba and the city of Accra respectively.

By far the longest river is the Volta and within its basin lies nearly three-quarters of the total land surface of the country. The Black Volta, the White Volta, the Oti and

Figure 5. Major reservoirs in Ghana. These include major irrigation projects.

No.	Name of Project	Storage Acre-ft	Irrigated Acres	Completed Acres	Crops
1.	Ashiaman	4200	430	430	Rice
2.	Vea	14100	2100	2100	Rice and vegetables
3.	Asutsuare		10000	4800	Rice and sugarcane
4.	Kamenda		8000	1000	Sugarcane
5.	Dawhenya	5300	1200	460	Rice
6.	Okyereka	2000	320	150	Rice
7.	Hankessim	4200	800		Vegetables and rice
8.	Akumadan	1295	2000	200	Vegetables
9.	Lake shore (Amate)		500	250	Vegetables
10.	Atife	5200	2200	2200	Rice
11.	Weija	52000	4200	500	Vegetables and maize
12.	Kpong		15000	380	Rice, cotton, sugarcane
13.	Ayensu	38640	8600		
14.	Aveyime		2200	200	Rice, sugarcane and Vegetables
15.	Bontanga	16500	1200	460	Rice and Vegetables
16.	Tono	62000	6000	6000	Rice and Vegetables
17.	Lake shore Kpendu Torkar		1000	100	Vegetables
18.	Subinja		150	150	Vegetables
19.	Tanaso	431	1600		Vegetables
20.	Kabewam	569	185		Rice
21.	Gatinga			70	Rice and Vegetables
22.	Linga			20	Rice and Vegetables

———	DAM
⬭	RESERVOIR
▨	IRRIGABLE AREA
⊗	PUMPING PLANT

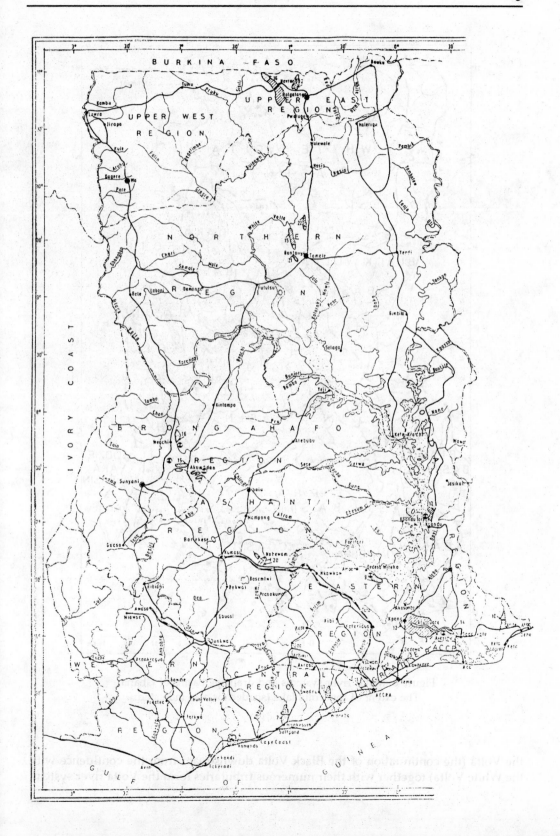

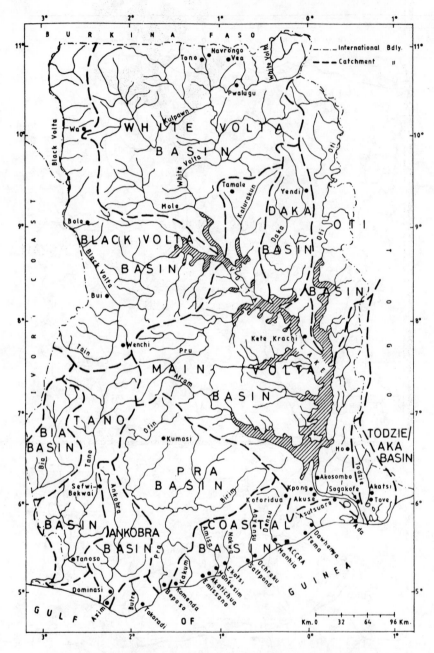

Figure 6. Major river systems and drainage basins of Ghana.
The extent of the Volta lake (shaded) is also indicated.

the Volta (the continuation of the Black Volta downstream from the confluence with the White Volta) together with their numerous tributaries form the Volta river system.

Increased flow in these rivers is associated with fluctuations in rainfall and surface run-off. Many of these rivers overspill their banks seasonally and flood low-lying areas giving rise to fringing floodplains. The recession of the seasonal floods leaves perennial or semi-perennial bodies of standing water on the floodplains including pools, lagoons, swamps or variously sized lakes.

(iv) Other Aquatic Habitats

Many aquatic habitats, natural and artificial other than rivers, natural and man-made lakes abound in the country especially in the less arid areas. The seasonal rainfall leads to the creation of many pools and small ponds. Some of these aquatic habitats are very temporary and include rain puddles which survive for at most a few days. Other habitats, such as pools in beds of ephemeral streams or rivers and rice paddy fields, persist for several months over the dry season whilst others, such as semi-permament streams and ponds more commonly persist over the rainy season.

The cultivation of rice especially in rainfed upland, rainfed lowland, inland swamp and irrigated areas, is becoming increasingly widespread. The irrigated areas are concentrated in the Interior Savanna belt which constitutes about 57% of the total land area of the country. These seasonally flooded paddy fields and the irrigated fields are all ideal shallow-water environments for the development of aquatic biota.

The ephemeral waters reflect the immediate climate and meteorologic regime far more than the permanent water bodies. The biota of these transitory waters are subjected to unusual environmental factors including widely varying physico-chemical conditions such as temperature, oxygen and salinity. Studies on these water bodies are, however, lacking.

There are in addition to these water bodies many aquatic habitats which persist throughout the year. A number of these habitats undergo considerable contraction in size over the drier months. These include fish ponds, ornamental ponds, springs, open drainage, cattle-watering holes of moderate sizes and irrigation ditches.

A survey (FAO 1989) has shown that as late as January 1988, there were about 2,033 fish ponds covering an area of 166.12 ha all belonging to registered private farmers. In addition to these, Government fish farms covered an area of about 56.9 ha.

RESEARCH ON VARIOUS AQUATIC ECOSYSTEMS

Natural Lake: Lake Bosumtwi

Lake Bosumtwi, a meteoritic crater lake, situated about 30 km south-east of Kumasi in the rainforest zone of Southern Ghana (6° 30'N; 1° 25'W), is the only natural freshwater lake of any size in the country. The main morphometric features of the lake are presented in Table 1 and Figure 4.

The lake lies in a deep almost circular crater surrounded by very steep hills which rise to a height of over 364 m above sea level. It has a diameter of 8 km, an area of 49 km^2 and a maximum depth of ca. 78 m. The present surface of the lake is about 105 m below the lowest point in the surrounding rim of hills and the lake is from 100 to 200 m lower than the land surrounding the crater. The basin which has a radial drain-

Table 1. Some of the main morphometric features of the major lakes, reservoirs and lagoons

Name	Date of closure	Location	Altitude (m)	Surface area (km²)[e]	Max. length (km)	Max. width (km)	Max. volume ($\times 10^6 m^3$)	Max. depth (m)	Mean depth (m)	Length of shoreline (km)	Major inflowing river	Major outflows	Reference
Natural Lake													
Bosumtwi	-	6°30'N; 1°25'W	1070	49	8	8	-	81	45	26.8	-	-	a
Reservoirs													
Barekese	Feb. 1970	6°44'N; 1°42'W	-	6.4	13	1.25	-	-	-	-	Ofin	Ofin	c
Dawhenya	1974	5°46'N; 0°4'E	-	2.2	-	-	-	-	-	-	-	Volta	-
Kpong	May 1981	6°9'N; 0°5'E	14.17	36.5	-	-	-	-	-	-	-	-	d
Tono	1975		200	18.60	-	-	0.09	-	-	-	-	-	d
Vea	1965		200	3.80	-	-	0.02	-	-	-	-	-	
Volta	May 1964	6°15'-9°00'N; 1°00'W-0°15'E	85	8482	400	23.8	165	74	19	4828	Black Volta, White Volta	Volta	a,b
Weija	Dec. 1974	5°35'N;0°22'W	14.1	33.61	14	2.2	30	-	14.1	-	Densu	Densu	e
Lagoons													
Aby-Tendo-Ehy Complex*		Cote d'Ivoire, Ghana 5°5'-23'N; 2°51'-3°21'W	-		410	52	-	14.9	5.0	-	Bia, Tano, Ochi	Channel to Atlantic Ocean	f
Amansuri		5°1'N; 2°35'W		3	-	-	-	-	-	-	-	Canal to Atlantic Ocean	f
Amisa		5°12'N; 1°1'W		50	-	-	1.5	-	-	-	-	"	
Angaw		5°48'N; 0°47'E		46	11	6	-	-	-	-	Volta	-	f
Avu		5°59'N; 0°45'E		4.5	-	-	-	-	-	-	-	Channels to Keta Lagoon	"
Benya		5°05'N; 1°21'W			-	-	-	-	1.1	-	Todzie	Channel to Atlantic Ocean	f
Keta		5°55'N; 0.56'W		330	29	13	-	-	0.8	-	Outflow from Avu lagoon	Channel to Atlantic Ocean	
Korle		5°32'N; 0°13'W		2.5	-	-	-	-	-	-	-	-	f
Mukwe		5°36'N; 0°3'W		0.04	2	-	-	1.5	-	-	-	-	
Sakumo 1-Accra		5°32'N; 0°17'W		23.6	5	0.14	-	-	-	-	Densu	-	f
Sakumo 2-Tema		5°37'N; 0°2'W		1.0	4.42	-	-	-	-	-	-	Canal to Atlantic Ocean	
Songaw		5°49'N; 0°28'W		18	20	8	-	0.88	0.50	-	-	- do -	a
Unvaiya		-		-	-	-	-	-	-	-	Volta	-	a

* International water; Ghana has about 25 km of shoreline along the Tendo-Ehyportia but no actual lagoon surface area.
a. Welcomme (1972), b. Czernin-Ghudentiz (1971), c. Allen and Gaudet (1978), d. ICOUR (1985), e. Aduma-Bossman and Mensah (1980), f. Bossche and Bernacsek (1990)

Table 2. Chemical composition of some major lakes, reservoirs and rivers. Values are means except for Lake Volta, and are expressed in mg L⁻¹ unless otherwise stated.

Name	Conductivity μS cm⁻¹	pH	Na	K	Ca	Mg	Fe	CO₂	Cl	NO₃	SO₄	SiO₂	Reference
Natural Lake													
Bosumtwi			204.0	36.0	12.0	28.0		103			6.0	16.0	Livingstone (1963)
Reservoirs													
Barekese													
Dawhenya		7.2-8.0											
Kpong		7.45	15.9	2.0	5.4	3.5			13.25	0.20	3.3	70.6	Thomas & Ratcliffe (1973)
Nungua													
Tono													
Vea	63-172*	6.8-8.5*	1.2-6.8*	1.5-6.0*	3.4-10.2*	2.4-7.1*	0-0.26*		1-4*	0.02-1.00*	trace	16-25*	Biney (1990), Czernin-Chudenitz (1971), Entz (1969)
Weija		7.3								0.13			
Rivers													
Bia		6.5-7.5*											
Black Volta	41-124*	6.5-7.3*	3.9	0.25	38**	11.86	0.82	11.3	17.5			125.5	Blanc and Daget (1957), Entz (1969) Welcomme (1972)
Oti		6.4-6.7*	3.2	0.22	30**	11.6		39	23.4			132	Blanc and Daget (1957) Welcomme (1972)
Pra	140	6.9-7.5*											
Red Volta		6.5	8.9	2.86	22**	13.4		71.7	17.5			148	Blanc and Daget (1957) Welcomme (1972)
Tano		6.9-9.0*								0.25			Biney (1990)
Volta		6.8											
White Volta	119	7.6	8.9	2.23	28**	12.4		84	17.5			150.6	Blanc and Daget (1957)

* range of values

** Ca figures were aberrantly high in the original publication and were reduced by a factor of 10 here.

age pattern extending to a radius of about 13 km from the centre of the lake, is wholly isolated from the general drainage system of the rest of Ghana. There is no river flowing out of the lake. It is thus an enclosed basin into which drain more than 37 streams with a total catchment of about 400 km^2. Only five of these streams-Abonu, Abrewa, Ebo Kwakye, Twiwaa and Konkoma are permanent streams and flow throughout the year; these streams arise from springs. The other streams flowing into the lake dry up during the dry season.

Detailed accounts of the origin, age, climate and physiography of this lake are given by Talbot and Delibrias (1977, 1980), Hall et al. (1978) and Talbot and Hall (1981).

Physico-Chemical Features

Very little is known of the physico-chemical features of this lake. Whyte (1975) briefly mentions these features in a paper devoted to the fish populations in the lake. The other published data on the lake are by Livingstone (1963) and by Beadle (1981); the latter is however based largely on Whyte (1975). Table 2 gives a summary of the physico-chemical features of the lake.

The chief mineral constituents of the lake water are the sulphates of sodium, calcium and magnesium; chloride and carbonates or bicarbonates of some of these elements are present in smaller amounts. The concentrations of solutes such as sodium, potassium and chloride are relatively high in the lake when compared to other water bodies in Ghana (see Table 2). Without an outflow, the lake basin exhibits two very different chemical environments: fairly dilute inflowing streams and a relatively concentrated soda lake.

Stratification in the lake is disturbed twice annually during when the hypolimnion, which is often deoxygenated below 7-10 m, becomes oxygenated. The main turnover associated with the violent mixing of the water column due to wind stress, at times of heavy cloud cover and low air temperatures, occurs betwen the two rainfall peaks around August. The overturned water occasionally contains hydrogen sulphide. A minor less violent turnover occurs during December and January as a result of the Harmattan wind which blows across the lake.

Whyte (1975) points out that the significant feature of the physico-chemical conditions in the basin is the extremely sharp chemical differences which exist between the riverine and lacustrine zones, with a narrower zone in which these factors change rapidly from the riverine to the lacustrine conditions.

Hydrobiological Features

There is a paucity of information on the phytoplankton and periphyton in the lake apart from what is given by Whyte (1975). The dominant taxa of the periphyton are diatoms which comprise approximately 53% of the taxa followed by cyanophytes (23%), chlorophytes (18%) and dinoflagellates (6%). Of the phytoplankton, the dominant taxa are the chlorophytes (40%) followed by cyanophytes (30%), diatoms (20%) and dinoflagellates (10%).

A descriptive representation of the zonal distribution of macro-invertebrates, zooplankton, periphyton and phytoplankton is shown in Table 3. The zooplankton, phyto-

Table 3. The zonal distribution of the food organisms in the lotic and lentic zones of the Bosumtwi basin (after Whyte 1975). These semi-quantitative results were obtained by the ranking of the different zones with respect to the quantity of each food item present.

Food Organisms	Source	Upper reaches	Middle reaches	Lower reaches	Upper reaches of estuary	Mouth of estuary	Littoral zone	Limnetic zone
Benthos	+	++	++++	+++	+++++	+++	++++	++
Zooplankton				+	++++	++++	+++	++
Phytoplankton			++		+	++	++++	+++
Periphyton				+	++++	++	+++	
Allochthonous plant debris	+++++	++++	++++	+++	++	+	++++	
Allochthonous fauna	++++	++++	++++	+++	++	++	++	
Aquatic macrophytes				+	+++	++	++	+

plankton and aquatic macrophytes, all of which are autochthonously produced predominate in the lacustrine zones whilst the allochthonously produced items predominate in the riverine zones.

With respect to the fishes there are 11 species of fish in the lake. These are:

Cyprinidae: *Barbus ablabes* (Bleeker, 1863); *Barbus trispilus* (Bleeker, 1863)
Cyprinodontidae: *Roloffia petersii* (Sauvage, 1882)
                    Epiplatys chaperi (Sauvage, 1882)
Amphiliidae: *Amphilius atesuensis* Boulenger, 1904
Clariidae: *Heterobranchus isopterus* Bleeker, 1863
Cichlidae: *Chromidotilapia guntheri* (Sauvage, 1882);
                    Hemichromis fasciatus Peters, 1857;
                    Tilapia busumana (Gunther, 1902);
                    Tilapia discolor (Gunther, 1902);
                    Sarotherodon multifasciatus (Gunther, 1902)

Of the cichlids, *Tilapia discolor* is the only endemic species. Two of the cichlid fishes, *Sarotherodon multifasciatus* and *Chromidotilapia guntheri* are mouth brooders whilst the remaining three species, *Hemichromis fasciatus*, *Tilapia busumana* and *Tilapia discolor* are substratum brooders.

The distribution of the fish populations is related partly to the distribution of their food items; the cichlid populations which feed on autochthonously produced food items predominate in the lacustrine zones, whilst the non-cichlid populations, which feed on allochthonous food resources, predominate in the riverine zones.

Man-Made Lakes (Reservoirs)

A great deal of attention has been focussed by limnologists on Lake Volta, the emphasis of the studies being on the ecological changes accompanying the transformation of the River Volta into a Lake. Other impoundments, though they are increasing in their numbers, have received scant attention by limnologists.

An estimate of the total number of reservoirs from 1967 to 1982 is given by Balarin (1988). By 1982, there were an estimated number of 169 reservoirs in the Upper East region, 90 in the Northern region and 51 in the Volta region. The Volta Lake is currently the world's largest man-made impoundment. It covers about 3 percent of the land area of Ghana and was formed following the closure of the Akosombo dam in May, 1964.

The distribution of the major reservoirs and the morphological features of some of these reservoirs are presented in Figure 5 and Table 1.

Physico-chemical Features

The major physico-chemical features are shown in Table 2. A brief review of the physico-chemical features of the Volta Lake is provided by John (1986). The Lake which has a highly dendritic shape, due mainly to the rivers which flow into it, has a depth ranging from 19 to 75 m; the depth decreases from south to north and from mid-lake to shore. These features of the lake, along with the climatic and topographic character of the basin influenced greatly the limnophysical and chemical character of the lake.

As the lake formed, the large quantities of suspended, dissolved and colloidal organic matter which entered with the flood water produced a turbid brown colour which reduced the transparency. The turbidity was further increased by the rainy season and the seasonal algal blooms and secchi disc readings of as low as 10 cm were recorded. Later, there was a north-to-south decreasing gradient in turbidity levels suggesting a gradual loss of suspended matter as the turbid water entering the lake flowed southwards towards the dam site. The transparency of the lake water increased in subsequent years as the suspended matter settled onto the lake floor or was flushed out of the system.

A decreasing surface-to-bottom temperature was observed at sampling stations along the axis of the lake over an eight year period; during this period the surface temperatures did not exceed 33°C and the bottom temperature did not fall below 23°C in any season (Obeng 1981). There was a north-to-south decreasing gradient of surface temperatures associated with a drastic lowering of surface temperatures due mainly to the dry harmattan winds from the Sahara. The surface temperatures were also affected by other external factors, including rain, wind and waves resulting in complete overturn in the deeper waters both in the northern and southern sectors of the lake.

There was an initial depletion of dissolved oxygen but subsequently, at most times, oxygen was usually present down to the bed in almost all sections of the lake. The mixing of the water contributed to the distribution of dissolved oxygen vertically and laterally throughout the water column.

Based on the nutrient levels alone, Lake Volta has been shown to be an oligotrophic water body. The concentration of minerals or ions in the lake water is generally low as reflected by the total range of dissolved solids (40 - 60 mg L^{-1}) at surface, and by the conductivity readings (40 - 70 μmhos cm^{-1}) (Obeng-Asamoah 1977, Obeng 1981). The levels of concentration varied with depth. The concentrations of phosphate, dissolved carbon dioxide, hydrogen sulphide, manganese and total iron increased downwards, while others including oxygen and pH, decreased with depth. For the chemical factors, no definite pattern of distribution was observed.

Information on the physico-chemical characteristics of the other reservoirs is very limited (see Table 2). References to the chemistry of the Weija and Barekese reservoirs may be found in unpublished reports of the Institute of Aquatic Biology (IAB 1976) and Biney (1979).

Hydrobiological Features

The only reservoirs which have received considerable attention are the Volta Reservoir and the Nungua reservoir. The most recent and detailed review of the biota of the Volta and Nungua reservoirs is given by John (1986). The paper deals with the seasonal periodicities, primary production, the community structure and dynamics of the algal flora including the phytoplankton, periphyton, and aquatic macrophytes as well as the short and long term effects of the impoundments.

Measurements of primary production are limited. The daily gross production of the Volta Lake is in the range of 2.1—14.0 g O_2 m^{-2} d^{-1} (mean 6.8 g O_2 m^{-2} d^{-1}) (Viner

1970b). The mean daily gross production of Nungua Reservoir is reported by Thomas and Ratcliffe (1973), for the months of April, July and November 1964, to be 8.76 g O_2 m^{-2} d^{-1}, 1.72 g O_2 m^{-2} d^{-1} and 3.96 g O_2 m^{-2} d^{-1} respectively.

Some measurements of the biomass of planktonic and periphytic algae have been made in the Volta Lake (John et al. 1980, Obeng-Asamoah et al. 1980).

In spite of the oligotrophic nature of the Volta Lake, plankton populations developed well, algal blooms were frequent and there was persistent development of aquatic macrophytes.

The algal flora of the Volta Lake consists of 143 taxa (John 1986). All the algae reported in the river Volta by Biswas (1968, 1970) before its impoundment are also present in the lake. The most diverse algal class in the lake are the chlorophytes which represent 32% of the known taxa. They are followed by the diatoms (27%), the desmids (17%), the cyanophytes (16%), the euglenophytes (5%) and others (3%).

The zooplankton population, less abundant at the time (1964—1969) was repre-sented largely by copepods, rotifers and cladocera. The most common zooplankton were *Bosmina, Moina, Ceriodaphnia, Bosminopsis, Filinia, Asplanchna, Keratella, Polyarthra* and *Trichocerca* (Obeng 1969).

The rapid establishment of communities of invertebrates was favoured by the expansion of the water column, the changes in chemical character of the water and other ecological factors. In the littoral zones, there was an increase in the populations of larval forms of terrestrial insects such as *Mansonia*, nymphs of mayfly especially *Povilla adusta* and *Caenis* species, dragonfly, caddisfly as well as truly aquatic organisms including some hemiptera, colleoptera, and aquatic molluscs such as *Bulinus* sp., and *Pila africana*. The benthic organisms of the river which had not survived well were represented mainly by chironomids and oligochaetes (Obeng 1975).

The establishment of the invertebrates was further supported by the development of aquatic plants floating and submerged. The floating *Pistia stratiotes* persisted on the lake and together with some grasses including *Scirpus cubensis* and *Cyperus* formed floating mats. These mats are now confined to the mouths of inflowing streams or rivers and to more wind-sheltered localities along the shore. The water surface, in some areas, was often covered by extensive spreads of small plants including *Azolla africana, Lemna paucicostata, Spirodela polyrhiza* and *Salvinia nymphellula*. Other plants were submerged *Ceratophyllum demersum* and *Utricularia inflexa*. Growths of the margi-nal grass *Vossia cuspidata* appeared within a year of the filling of the dam. Emergent plants including *Jussiaea repens, Echinochloa* sp. and *Alternanthera* sp. took over the shoreline shortly after, especially in low-lying areas (Hall 1969). Further information on the problem of aquatic weeds on the Volta Lake is provided by Lawson (1967), Piarce (1971), Okali and Hall (1974) and Opoku (1976).

Very little information exists on the hydrobiological characteristics of the remaining reservoirs. Quantitative and qualitative accounts of the algal communities in these reservoirs are limited; available information may be found in Frempong and Nijjhar (1973) and Biney (1990). In the Weija reservoir five main algal groups were represented namely, green, blue-green, diatoms, desmids and flagellates (Appler 1977).

Studies on the weed infestation in some of the reservoirs have been carried out by the Institute of Aquatic Biology (IAB 1980). Serious weed problems involving floating species (e.g., *Pistia*), submerged plants (e.g., *Ceratophyllum*), semi-aquatic vegetation (e.g., *Typha* and *Echinochloa*) and "sudd" vegetation existed in the Barekese, Dawhenya,

Kwanyarko, Okyereko, Owabi and Weija reservoirs. In the Weija reservoir, the sudd formed covered about 50% of the reservoir surface and 70% of the area between Weija and Machigeni. The species involved included *Pistia, Ficus, Typha, Echinochloa, Alternanthera, Scirpus* and *Leersia*. Weed infestation was related to the annual rainfall regime and relative influx of nutrients. The presence of the weeds hindered the use of the water resources for a variety of purposes eg. fishing and water supply.

An inventory of the macro-invertebrate fauna of some of the reservoirs may be found in unpublished reports of the Institute of Aquatic Biology. The predominant groups have been Ephemeroptera, Odonata and Trichoptera (IAB 1970).

Rivers, Floodplains and Swamps

Physico-chemical Features

Ghana is well drained by a large number of streams and rivers; the Volta basin alone accounts for 66 percent of the country's drainage system (Figure 6). The data on available surface water resources of Ghana (Government of Ghana 1966, Welcomme 1972, Nerquaye-Tetteh et al. 1984) have been updated by Opoku-Ankomah (1986) and are presented by river basins (Table 4).

Hydrological data on many of the rivers, and streams are limited. However, the hydrology of the Volta River is well documented by Nerquaye-Tetteh et al. (1984).

Some of the characteristics of the major rivers in Ghana are also given in Table 4. The chemical composition of some of the river waters is presented in Table 2.

Further information is also given by the Institute of Aquatic Biology on the chemical and physical nature of a number of rivers in Ghana (IAB 1970, 1973, 1978). Most of the rivers lie within the Volta basin, there is thus not much difference in their chemical nature from that of the Volta river. Some rivers, however, which are outside the Volta basin often have marked differences in concentrations of solutes as compared to those from rivers in the Volta basin. The nitrate, ammonia and alkalinity levels tended to be high in rivers with much human connection.

Extensive marshes and swamps occur around the borders of the coastal lagoons; there are, however, no quantified data on these habitats.

Hydrobiological Features

Despite the importance of lotic environments in agricultural and fishery production, our knowledge of the ecology of these environments is still very poor. The most comprehensive treatment is on the Volta River system. The physico-chemical characteristics have been described by Blanc and Daget (1957), Biswas (1968), Entz (1969b), Viner (1970) and John (1986). Studies on the planktonic algae and the aquatic macrophytes have been reported by Biswas (1968), Hall and Pople (1968) and Hall et al. (1969).

The effect of dams on the downstream of River Volta has been described by Hilton and Kowu-Tsri (1970), Lawson (1970), Chisholm and Grove (1985) and John (1986). Some of the physical, chemical and biological features of the Lower Volta river have been given in a review of some of the characteristics of freshwater and coastal ecosystems in Ghana (Biney 1990). There is a paucity of information on other downstream rivers.

Table 4. Surface water resources and distribution by basins

Major River System	Altitude m	Length km	Drainage Area km²	Flow range (Annual mean) x 10³ m³ s⁻¹	Run off x 10⁶ m³ day⁻¹*		
					Annual Mean	Monthly Max.	Monthly Min.
Volta Basin			165700	- (0.057)			
Black Volta**	300	650	31105	0.01-1.10 (0.135)	4.92	53.83	0.17
White Volta**	298		45800	0.1-1.41 (0.112)	10.28	104.98	0.09
Oti	640	900	16215	0.01-1.27 (0.141)	9.59	73.44	0.17
Volta	14.3	86	68580		12.10	249.70	0.17
Bia**	306	200	6470	0.13 (0.08)	3.63	40.95	0.17
Tano**	430	625	1490	0.03-0.78 (0.13)	6.39	45.27	0.17
Ankobra			8460	0.11	10.45	40.61	1.30
Pra	550	445	23200	0.03-0.92 (0.24)	20.74	94.18	1.38
Ochi-Amissa			1370	0.05			
Ochi-Nakwa			1500	0.05			
Ayensu			1700	0.001-0.06			
Densu			2550				
Subri-Amansuri			840				
Butre			460				
Kakum-Saruwi			980				
Todzie			1860	0.06	1.38	155.52	0.09
Aka (Keta Lagoon)			1720				
Minor Coastal Streams							
Total		6150	237870				

Sources: Opoku-Ankomah (1986); Bossche and Bernacsek (1990) ** International water
* Run off values are for flows from within basins in Ghana and exclude flows entering from upstream

Information on the aquatic and semi-aquatic vegetation in the southern reaches of some of the major rivers like the Ankobra, Ayensu, Densu, Otchi and Pra may be found in unpublished reports of the Institute of Aquatic Biology (IAB 1977). In all the rivers there was generally no threat of a weeds problem. Weeds which need attention, in rivers which are likely to be impounded, are *Vossia* and *Phragmites* in the Pra river and *Typha, Echinochloa, Pistia* and *Polygonum* in the Ayensu system.

There has been no attempt to measure primary production in any of the river systems. Other published information on rivers with respect to the invertebrates and fish fauna, is scattered in various publications and official reports, e.g. IAB (1988).

The fauna and flora of the floodplains have been little studied. Scattered information on the floodplains of Ghana and the importance of the fisheries associated with these areas are mentioned in a review by Welcomme (1979).

Coastal Lagoons

There are about 50 brackishwater lagoons situated along the coast of Ghana with a total surface area of 400 km^2 (FAO/IFAD 1981) (see Figure 7). Morphological data on some of the major lagoons are given in Table 1. The largest of these lagoons is the Keta Lagoon, which is situated around the delta of the Volta River.

Table 5. Physical and chemical data of some of the major lagoons in Ghana
(after Biney 1984)

Lagoon	T°C	pH	Transparency (cm)	DO	BOD	PO$_4$-P	NO$_3$-N	NH$_3$-N
Amisa	30.1	7.0	22	6.11	3.34	0.026	0.058	0.675
Angaw	29.4	7.2	85.3	2.37	1.02	0.013	0.641	0.004
Benya	27.5	9.4	100	6.63	3.90	0.016	0.0	0.105
Chemu	36.3	8.1	-	0.0	71.2	0.585	0.295	1.28
Fosu	28.5	7.8	23	8.29	23.76	0.066	0.018	0.262
Gao	29.6	8.1	70	8.06	6.37	0.038	0.868	0.009
Keta	32.3	8.1	35	7.22	3.41	0.023	0.173	0.101
Korle	25.9	7.1	24.7	4.37	80.0	0.859	0.303	3.79
Kpeshie	29.4	8.0	-	7.32	5.04	0.111	0.335	0.294
Laiwi	28.8	8.1	48	7.56	4.79	0.012	0.273	0.016
Muni	28.3	7.0	60	7.21	4.47	0.046	0.026	0.159
Nakwa	28.5	7.6	56	8.08	3.82	0.063	0.021	0.521
Oyibi	28.1	7.0	19	3.82	2.78	0.078	0.193	0.08
Sakumo 1	25.5	7.0	43.8	6.26	3.95	0.033	0.479	0.012
Sakumo 2	28.9	8.2	14	8.0	20.16	0.084	0.184	0.15
Songhaw	29.2	9.2	-	4.52	1.82	0.0	0.839	0.019

The biological, chemical and hydrological characteristics as well as the fisheries of the coastal lagoons are described in detail by Kwei (1977) and Mensah (1979). In a

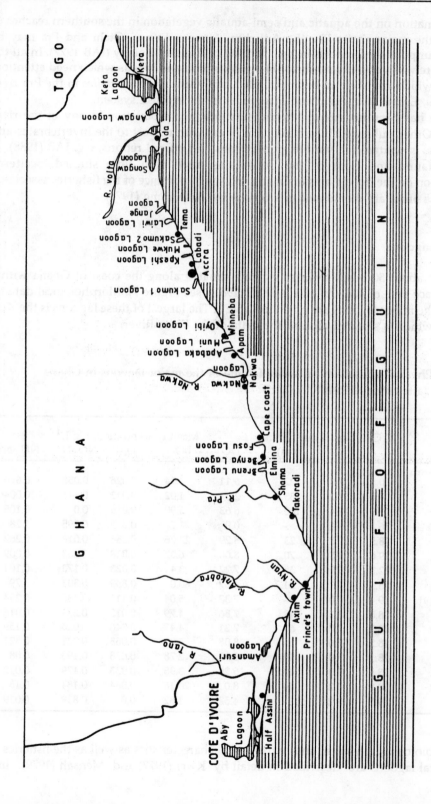

Figure 7. Map of southern Ghana showing the principal lagoons (from M.A. Mensah, in Weigel 1985)

recent review, Biney (1990) discussed the physico-chemical characteristics, nutrients and the diversity of phytoplankton in six of the coastal lagoons. The major physico-chemical features of the lagoons are presented in Table 5.

High phytoplankton counts dominated by blue-green algae occurred in the Korle, Sakumo-2 and Fosu lagoons, in which orthophosphate and ammonia-nitrogen concentrations were high. The major groups of blue-green algae found were *Anabaena, Nostoc, Microcystis, Oscillatoria* and *Lyngbya*. Diversity indices were low in these nutrients-rich lagoons (Table 6).

Table 6. Phytoplankton numbers, diversity and ratio of green algae, cyanophytes and diatoms in some lagoons (after Biney 1990)

Lagoon	Counts ml^{-1}	Diversity index	Green algae	Cyanophytes	Diatoms
Fosu	6872 ± 950	0.097	1	48	0
Korle	1145 ± 725	0.13	1	111	0
Laiwi	36 ± 9	0.83	0	1	30
Sakumo-Accra	110 ± 45	1.53	1	2.7	2.5
Sakumo-Tema	7800 ± 2000	0.034	0	7800	0

Fish and Fisheries Resources

Fish is the most important source of animal protein in Ghana; it constitutes about 52.1% of all animal products consumed in common household diets and contributes 75% to animal protein intake (Balarin 1988). The national production of fish has fluctuated around 300,000 mt yr^{-1}. It has been estimated that there is a current nutritional shortfall of around 200,000 — 300,000 mt of fish per year (FAO 1989). Fish production, thus ought to be raised between 500,000 - 600,000 mt yr^{1} from the current level to offset the shortfall.

Various aspects of the state of the fisheries resources in Ghana have been reviewed by Denyoh (1969, 1985), Welcomme (1979), FAO/IFAD (1981), Vanderpuye (1984) and Balarin (1988). The main feature of the inland fishery is the Volta Lake which produces an estimated 40,000 t yr^{1} (FAO 1978). Catch from other inland waters and the coastal lagoons is estimated to be 7,000 t. The potential annual yield for the inland waters is estimated to be 40,000 — 69,000 t (Balarin 1988). No information, however, is available for the catch range in a number of the reservoirs e.g., Barekese, Dawhenya, Kpong and Weija and the other lagoons and rivers.

During the first three months of the formation of the Volta Lake, sixty species of fishes were recorded; the closing of the dam trapped the river fishes within the rising waters. *Alestes* sp., *Clarias* sp. and *Ctenopoma* sp. were then the most abundant fish. The cichlids were represented by four *Tilapia* species which became prolific and are now caught in all areas of the lake. Some fish species were killed due to the alteration of some of the physical and chemical factors in the new environment, particularly the initial depletion of dissolved oxygen by the decomposition of the submerged vegetation. Apart from the *Tilapia* species, some of the important species as indicated by the weight of the species in the total catch, are *Alestes macrolepidotus, Hydrocynus forskalii, Labeo cubio* and *Lates niloticus*. The quantitative and qualitative aspects of the fish population are described by Denyoh (1969), Evans and Vanderpuye (1973) and Vanderpuye (1982, 1984).

Information on the fish and fisheries of water bodies outside the Volta system is scanty; the available data are mainly in the form of unpublished data from the Institute of Aquatic Biology. Studies have been carried out by the Institute on fish composition and food habits of fish in three reservoirs, namely Weija, Dawhenya and Kpong (Dassah and Abban 1979).

In the Weija reservoir, nine species representing about 50% of the original fish fauna of the Densu river system had established themselves as the major fishes in the reservoir. The fishes were *Hepsetus odoe, Clarias senegalensis, Heterobranchus longifilis, Tilapia zilli, Sarotherodon galilaeus, S. heudeloti, Chrysichthys nigrodigitatus, Hemichromis fasciatus* and *Ophiocephalus obscurus*. Among these species were plankton feeders, benthic fauna feeders, weed feeders, detritus feeders and piscivorous fishes. Six potentially economic species including the prawn, *Macrobrachium vollenhoveni* were reported to be present in the Dawhenya reservoir. *Sarotherodon galilaeus* constituted over 80% of the fish biomass. In the Kpong reservoir, ten major economic fish species including *Tilapia zilli, Hemichromis fasciatus* and *Alestes macrolepidotus* were reported.

Frempong and Nijjhar (1973) provide information on the fish fauna of Barekese reservoir. Nineteen species of fish were recorded. The Tilapias constituted 59.7% of the total catch and of this, 31.6% was made up of *Tilapia busumana*. Other fish reported include *Marcusenius brachystius, Hepsetus odoe, Alestes nurse, Micralestes occidentalis, Labeo senegalensis, Barbus trispilus, Barbus parablabes, Barbus sublineatus, Heterobranchus isopterus, Chrysichthys nigrodigitatus, Cynodontis eupterus, Aplocheilichthys schioetzi, Hemichromis fasciatus, Hemichromis bimaculatus, Chromidotilapia guntheri, Ophiocephalus obscurus* and *Mastacembelus nigromarginatus*. Of these species only three *Tilapia busumana, Heterobranchus isopterus* and *Hepsetus odoe* were caught in the open lake. The largest number of fish was taken in cast nets from the water below the dam.

An inventory of the freshwater fishes of major rivers and their distribution in Ghana have been undertaken by the Institute of Aquatic Biology. The rivers studied included the Ankobra, Pra, the Red, White and Black Voltas, Oti, Daka, Densu, Birim, Dayi and Wawa. Approximately 115 fish species have been identified in these rivers. More than 90% of the fishes were either of food or commercial aquarium importance or both (IAB 1976, 1978, 1982).

The construction of the Akosombo dam has affected the catch downstream as well as the freshwater clam (*Egeria radiata*) fishery in the lower Volta river below Akuse and the fisheries of some of the coastal lagoons.

Studies have been carried out on parasitic infections of fishes from rivers, streams, lakes, reservoirs and ponds in Southern Ghana over the years. There was a high rate of helminth and copepod infection among fish from ponds, small lakes and reservoirs while infection was insignificant in the fish from the Volta Lake and the rivers which drain into it (Prah 1969).

Documented statistics of aquaculture production is given by Denyoh (1985) and FAO (1989). Fish ponds for registered private farmers and government fish farms cover an area of approximately 223 ha. Most of the fish ponds have sizes less than 0.5 ha, although a few go beyond this size and up to 3 ha.

Production of fish from fish ponds is generally low; the average yield is mostly below 0.5 t ha^{-1} yr^{1}. The Ashanti region has recorded the most active growth since 1984, with some ponds in the region averaging between 1.5 t ha^{-1} yr^{1} and 2.0 t ha^{-1} yr^{1} (FAO 1989). Currently, aquaculture contributes less than 0.5% of the national fish production.

The most commonly used fish species for culture in Ghana are the tilapias, mainly *Oreochromis niloticus* which forms the basal stock on most farms. Other species also cultured are *Heterobranchus* sp., *Clarias* sp., *Heterotis niloticus, Ophiocephalus obscurus,* and *Gymnarchus* sp. The rest, which could be considered as incidentals include: *Chrysichthys nigrodigitatus, Hemichromis* sp., *Lates niloticus* and *Hydrocyon brevis.*

The principal constraints in the aquaculture sector have been reviewed by several authors including Denyoh (1985). Information on aquaculture dealing with feed and feeding habits of the fish as well as the physico-chemical and biological characteristics of fish ponds are also available from unpublished project reports (e.g., IAB 1976 and Williams 1992).

Taxonomic Works

The algal flora of some freshwater and brackish waters in Ghana are documented in two checklists by Lawson (1960, 1965) in which over 200 algae are mentioned. Other taxonomic treatments of freshwater algae are those by Biswas (1968) on River Volta and by Biswas (1970) and Anon (1974) both on Volta Lake. The most important publication on Ghanaian freshwater diatoms is by Foged (1966). It lists 685 diatom taxa which include 135 new species as well as five new varieties.

Hall (1971a, 1971b) has described some new species of aquatic plants. Details of aquatic macrophytes in Ghana are included in a comprehensive review of the subject by John (1986). The paper also deals with the dynamic aspects of macrophytic vegetation including the seasonal changes and long-term succession.

An inventory of the macro-invertebrate fauna of the inland waters of Ghana is under preparation by the Institute of Aquatic Biology (IAB 1968, 1969, 1970); data are still being collected. The predominant groups have been the Ephemeroptera, Odonata and Trichoptera. It has not been possible to identify all the specimens so far collected; this requires the services of various specialists in the respective families.

A cooperative project on the biosystematics of Chironomids of Ghana between the Department of Zoology at the Museum of Zoology in Bergen, Norway and the Institute of Aquatic Biology, Accra, Ghana is in progress. It is financed by the Norwegian Research Council and the University of Bergen.

A checklist of Chironomidae (Diptera: Nematocera) from Ghana based on published records upto 1993 has been prepared by Amakye (1993). A list of 87 chironomid species in 31 genera belonging to three subfamilies is provided. Tanypodinae is represented by 12 species, Orthocladiinae by 6 species and Chironominae by 69 species. The regions most intensively studied are the Volta region, the Greater Accra region and the Eastern region with 49, 45 and 36 recorded species respectively. No species is reported from the Western, Central and Northern regions.

Four Afrotropical species *Microtendipes lentiginosus* Freeman, *Collartomyia hirsuta* Goetgheuber, *Henrardia quadrispinosa* Goetgheuber and *Dicrotendipes multispinosa* (Freeman) (Diptera: Chironomidae) have been redescribed in both sexes and all stages by Amakye and Saether (1992).

An expanded cooperation, for the period 1992-1996, between the Institute of Aquatic Biology, the Department of Zoology, University of Ghana, Legon, Accra, and the Museum of Zoology, University of Bergen also exists. The objective of this colla-boration is to develop a better knowledge of the freshwater invertebrates of Ghana. It is expected that the cooperation will lead to the establishment of a freshwater entomo-logy laboratory at the Institute of Aquatic Biology, the offering of courses in freshwater entomology, including systematics, ecology, zoogeography and phylogeny at the Department of Zoology, University of Ghana and also to the provision of necessary training of technicians and graduate students at the Museum of Zoology in Bergen.

A provisional checklist of the freshwater fishes in the Volta basin has been provided by Roberts (1967). A key for the field identification of freshwater fishes in the Volta reservoir has been prepared by Lowe McConnell (1972). Whyte (1975) discusses the systematics of the species of fish recorded from the Bosumtwi basin. Other taxonomic references on the freshwater fishes of Ghana are given by Irvine (1947) and IAB (1972, 1976, 1978, 1982).

Water Quality and Pollution

Associated with the ever increasing demand for freshwater, due to the rapidly growing population (2.7% per annum), is the ever present problem of water pollution. Water is the major means by which waste, a by-product of socio-economic development is disposed of. Wastes present in sufficient quantities render water unfit for consumption, production and irrigation. ·

The major sources of pollution of the aquatic ecosystem are through:
 i. the disposal of domestic and municipal waste including garbage, excreta and liquid
       household wastes,
 ii. agricultural run-offs,
 iii. industrial, including mining effluents and
 iv. land degradation practices.

i. *Domestic and Municipal Wastes*

The volume of these wastes will increase because of the rapid population growth rate. Currently, disposal is by land filling and by inceneration. Leachates resulting from improper land filling result in pollution as they are washed off by rain into water-bodies. The existence of central sewerage systems only in parts of Accra, Akosombo, and Tema reflect the intensity of the problem of excreta disposal in the urban areas. The promotion of the use of Ventilated Improved Pit Latrines in cities, towns and in rural areas is an attempt to find a solution to the problem. Both treated and raw excreta may eventually find their way into surface and underground waters. The disposal of liquid wastes from households and commercial houses also poses a serious problem. The extent of contamination by all these wastes is, however, not well documented.

ii. *Agricultural Run-off*

The use of agro-chemicals like fertilizers, pesticides and herbicides for agricultural activities contributes to contamination of water bodies. Fertilizers are used over the country on both rainfed and irrigated farms, but particularly farms in areas such as the northern and upper regions where soils are poorer in quality. In these regions, the main receiving waters are in the Volta system.

The widespread use of pesticides and their presence in waterbodies are of particular concern. The use of pesticides for agriculture in developing countries is on the increase; it was estimated to be about 40% of the world total in 1975 (Alabaster 1981). Many of the insecticides, and fungicides used in the country have been totally or partially banned from the industrialized countries. These include gramoxone, D.D.T., dieldrin and aldrin. The increased use of these persistent and often environmentally damaging chemicals is due partly to their ready availability on the market and lack of effective controls on their importation.

There has, however, been no systematic programme for the continuous monitoring of the effects of fertilizers and pesticides on the quality of waterbodies and on the aquatic life. The results of contamination by some of these pesticides are evidenced by fish kills. The application of chlorphoxim for the control of *Simulium damnosum* in the Volta River basin was found to have adverse effects on fish brain at a concentration of 0.25 mg L^{-1} (Antwi 1981).

The monitoring of the fish populations and the invertebrate productivity in some of the rivers in the WHO Onchocerciasis Control Programme (OCP) area was carried out by the Hydrobiology division of the Institute of Aquatic Biology. The rivers, viz., Oti at Sabari, Black Volta at Bamboi and Pru at Asubende were treated regularly with four larvicides - carbosulfan, chlorphoxim, permithrin and *Bacillus thuringiensis* (H. 14), to control Simulium. In general the drift indices of the predominant invertebrates - Baetidae, Caenidae, Chironomini, the non-target Diptera, Ephemeroptera, Leptophlebiidae, Heptageniidae, Hydracarina and Tricorythidae, were very low compared with the pretreatment values. In the case of the fishes higher catches per unit effort were recorded in all the three rivers as compared to the previous year. The detailed results are reported in the Hydrobiological Monitoring Report (IAB 1988).

Agro-chemical pollution of groundwater has not yet been studied in the country; the possibility of its occurrence cannot be over-ruled.

iii. *Industrial Effluents*

There is evidence of industrial pollution due to the discharge of large volumes of untreated effluents from industries into waterbodies (Mensah 1976). Such wastes come from the breweries, chemical, food, mining, tanning, textile and rubber industries. The major waterbodies found receiving industrial effluents included the Volta, Birim, Densu, Ofin and Ankobra rivers as well as the Korle Lagoon. High concentrations of these effluents result in accelerated nutrient enrichment, objectionable smell, bad taste and other nuisances.

In the mining areas, cyanide and arsenic concentrations as high as 4.0 and 5.9 mg L^{-1} respectively, were found in rivers into which effluents were discharged (Mensah 1976, WRRI 1988). These levels are a risk to human health and lethal to aquatic life.

In a recent work on the environmental impact of the gold mining industry in Ghana, Bamford et al. (1990) have shown that gold ore and gold tailings are some of the sources of pollution. Inland waters receiving effluent from the mines showed the presence of Fe and Zn at concentration levels of $0.08 - 2.4 \ \mu g \ mL^{-1}$. The sediments of these waters showed the presence of most of the heavy metals, viz., Cr, Mn, Fe, Cu, Zn, As, Pb, Hg, Rb, Sr, Y, Zr and Cd within a concentration range of 0.08 ppm – 4.9 ppm. Most of the heavy metal pollution thus exist in particulate form and settle into the sediment of the receiving waters.

iv. *Land Degradation Practices*

The main practices in land utilization which contribute to pollution in inland waters include: the felling of forest trees for timber, the extensive exploitation of fuel-wood to provide energy for household needs in both the rural and urban areas, bush-burning as a means of land preparation and for hunting and over-grazing by livestock. These practices have the effect of baring the land, thus enhancing soil erosion by water and wind and ultimately increasing the nutrient and sediment loads in receiving waters.

The siltation of dams and dug-outs and desertification are already evident in the Northern and Upper East regions of the country. Farming activities in the catchment area of the Tono river are causing increased erosion which in turn has resulted in increased siltation of the Vea and Tono reservoirs.

Research into the effects of land degradation on water resources is virtually non-existent. The National Plan of Action to combat desertification is yet to be fully implemented (EPC 1987).

Water-Borne Diseases

The creation of man-made lakes has in a number of ways led to some new problems and intensified some pre-existing ones.

In general, there has been an increase in the incidence of some waterborne diseases over the past few years as reflected in the national morbidity data (Table 7). Derban (1975) has summarized the trends in the incidence of waterborne and water-associated diseases in the Volta reservoir area. It was noted, for example that the prevalence of schistosomiasis among school children increased sharply from 5% in 1960 to 90% in 1967 after the completion of the Akosombo dam in 1964. In other localities along the Volta system where the infection rate was previously nil or moderate gradual increases have been observed. Odei (1979) in a survey on schistosomiasis in some river basins and reservoirs in Ghana, also recorded an increase in the prevalence rates. Information on the freshwater snails responsible for the transmission of schistosomiasis in various regions and major river basins of Ghana is available in Odei (1975 a,b, 1982).

The prevalence rate of onchocerciasis among people over 15 years of age has also been observed to be as high as 90% in some areas (Derban 1975). A comprehensive programme of control of onchocerciasis within the Volta system by WHO, was initiated in 1974.

Studies on the control of the vectors of malaria using larvivorous fish *Poecilia reticulata* and *Bacillus sphaericus* are still in progress (IAB 1987, Ofori 1987).

Table 7. National mortality data for water borne diseases (1980-1987)

| | Mortality for various years | | | | | | |
	1980	1981	1982	1983	1985	1986	1987
Bilharzia	3300	2032	2058	2018	9142	11079	11635
Cholera[2]	-	943	11086	15032	25*	25*	-
Diarrhoea	48937	41099	50324	52295	132102	165768	219798
Guinea Worm[1]	1371	768	741	457	4608	3234	4066
Malaria[1]	242781	173765	212524	210863	593368	807017	1141893
Onchocerciasis[1]	4534	4213	2143	1975	1811	4456	5504
Typhoid[1]	462	663	910	2018	9142	11079	11635

Source: Centre for Health Statistics, Ministry of Health
1 = 1980-1983 Figures from H.O.P.I. Compilations.
    1984 was a trial period for Monthly Activity Report Form
1 = 1985-1987 Figures from Monthly Activity Report Compilation
2 = 1980-1987 Figures for Epidemiological Bulletin
*   Jan.-June Figures

Conservation

The need to conserve various water bodies in the country and to prevent their pollution appears to have been recognized by Government. Various agencies such as the Environmental Protection Council, the Ghana Water and Sewerage Corporation, the Irrigation Development Authority, Minerals Commission and the Volta River Authority have thus been empowered by the laws establishing them to make the necessary regulations to protect the aquatic environment. However, no such regulations have so far been made by any of these agencies, leaving the waters at the mercy of various industrial concerns (EPC 1989). There is thus the need for the appropriate authorities to enforce the law to prohibit pollution of various waterbodies.

TRAINING, RESEARCH INSTITUTIONS/ORGANIZATIONS AND AGENCIES

A number of institutions and organisations are associated with limnological research and development in the country. The functions of these institutions are indicated in Table 8. Inspite of their number, there is a complete lack of cooperation and coordination among these establishments leading to overlaps in activity and duplication of efforts.

With cooperation between the universities and research institutes and the effective utilization of the limited resources, the training of competent young scientists capable of initiating and undertaking basic research in limnology could be achieved.

Facilities at the universities for the training of high-level personnel in limnology are limited and highly inadequate. At the undergraduate level the scope and depth of

Table 8. Institutions, organisations/agencies involved in the water sector, their main

Institution	Date of Establishment	Main Objectives
Environmental Protection Council	1973	To ensure the observance of proper safeguard in the planning and execution of all development projects that are likely to interfere with the quality of the environment.
Ghana Water & Sewerage Corporation (*reorganized from Hydraulic Division, Water Supply Division of P.W.D. and Department of Rural Water Development)	1965/1900*	Domestic and industrial water supply and sewage disposal. Data collection in respect of above.
Hydrological Division of Architectural and Engineering Services Corporation (*formerly Hydrological Branch of Public Works Department)	1974/1951*	Surface water hydrological data collection, flood control and coastal erosion
Institute of Aquatic Biology	1965	Undertakes research, both fundamental and applied into the resources of the inland water system, estuaries, lagoons and coastal waters of Ghana. Provides necessary information for the proper development, management and exploitation of these waterbodies.
Irrigation Development Authority (*reorganised from Department of Irrigation and Drainage)	1977/1962*	Irrigation and drainage.
Meteorological Services Department	1937	Hydrometeorology and Agro-climatology
University of Cape Coast Botany Department	1962	Teaching and Research
Zoology Department	1962	Teaching and Research
University of Ghana Botany Department	1948	Teaching and Research
Zoology Department	1948	Teaching and Research
University of Science and Technology Biological Sciences Department	1961	Teaching and Research
Civil Engineering Department		Engineering graduates and Diplomates

objectives, professional staff, and types and areas of research

Strength, type and qualification of professional staff	Types and duration of courses offered	Types and Areas of Research	Training/Research facilities
1 M.Sc. (Asst Research Officer)	None	Aquatic Biology, Water Pollution	None
- -	None	Water quality monitoring of some rivers, reservoirs and groundwater. Groundwater level fluctuations data collection in respect of research	- -
- -	None	River water quality monitoring, River level & discharge data collection in respect of research	- -
4 Ph.D. (3 Sr Res. Officers, 1 Principal Res. Officer), 9 M.Sc. (2 Principal Res. Officers, 3 Sr Res. Officers and 4 Res. Officers), 7 B.Sc. (1 Res. Officer and 6 Asst Res. Officers)	None	Limnochemistry, Hydrobiology, Fisheries Biology, Parasitology, Entomology, Microbiology	Aquaculture Research & Development Centre, GLC, Flame Analyser
- -	None	- -	- -
- -	None	Evaporation, humidity, temperature and rainfall data collection	
1 Ph.D. (Lecturer) 4 Ph.D. (2 Professors and 2 Senior Lecturers	B.Sc.; 3 years B.Sc.; 3 years	Ecology of algae Fisheries Biology	Basic laboratory equipment available - do -
2 M.Sc. (2 Lecturers)	B.Sc.; 3 years	Aquatic Macrophytes Aquatic microbiology	Basic laboratory equipment available
1 Ph.D. (Professor) 2 M.Sc. (1 Lecturer, 1 Research Fellow)	B.Sc.; 3 years	Hydrobiology Fisheries Biology	- do -
1 Ph.D. (Senior Lecturer)	B.Sc.(Hons); 4 years	Hydrobiology, Aquaculture, Fisheries Biology	Basic laboratory equipment available
1 M.Sc. (Lecturer)	M.Sc. Sanitary Engineering; 1 year	Water quality, Environmental impact assessment	- do -

Table 8. (contd)

Institution	Date of Establishment	Main Objectives
Institute of Renewable Natural Resources	1982	Teaching and Research
Volta Basin Research Project	1963	To carry out limnological as well as sociological and archaeological observations on the Volta Basin
Volta Lake Research and Development Project	1968 (dismantled in 1986)	Investigations on the limnology, fisheries resources of Volta Lake as well as on resettlement and public health problems
Volta Lake Transport Company	1970	Water transport on Lake Volta for movement of passenger and cargo

limnology taught in the various universities are very limited. In most cases the only area of concentration is on Fish and Fisheries Biology or Aquaculture.

The proper management and efficient utilization of our water resources require a sound background knowledge, and hence the need to consciously intensify our training and research programmes in the various areas of limnology.

SCIENTIFIC SOCIETY

Currently there is no scientific society specifically concerned with limnology in the country. Plans have, however, been initiated to establish a National branch of the International Association of Limnology (SIL).

The Ghana Science Association (GSA), in general, embraces all scientists working in any aspect of limnology and is open to all others to further scientific research and its application or foster the understanding and teaching of science in Ghana. The Association presently has a membership of 400. Its postal address is: GSA, P.O. Box 7, Legon, Ghana.

The official organ for scientific publications is the *Ghana Journal of Science* which is published jointly by the Council of Scientific and Industrial Research of Ghana and the GSA. The Journal is open to all papers of a scientific and technological nature from Ghana and elsewhere and is issued twice a year in April and October.

CONCLUSIONS AND RECOMMENDATIONS

1. There are evidently very large gaps in the collection of water cycle data, i.e. hydro-

Table 8. (contd)

Strength, type and qualification of professional staff	Types and duration of courses offered	Types and Areas of Research	Training/Research facilities
3 M.Sc. (3 Lecturers)	B.Sc.; 3 years	Hydrobiology and Aquaculture	Basic laboratory equipment available
3 M.Sc. (3 Lecturers)	None	Aquatic microbiology	- do -
- -	None	Limnology Fisheries Biology	- do -
- -	None	- -	None

meteorological, hydrological and hydrogeological data, as well as physiographic data in the country. A review of the data collection programme and the provision of adequate resources in order to maintain, rehabilitate and expand existing networks are necessary.

2. The present knowledge on the assessment of surface and groundwater resources needs to be updated and expanded both qualitatively and quantitatively to cover all river basins.

3. There are serious deficiencies in our limnological knowledge not only of the larger man-made lakes e.g., the Volta lake and rivers, but also of the smaller ecosystems along with their catchments. More attention needs to be given to the much neglected smaller waterbodies such as ephemeral streams, ponds, floodplain pools and rice paddy fields.

4. Over the past decade, little or no attention has been given to the following areas of research: metabolism of lake waters, nutrient loading and recycling from sediments, the ecology of the benthic fauna, trophic changes in major reservoirs, improvement of fish stock and the composition and dynamics of river plankton. Research on all these aspects of the limnology of the inland waters should be undertaken.

5. Diel cycles exert considerable influence on community metabolism and structure and constitute the basic foundation upon which seasonal and annual variations are superimposed. Information on these areas of research is virtually non-existent.

6. The importance of undertaking baseline surveillance or regular monitoring so as to follow any changes that take place as a result of man increasingly modifying the aquatic ecosystem should be recognized to allow for more reliable data upon which proper planning could be based.

7. There is an urgent need for more comprehensive research, than what presently

exists, on the pollution of aquatic ecosystems in the country with a view to identifying the sources, types of pollutants, their consequent effect on the environment and the appropriate measures to be taken to offset such effects.

8. There are weaknesses in the institutional framework for the efficient management and conservation of water resources. The establishment of a Water Resources Commission as proposed by WRRI (1987) should thus be given priority.

9. Research institutions, universities and other organisations involved with limnological research need to be strengthened in terms of the provision of funds, relevant equipment and facilities in order to achieve any meaningful results.

10. There are still very many official reports and students' theses which contain relevant information but which have not been published thus making them inaccessible to many people. Important findings locked up in such sources should be published in widely distributed national and international journals to make them readily available to other limnologists. To this end a national limnological journal may be necessary. Currently none of the major limnological journals is subscribed to by the research institutes and most of the universities in the country.

11. It is essential to establish a DATABASE, an information system to support fisheries, aquaculture and limnological research in the country. It should contain information on morphometrics, distribution, ecology, population dynamics, nomenclature etc. Such a database will provide fast access to the necessary information as well as allow for comparative studies between species groups or various ecosystems.

12. There is a need, as a matter of urgency, for the training of middle and high level personnel capable of initiating and carrying out research in the various areas of limnology; the relatively few numbers of limnologists currently available in the country cannot cope effectively with the necessary research related to the drastic changes in the aquatic environment.

REFERENCES

Abban, E.K. 1982. Pretreatment observations on the fish fauna of River Pru. Technical Report No. 97. Institute of Aquatic Biology, Council for Scientific and Industrial Research, Accra, Ghana. 20 pages.

Ackermann, W.C., White, G.F. and Worthington, E.B. (Editors). 1973. Man-made Lakes: Their problems and environmental effects. Geophysical Monographs 17. American Geophysical Union, Washington, DC. 847 pages.

Alabaster, J.S. 1981. Review of the state of aquatic pollution of East African inland waters. Committee for Inland Fisheries of Africa (CIFA) Occasional Paper 9: 35 pages.

Allen, G. and Gaudet, J.J. 1978. Assessment of aquatic weed problems and their economic significance in Ghana. Prepared for United State Agency for International Development, and Ghana Water and Sewerage Corporation. 12 pages.

Amakye, J.S. 1993. A checklist of Chironomidae (Diptera: Nematovera) from Ghana based on published records up to 1993. Norwegian National Committee for Development Research and Education (NUFU) Project 38/91. Ghana Freshwater Entomology Report no. 1. 17 pages. Museum of Zoology, University of Bergen, Bergen, Norway.

Amakye, J.S. and Saether, O.A. 1992. The immatures and imagines of the Afrotropical species *Microtendipes lentiginosus* Freeman and *Collartomyia hirsuta* Goetgheuber (Diptera: Chironomidae). Entomologica Scandinavica 23: 429-442.

Amakye, J.S. and Saether, O.A. 1993. Redescription of the Afrotropical Henrardia quadrispinosa Goethgheuber and Dicrotendipes multispinosa (Freeman) (Diptera: Chironomidae). Journal of the Kansas Entomological Society 66 (3): 263-273.

Anon. 1974. Environmental aspects of a large tropical reservoir. A case study of Volta Lake, Ghana. Report of the Office of Science and Technology. Agency for International Development, Washington, DC. xv + 340 pages.

Antwi, L.A. 1981. The effect of Chlorphoxim on fish brain Acetylcholinesterase. Report submitted to Onchocerciasis Control Programme (OCP)/World Health Organisation (WHO), Ouagadougou, Upper Volta. 24 pages.

Appler, H.N. 1977. Studies on the community structure of the algae present at the Weija dam site during the period July - December 1976. Technical Report No. 75, Institute of Aquatic Biology, Council for Scientific and Industrial Research, Accra, Ghana. 12 pages.

Balarin, J.D. 1988. National reviews for aquaculture development in Africa. 18. Ghana. Food and Agriculture Organisation (FAO) Fisheries Circular 770 (18): 121 pages.

Bamford, S.A., Osae, E., Aboh, I., Biney, C.A. and Antwi, L.A. 1990. Environmental impact of the gold mining industry in Ghana. Biological Trace Element Research 26: 279-285.

Beadle, L.C. 1981. The Inland Waters of Tropical Africa. An Introduction to Tropical Limnology. Second edition. Longman, London/New York. 475 pages.

Biney, C.A. 1979. Chemistry of the Densu Reservoir. pp. 1-6, In: Dassah, A.L. and Abban, E.K. (Editors), The potential for fishery in the Densu (Weija) reservoir. Proceedings of the Institute of Aquatic Biology. Technical Report No. 89, 73 pages.

Biney, C.A. 1984. Preliminary studies on coastal pollution in Ghana. 1. Oxygen, nutrients and some physical properties. Technical Report No. 105. Institute of Aquatic Biology, Council for Scientific and Industrial Research, Accra, Ghana.

Biney, C.A. 1990. A review of some characteristics of freshwater coastal ecosystems in Ghana. Hydrobiologia 208: 45-53.

Biswas, S. 1968. Hydrobiology of the Volta River and some of its tributaries before the formation of the Volta Lake. Ghana Journal of Science 8: 152-166.

Biswas, S. 1970. Changes in the phytoplankton in the developing Volta Lake. Ghana Journal of Science 10: 85-92.

Biswas, S. 1972a. Ecology of phytoplankton of the Volta Lake. Hydrobiologia 39: 277-288.

Biswas, S. 1972b. Distribution of phytoplankton during the early development of Volta Lake (1964-68), Hydrobiologia 40: 201-207.

Biswas, S. 1978. Observations on phytoplankton and primary productivity in Volta Lake Ghana. Verhandlungen der internationale Vereinigung für theoretische und angewandte Limnologie 20: 1672- 1676.

Blanc, M. and Daget, J. 1957. Les eaux et les poissons du Haute Volta. Memoires de l'Institut français d'Afrique noire, 50: 100-169.

Brooks, M. 1969. A bibliography of hydrobiological work in Ghana, including references to onchocerciasis, bilharziasis and dracontiasis (excluding yellow fever, malaria, trypanosomiasis). Volta Basin Research Project, University of Ghana. Technical Report No. X31. 25 pages.

Chisholm, N.G. and Grove, J.M. 1985. The lower Volta. pp. 229-250. In: Grove, A.T. (Editor) The Niger and Its Neighbours. A.A. Balkema, Rotterdam/Boston.

Dassah, A.L. and Abban, E.K. 1979. The potential for fishery in the Densu (Weija) Reservoir. Proceedings of the Institute of Aquatic Biology, Accra, Ghana. Technical Report No. 89. 73 pages.

Denyoh, F.M.K. 1969. Changes in fish population and gear selectivity in the Volta Lake. pp. 206-219. In: Obeng, L.E. (Editor) Man-Made Lakes: the Accra Symposium. Ghana Universities Press, Accra. 398 pages.

Denyoh, F.M.K. 1985. Status of Aquaculture. Proceedings of Workshop on Village Level Aquaculture Development in Africa. Freetown. 8 pages.

Derban, L.K.A. 1975. Some environmental health problems associated with industrial development in Ghana. Institute of Aquatic Biology, Council for Scientific and Industrial Research, Accra, Ghana. 22 pages.

Dickson, B. and Benneh, G. 1970. A New Geography of Ghana. Longman, London. 173 pages.

Dunn, J.S. 1947. Mineral analysis of Gold Coast waters. Gold Coast Geological Survey Bulletin 15: 57-66.

Entz, B. 1969a. Limnological conditions in Volta Lake, the greatest man-made lake of Africa. Nature and Resources, UNESCO 5: 9-16.

Entz, B. 1969b. Observations on the limnochemical conditions of the Volta Lake. pp.110-115. In: Obeng, L.E. (Editor) Man-Made Lakes: the Accra Symposium. Ghana Universities Press, Accra. 398 pages.

Evans, W.A. and Vanderpuye, J. 1973. Early development of the fish populations and fisheries of Volta Lake. pp. 114-120, In: Ackermann, W.C. White, G.F. and Worthington, E.B. (Editors) Man-made Lakes: their problems and environmental effects. American Geophysical Union, Washington, D.C. 847 pages.

Environmental Protection Council (EPC). 1987. National Plan of Action to Combat Desertification. Environmental Protection Council, Accra. 83 pages.

Environmental Protection Council (EPC). 1989. Environmental Action Plan. Water management component. Environmental Protection Council, Accra. 90 pages.

Ewer, D.W. 1966. Biological investigations on the Volta Lake. May 1964 to May 1965. pp. 21-31. In: Lowe-McConnell, R.H. (Editor) Man-made Lakes. Academic Press, London. 218 pages.

FAO. 1978. Ghana: Agro-industrial development. FAO/TCP 6/GHA 02/1, 85 pages.

FAO. 1991. Technical assistance and investment framework for aquaculture in Ghana: where are the best opportunities for fish farming in Ghana? The Ghana Geographical Information System as a decision-making tool for fish farming development. F1:TCP/GHA/0051. Field Technical Report 5. FAO, Rome. 59 pages.

FAO/IFAD. 1981. Ghana artisanal fisheries project. Identification report. FAO/IFAD Coooperative Programme (17/81 DDC GHA 11). 50 pages.

Foged, N. 1966. Freshwater diatoms from Ghana. Biologiske Skrifter, Kongelige Danske Videnskabernes Selskab 15: 1-169.

Frempong, E. 1980. Limnological research in Ghana: some perspectives. pp. 131-136. In: Mori, S. and Ikusima, I. (Editors), Proceedings of the First Workshop for the Promotion of Limnology in Developing Countries, Kyoto. 172 pages.

Frempong, E. and Nijjhar, B. 1973. Some preliminary observations on the fauna and flora of Barekese Lake, Ghana. Bulletin de l'Institut Fondamental d'Afrique noire, Series A, 35: 67-78.

Government of Ghana. 1966. River basins of Ghana. Water yearbook 1966-1967. Ghana Publishing Corporation, Accra/Tema. 335 pages.

Gunther, A. 1902. Last account of fishes collected by Mr. R.B.N. Walker, C.M.Z.S., on the Gold Coast. Proceedings of the Zoological Society, London: 330-339.

Hall,J.B. 1971a. New Podostemaceae from Ghana with notes on related species. Kew Bulletin 26: 125-136.

Hall, J.B. 1971b. Observations on Isoetes in Ghana. Botanical Journal of the Linnean Society 64: 117-139.

Hall, J.B., Laing, E., Hossain, M. and Lawson, G.W. 1969. Observations on aquatic weeds in the Volta Basin. pp. 331-336. In: Obeng, L.E. (Editor) Man-Made Lakes: the Accra Symposium. Ghana Universities Press, Accra. 398 pages.

Hall, J.B. and Pople, W. 1968. Recent vegetation changes in the lower Volta River. Ghana Journal of Science 8: 24-29.

Hall, J.B., Swaine, M.D. and Talbot, M.R. 1978. An early Holocene leaf flora from Lake Bosumtwi, Ghana. Palaeogeography, Palaeoclimatology, Palaeoecology 24: 247-261.

Hilton, T.E. and Kowu-Tsri, J.Y. 1970. The impact of the Volta scheme on the lower Volta floodplains. Journal of Tropical Geography 30: 29-37.

Institute of Aquatic Biology (IAB). 1968. Third Annual Report. Institute of Aquatic Biology, Council for Scientific and Industrial Research, Accra, Ghana. 37 pages.

Institute of Aquatic Biology. 1970. Fourth Annual Report. Institute of Aquatic Biology, Council for Scientific and Industrial Research, Accra, Ghana. 109 pages.

Institute of Aquatic Biology. 1972. Some freshwater fishes of Ghana. Technical Report No. 41. Institute of Aquatic Biology, Council for Scientific and Industrial Research, Accra, Ghana. 13 pages.

Institute of Aquatic Biology. 1973. Chemistry of River Klemu, Ho. Fifth Annual Report. Institute of Aquatic Biology, Council for Scientific and Industrial Research, Accra, Ghana. 101 pages.

Institute of Aquatic Biology. 1976. Inventory of fishes of the White Volta at Pawlugu. Annual Report. Institute of Aquatic Biology, Council for Scientific and Industrial Research, Accra, Ghana. 107 pages.

Institute of Aquatic Biology. 1977. Survey of the aquatic and semi-aquatic vegetation along certain stretches of selected large rivers (Ankobra, Pra, Otchi and Ayensu) in Ghana. Annual Report. Institute of Aquatic Biology, Council for Scientific and Industrial Research, Accra, Ghana.

Institute of Aquatic Biology. 1978a. Inventory of fish species in Northern Ghana. pp. 20-24, In: Institute of Aquatic Biology/Onchocerciasis Control Programme Hydrobiological Monitoring Report, January 1978. Special Report no. 1. Institute of Aquatic Biology, Council for Scientific and Industrial Research, Accra, Ghana. 36 pages.

Institute of Aquatic Biology. 1978b. Impoundment studies of the Densu River. Quarterly Report, April 1978. Institute of Aquatic Biology, Council for Scientific and Industrial Research, Accra, Ghana. 15 pages.

Institute of Aquatic Biology. 1978c. Preliminary studies of the chemical characteristics of the Oti, White and Black Volta rivers. Quarterly Report, May 1978. Institute of Aquatic Biology, Council for Scientific and Industrial Research, Accra, Ghana. 15 pages.

Institute of Aquatic Biology. 1980. Weed infestation in some impounded water bodies in Ghana. Annual Report. Institute of Aquatic Biology, Council for Scientific and Industrial Research, Accra, Ghana. 12 pages.

Institute of Aquatic Biology. 1987. Annual Report. Institute of Aquatic Biology, Council for Scientific and Industrial Research, Accra, Ghana. 19 pages.

Institute of Aquatic Biology. 1988. Onchocerciasis Control Programme in the Volta Basin in Ghana. Annual Hydrobiological Monitoring, Technical Report No. 119. Institute of Aquatic Biology, Council for Scientific and Industrial Research, Accra, Ghana. 34 pages.

Institute of Aquatic Biology. 1990. Annual Report. Institute of Aquatic Biology, Council for Scientific and Industrial Research, Accra, Ghana. 27 pages.

Irvine, F.R. 1947. The Fishes and Fisheries of the Gold Coast. Crown Agents. 352 pages.

John, D.M. 1986. The Inland Waters of Tropical West Africa: An introduction and botanical review. Archiv für Hydrobiologie, Beiheft Ergebnisse der Limnologie 23: 1-244.

John, D.M., Obeng-Asamoa, E.K. and Appler, H.N. 1980. Periphyton in the Volta Lake. II. Seasonal changes on wooden blocks with depth. Journal of the West African Science Association 6: 122-136. Hydrobiologia 76: 207-215.

Kesse, G.O. 1985. Options open to Ghana for economic recovery with regards to her mineral resources. pp. 33-59. In: Proceedings of the 14th Biennial Conference, Ghana, Science Association, Kumasi, Ghana. 153 pages.

Kwei, E.A. 1977. Biological, chemical and hydrological characters of coastal lagoons of Ghana, West Africa. Hydrobiologia 56: 157- 174.

Lawson, G.W. 1960. A preliminary check-list of Ghanaian fresh- and brackish-water algae. Journal of the West African Science Association 6: 122-136.

Lawson, G.W. 1963. Volta Basin Research Project. Nature, London 199: 858-859.

Lawson, G.W. 1965. Additions to a preliminary check-list of Ghanaian freshwater and brackish-water algae. Journal of the West African Science Association 10: 45-55.

Lawson, G.W. 1967. "Sudd" formation on the Volta Lake. Bulletin de l'Institut Fondamental d'Afrique noire, Series A 29: 1-4.

Lawson, G.W. 1970. Lessons of the Volta - a new man-made lake in tropical Africa. Biological Conservation 2: 90-96.

Livingstone, D.A. 1963. Chemical composition of rivers and lakes. In: Fleischer, M. (Editor). Data of Geochemistry. Edition 6. U.S. Geological Survey Professional Paper 440 G. Government Printing Office, Washington, DC.

Lowe-McConnel, R.H. 1972. Freshwater fishes of the Volta and Kainji Lakes. Ghana Universities Press, Accra. 22 pages.

Mensah, G.G. 1976. Water quality and pollution survey of inland and coastal waters of Ghana. Water Resources Research Institute, Accra, Ghana. Technical Report. 27 pages.

Mensah, M.A. 1979. The hydrology and fisheries of the lagoons and estuaries of Ghana. Fisheries Research Unit, Ghana. Marine Fisheries Research Report No. 7. 14 pages.

Nerquaye-Tetteh, F.O., Larmie, S.A. and Akrasi, S.A. 1984. Surface water resources of the Volta Basin. Subregion Workshop on water resources of the Volta Basin: 10 pages. (mimeo).

Obeng L.E. (Editor). 1969. Man-Made Lakes: the Accra Symposium. Ghana Universities Press, Accra. 398 pages.

Obeng, L.E. 1973. Volta Lake: Physical and biological aspects. Geophysical Monograph (American Geophysical Union) 17: 87-98.

Obeng, L.E. 1981. Man's impact on tropical rivers. pp. 265-288, In: Lock, M.A. and Williams, D.D. (Editors), Perspectives in Running Water Ecology. Plenum Press, New York/London.

Obeng-Asamoah, E.K. 1977. A limnological study of the Afram arm of Volta Lake. Hydrobiologia 55: 257-264.

Obeng-Asamoah, E.K., John, D.M. and Appler, H.N. 1980. Periphyton in the Volta Lake. 1. Seasonal changes on the trunks of flooded trees. Hydrobiologia 76: 191-200.

Odei, M.A. 1973. Observations on some weeds of malacological importance in the Volta Lake. Bulletin de l'Institut Fondamental d'Afrique noire, Series A 35: 57-66.

Odei, M.A. 1975a. Distribution and dynamics of population of snails transmitting schistosomiasis in Ghana. Proceedings of the Afro-Brazilian Symposium on Schistosomiasis. Brazil, March 3-13, 1974. Brasilia Medica II (1 & 2): 13-26.

Odei, M.A. 1975b. The prospects of some water borne diseases in the area of the proposed Weija Dam reservoir near Accra. Ghana Journal of Science 15(2): 219-224.

Odei, M.A. 1979. Schistosomiasis and water development with record of some infested river basins in Ghana. A working paper for the National Health Committee on Water Resources Development. Institute of Aquatic Biology, Accra, Ghana. 10 pages.

Odei, M.A. 1982. Survey for the distribution of vector snails and the trematodes of medical and veterinary importance which they transmit. Final Report 1982 on WHO Research Grant No. SCH T16/181/B2/20. 12 pages.

Ofori, J.C. 1987. Isolation of some toxic strains of Bacillus sphaericus and larvicidal activity on Culex quinquefasciatus. Proceedings of the joint 15th and 13th Biennial Conference of the Ghana Science Association, and the West African Science Association, Accra. 11 pages.

Okali, D.U.U. and Hall, J.B. 1974a. Colonization of Pistia stratiotes L. mats by Scirpus cubensis Poepping & Kunth on the Volta Lake. Ghana Journal of Agricultural Science 7: 31-36.

Okali, D.U.U. and Hall, J.B. 1974b. Die-back of Pistia stratiotes on Volta Lake, Ghana. Nature, London 248: 452-453.

Opoku, A.K. 1976. The development of aquatic weeds, their contribution and economic importance in the Volta Lake during the first ten years of the Lake (1964-1975). Paper presented at the Conference on the Volta Lake and National Development, University of Ghana, Legon. 6 pages.

Opoku-Ankomah, Y. 1986. Annual stream flow characteristics of the major Ghanaian rivers. Water Resources Research Institute, Council for Scientific and Industrial Research, Accra.

Owusu, D.A. 1972. Hydrobiological studies on the Volta Lake. pp. 909-912. In: Kajak, Z. and Hillbricht-Ilkowska, A. (Editors). Productivity Problems of Freshwaters. Polish Science Publishers, Warsaw.

Pierce, P.C. 1971. Aquatic Weed-Development, Impact and Control at Volta Lake 1967-1971. United States Agency for International Development (USAID) Volta Lake Technical Assistance project (641-11-190-028). USAID-Ghana, Accra. 90 pages.

Prah, S.K. 1973. Observations on parasitic infections in freshwater fishes of Ghana. pp. 261-268. In: Obeng, L.E. (Editor). Man-Made Lakes: the Accra Symposium. Ghana Universities Press, Accra. 398 pages.

Roberts, T.R. 1967. A provisional check-list of the freshwater fishes of the Volta Basin with notes on the species of possible economic importance. Journal of the West African Science Association 12(1): 10-18.

Talbot, M.R. and Delibrias, G. 1977. Holocene variations in the level of Lake Bosumtwi, Ghana. Nature, London 268: 722-724.

Talbot, M.R. and Hall, J.B. 1981. Further late Quaternary leaf fossils from Lake Bosumtwi, Ghana. In: Coetzee, J.A. and van Zinderen Bakker, E.M. (Editors). Palaeoecology of Africa and the surrounding Islands 13: 83-92. A.A. Balkema, Rotterdam.

Thomas, J.P. and Ratcliffe, P.J. 1973. Observations on the limnology and primary production of a small man-made lake in the West African Savanna. Freshwater Biology 3: 573-612.

Vanderpuye, C.J. 1982. Further observation of the distribution and abundance of fish stocks in Volta Lake, Ghana. Fisheries Research 1: 319-343.

Vanderpuye, C.J. 1984. Volta Lake (Ghana), pp. 261-320. In: Kapetsky, J.M. and Petr, T. (Editors) Status of African reservoir fisheries. CIFA Technical Paper. CPCA (10): 326 pages.

Viner, A.B. 1970a. Hydrobiology of Lake Volta, Ghana. I. Stratification and circulation of water. Hydrobiologia 35: 209-229.

Viner, A.B. 1970b. Hydrobiology of Lake Volta, Ghana. II. Some observations on biological features associated with the morphology and water stratification. Hydrobiologia 35: 230-248.

Water Resources Research Institute (WRRI). 1987. Report of workshop on the proposed Water Resources Commission for Ghana. Water Resources Research Institute, Council for Scientific and Industrial Research, Accra, Ghana. 74 pages.

Welcomme, R.L. 1972. The inland waters of Africa. Committee for Inland Fisheries of Africa (CIFA) Technical Paper 1. 117 pages.

Welcomme, R.L. 1979. The inland fisheries of Africa. Committee for Inland Fisheries of Africa (CIFA) Technical Paper 7. 77 pages.

Whyte, S.A. 1975. Distribution, trophic relationships and breeding habits of the fish populations in a tropical lake basin (Lake Bosumtwi-Ghana). Journal of Zoology, London 177: 25-56.

Gopal, B. and Wetzel, R.G. (Editors) **Limnology in Developing Countries**: 41-61
© 1995, International Association for Limnology

Limnology in Tunisia

Jeanne Zaouali

Institut National Agronomique de Tunisie, 43 av. Charles Nicolle, Tunis, Tunisia

ABSTRACT

Following the study of general geographical and climatological characteristics, a review and a description of main Tunisian hydrographical regions, lakes, sebkhas, and man-made water bodies are done.

The major results pointed out that although biological research focussing on land water resources was very active at the beginning of our century, they were later on almost abandoned and started again only some 20 years ago. This recent effort must be carried on as there are, still, numerous gaps in this field which remain to be filled.

INTRODUCTION

Tunisia, which is located in the arid part of the climatological mediterranean region has very few permanent water resources. Therefore, the scientists who investigated the country at the end of the 19th century were immediately attracted by the original flora and fauna that they found in this stressed environment and produced numerous publications emphasizing the characteristics of these organisms. However, these studies were carried out individually without any coordination and with hardly any reference to ecological problems.

For the last 20 years, it was most often with the support of European cooperation that a few small groups have been able to work in the field of limnology and to try to integrate their biological results at the geographical and ecological characteristics.

Geographical Location

Tunisia covers approximately 155,830 km² in the Eastern part of North Africa and it has a long coastal line of 1,200 km (Figure 1). The country is located between the 37° and 31° North Latitude. It is exposed to mild masses of air coming in from the Mediterranean sea as well as to masses of continental origin and is subject to wide temperature variations. The main reliefs (Dorsale) are of West-East orientation, they are relatively sort (average height is 300m and the highest mountain the Jebel Chambi is 1,544m) and are to be found in the North-Eastern part of the country. Rivers as such are to be found North of the Dorsale and the only one deserving that name in the country is the Mejerda. Everywhere else the hydrographic network is irregular and represented by "oueds" (temporary watercourses) which, most of the time, find their outlets in closed hollows which dry up periodically ("Sebkhas") and are not connected with the sea.

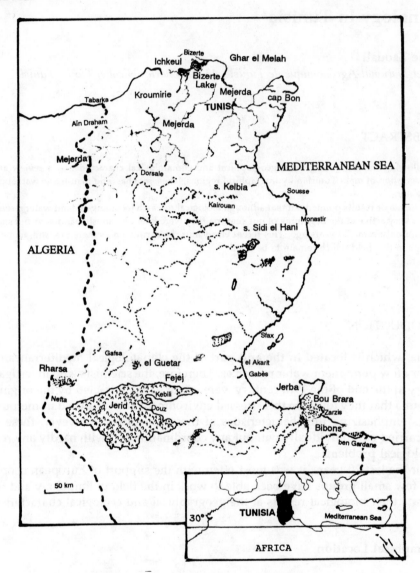

Figure 1. **Map** of Tunisia with its drainage system.

Climate

The overall temperature pattern (Figure 2) shows a significant difference between those of the coastal areas where the margin is fairly narrow and the interior of the country.

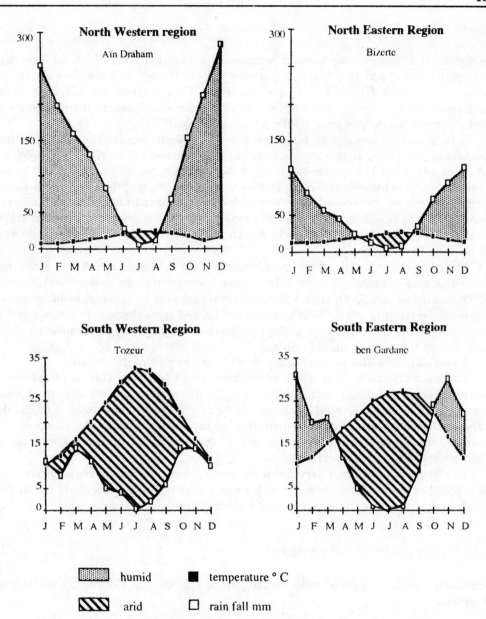

Figure 2. Temperature and rainfall cycles

Continental Area

Average annual temperatures vary on the mainland between 14.3°C at Felja (in the Northern region) and 21.3°C at Tozeur (in the Southern region) with major variations between absolute minimum and maximum temperatures and more particularly in the South (Felja -6.5° in December, 49° in August; Gafsa: -6° in February, 53° in July). Days of frost are almost as numerous in the South (6) as in the North (7).

Coastal Area

In the coastal area average annual temperatures vary between 17.9°C at Tabarka, (Algerian border) and 19.5°C at Ben Gardane (Libyan border) and absolute variations remain fairly high (Tabarka -1°C in December, 47° in August; Ben Gardane 5° in December, 55° in August). Days of frost are, however, less frequent than in Western part (North: 3.3 days per year, South: 0.5 days per year).

Rain is mainly brought in by North-West and North winds. The impact of the Dorsale is, therefore, at the origin of an obvious contrast between the North-West, which as an annual average rainfall of more than 400 mm, mainly in winter, and in the East and South of the country which receive much smaller quantities of rain (especially in the autumn for the coastal area, and in the spring for mainland Tunisia). Discrepancies may be noted in the amount of rainfall and its frequency: an annual average of 1582 mm falling during 118 days in Ain Draham (North) and 99 mm falling during 22 days in Tozeur (South).

The main characteristic of the rainfall distribution in Tunisia is that it is erratic on an annual and pluriannual scale: a dry season lasting 5 months in the North from 9 to 11 months in the South with variations from one year to another, from single to double the quantities of rain North of the Dorsale, and from single to five-times in the Far-South of the country where during the course of a single day torrential rainfalls may exceed the normal annual rainfall.

Snowfall is rare and occurs mainly in the western part of the country.

The main directions from which winds blow are in Northern Tunisia from North-North-West, in the South from South-West (in the mainland part) and from East (coastal region) and in Central Tunisia from the North-West. Wind speed is moderate varying between 3 and 6 m s^{-1}. Hurricanes are rare and limited to the North of the country. Small cyclones of short duration may occur in the South in the area around Gabes: they generally generate rainfall.

The "sirocco", a dry and very hot wind coming from the Sahara blows from May to September more or less strongly; its influence may be more 1xrticularly felt in the South and, even more, in the steppes of Central Tunisia (28 days per year).

THE HYDROGRAPHIC NETWORK

Mainland Tunisia has three major hydrographic regions: the Northern, Central and Southern.

The Northern Region

This part of the country which benefits from relatively regular rainfall is the only one to have permantnt rivers. The most important one is the Mejerda which meanders between the Kroumirie mountains in the North and those of the Dorsale in the South (460 km long and a drainage area spreading over 23,700 km² carrying on annual average around 1 billion cubic metres of water). Its source is located in the North-Eastern Algerian mountains (Sedrata region) from where it winds South-West to North-East to flow into the sea near Ghar-el-Melah (formerly Porto-Farina). Its constantly migrating delta-like mouth has been subject of multiple peregrinations which are materialised in a progressive movement of its mouth towards the North away from Tunisia.

In the Eastern part of the Northern zone, the fluviatile network flowing North-South or West-East ends in the endoreic depression formed by Lake Ichkeul into which flow yearly approximately 320 million cubic metres. Finally, in several places in the Kroumirie mountain (North) are ponds which apparently are a habitat of a fairly original flora and fauna.

Altogether the chemico-physical patterns of these waters courses are very diversified, especially those of the Southern tributaries of the Mejerda which, as they flow through Triassic salt-dome areas, are often strongly chlorinated. Moreover, they generally carry multiple clay particles, and are often extremely polluted as is the case of Oued Beja which flows into the Sidi Salem dam.

The Central Region

This region, which is characterised by vast steppe-like plains accounts for a low, irregular rainfall (the annual rainfall is 150 mm). Its endoreic hydrographic network ic constituted of large torrents with temporary water courses (oueds Mergeullil, Nehbana and Zeroud) which flow into large closed depressions which dry up during the arid season when they are covered with a thin salt layer. The sebkha Kelbia (140 km²), North of Kairouan, and the sebkha Sidi el Hani (350 km²), South of Kairouan, collect the water of drainage basin collected estimated to be around 165 million cubic metres. Smaller depressions may also collect temporary water inflows, but they are not salt-covered: these are the "r'dirs" or "dayas".

The Southern Region

Besides the oases, where rivulets (the "seguias") flow from underground artesian and often thermal wells, is a desert. There, remain, however, a few rare temporary oueds (annual average inflow in the Gafsa area: 100 million cubic metres) which often drain salty and sometimes very salty waters (the salt content of oued Magroun which flows into chott Rharsa is higher than 20‰). There are numerous basins, some very small, which may be quasi-permanent ("gueltas") or temporary ("kraouis") and others far larger, which are coverd with a thick, more or less solid salt layer depending on the season. These latter are immense endorheic depressions, the "chotts" Fejej (800 km²), Jerid (4,600 km²) and Rharsa (600 km²) between the Algerian frontier and the region of Gabes, and slightly more to the North, Chott el Guettar. These, according to a wide-spread theory, are witnesses of former humid times, between 200,000 and 90,000 years B.P.

The Fluvial Network of the Coastal Area

The coastal area has practically no fluvial network. Nevertheless, in an embryonic state, it does exist in three points. The Northern region accounts for some torrential-like rivers along the Northern coast and flowing down from Kroumirie mountains. They are mostly dry during the summer and flow into the sea after covering a very short South-North course. Their drainage area covers approximately 1950 km² with an estimated annual water inflow of 350 million cubic metres.

Except for Oued Miliane (150 km) which flows into the Gulf of Tunis, South of the capital itself, the North-Eastern region accounts for several very short oueds flowing down into the sea from the mountains which make up the centre of the Cap Bon peninsula (annual average water inflow of 290 million cubic metres).

In the Southern region, after a break covering the entire Central Region coast (the rare streams of the Sahel of Sousse and Sfax account for hardly more than an annual average water inflow of 80 million cubic metres) there is paradoxically a network of very short permanent rivers, a few kilometres long only, which feed on artesian, often thermal, wells (120 million cubic metres of water annually). Another paradox is that the mouths of these rivers assume the form of estuaries engendered by tidal movements which are fairly important in the Gulf of Gabes. Other oueds which materialise only every 10 years, and even 100-year floods flow into coastal sebkhas.

Outside these regions the coast which is generally flat and deeply indented has contributed to the creation of numerous parallel stretches of water: lagoons and sebkhas.

Lakes

Only Lake Ichkeul (120 km² and approximately 1 m deep) located in the North-Eastern part of the country has the characteristics that allow it to be considered a lake. It is an endoreic basin linked to the lagoon of Bizerte by a natural channel (oued Tinja) and surrounded by major stretches of marshes.

Sebkhas

They are also divided in three regions beginning in the vicinity of Tunis. There are two of them on the outskirts of Tunis, but of varying aspect; the Sebkha Ariana (20 km²) which is a "dead lagoon" located North, near the sea, and the Sebkha Sejoumi (25 km²) to the West which is an endoreic basin.

Except in the coastal region at the bottom of the Gulf of Gabes the central coastal region, which stretches the Eastern Cap Bon down Jerba, accounts for an almost unbroken series of sebkhas which are located parallel to the coast and often flooded by the sea during the gales blowing in winter. They are generally small, except for the network formed by Sebkhas Assa el Jerida and Halk el Menzel (30 km²) located in the Sahel North of Sousse.

In the far-south there are two large sebkhas which catch the water from the surrounding reliefs when they are torrential outflows. The first one is, near the Bou Gara lagoon, the Sebkha Ain el Mader and the second one, near the Biban lagoon is the Sebkha Bou Jmel. Between these two formations, South of the town of Zarzis, there is a major "fossil" sebkha : the Sebkha el Melah (160 km²) with an haline crust of more than 10 m thickness.

Artificial Water Bodies

Dams, Hill-side Reservoirs and Major Canals

The water resources of an almost barren country must, as much as possible, be preserved, not only for supplying the big cities with drinking water but also for fostering agriculture through irrigation. Tunisia has undertaken the construction of numerous dams, hill-side reservoirs, culverts and canals (Figure 3).

Dam construction started in 1925 with the Kebir dam site on Oued Mellegue which is the main affluent or the Oued Mejerda. After a long period of stagnation, dam building was resumed in the 1950s and as been carried on steadily with about one dam

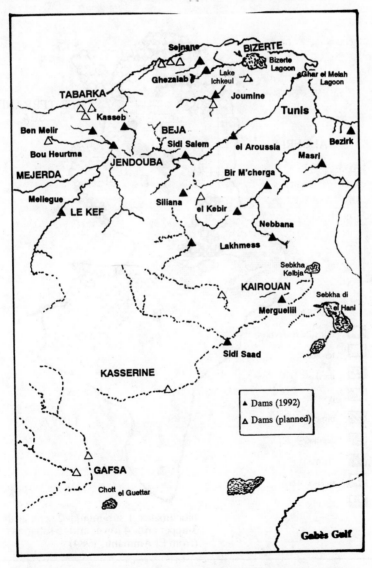

Figure 3. Dams and reservoirs in Tunisia (from Laroussi 1991)

every two years. At present, Tunisia has 18 major dams, with a total storage capacity of 1,704 million cubic metres, which are distributed in the Centre and North; 15 hillside reservoirs in the North and the Cap Bon area with a total storage capacity of 13 million cubic metres and two major canals which take their water from dams built on the Mejerda river: the lower Mejerda valley canal and the Mejerda-Cap Bon canal. The latter is a1xajor 120 km long water work which flooded for the first time in 1984. It allows for the irrigation to the South-East of all the plains it crosses, and it supplements the drinking water supply of Tunis and Cap Bon cities. This canal carries 470 million cubic metres of water every year.

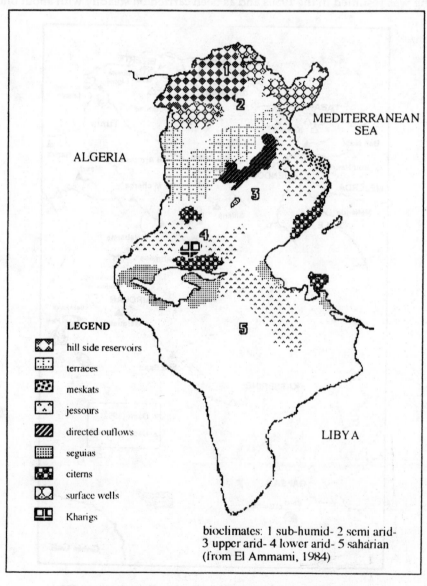

Figure 4. Traditional water harvesting works in Tunisia

Traditional Water Harvesting Works

It is impossible to construct major dam in the South; yet the cultivated area, oases and hillsides are covered by a major irrigation network (Figure 4) which dates over a thousand years ago (El Ammami 1984). In the Sahel region little catchment basins occur around some areas: the "meskets". In the oases the network is composed of "seguias", which are irrigation culverts fed by artesian wells; the "kharigs" (which corresponds to "Foggara" in Algeria) are subterranean networks located at the hillsides where water from the groundwater table is recovered at sources; and finally in the hills areas, West of Sahel region near Sousse, North of Jerid and in Matmata mountains (West of Gabes) "jessours" have been built; they are in fact a series of small earthen or stone dams built terrace-like (or following the staircase pattern) in ravines or gullies, and cover approximately 400,000 ha.

Exploiting of the Groundwater

Groundwater feeding wells exist all over the country. Their main use is for irrigation and they rely on a balance system called "khottare". In the South these wells may go as deep as 70 m. Water resources from these wells reach an estimated annual average 320 million cubic metres in the North, 280 million cubic metres in the Centre and 530 million cubic metres in the South.

Exploiting Fossil Water Resources

At present, numerous generally very deep bore holes (1,000 m) in and around the oases have allowed for increasing the output of artesian wells by tapping directly the deep-water tables of the "terminal continental" (age between -6000 and -24000 years) and or the "intercalary continental" (age between -28000 and -45000 years).

Water Use

The salinity of the surface and deep waters varies most of the time between 1 and 3.5 g dry residue L^{-1} (where NaCl predominates). The proportion of strongly saline water is 10% in the North, 20% in the Centre and 50% in the South. According to the degree of salinity, the usefulness of water may therefore be graded as low for urban use (200 million cubic metres per year), average for agriculture (1,300 million cubic metres per year) and high for industrial use (100 million cubic metres per year).

LIMNOLOGICAL STUDIES

Potamology - Rivers and Oueds

The Mejerda and the Rivers of Northern Tunisia and the Cap Bon

Although study of this environment started at the end of the 19th century, biological and especially ecological knowledge had remained very fragmentary until recently.

During the last century, a fairly comprehensive review of fish species was made by Gervais et al. (1879), to be taken up again and completed at the beginning of this century by de Chaignon (1904) who related the presence of several fish species: *Barbus callensis, Phoxinellus (Leuciscus) chaignoni, Anguilla chaignoni* (in fact, *A. anguilla), Cyprinodon carinatus*, the shrimp *Atyaephyra desmaresti*, the crab *Potamon edulis* and the tortoises *Emys leprosa* and *Cistudo europea*. The list was again expanded by Pellegrin (1921) and twenty years later, Seurat (1940) supplied information on the fishes living in the rivers of Cap Bon.

Besides reviews of the fish fauna, Simon (1885) and Gurney (1909) initiated the first carcinological studies, to be extended later by Sollaud (1927) on shrimp populations, by Gauthier (1928) on Entomostraca and other organisms. The malacological fauna was studied by Bourguignat (1868), Bourguignat et al. (1987) and Pallary (1923) and the flora by Gauthier-Lievre (1931).

Such faunistic and floristic works were almost totally abandoned until the 1970s and 80s when studies were taken up again, up-dated and complimented with environmental considerations (Khallel 1974), and Boumaiza (1984) on physico-chemical patterns and elements of the fauna which had not yet been indexed. Studies by Kraiem (1983) on fish showed that although the fish fauna was relatively abundant in most rivers, it was little diversified and dominated by two species; *Barbus callensis* and *Pseudophoxinellus callensis*.

The Mejerda Delta

Owing to the fact that the river mouth migrated numerous times, it has been particularly well investigated from the geological (Mansouri et al. 1979) as well from the geomorphological points of view (Pimienta 1953, Paskoff 1981). The biotic environment has, however, never been studied.

Central Tunisian Oueds

Because of their sporadic but always torrential flow, they have been impossible to study.

Rivers of the Gulf of Gabes and Irrigation Systems in the Oases

The geographical (river estuaries flowing into the Gulf) or thermic features (numerous hot water springs and wells all over the South) have for a long time already been able to attract the attention of a number of researchers.

Among the most important publications, the studies on fish fauna (Blanc 1895, Seurat 1941), and cenoses by Seurat (1922, 1927, 1934, 1938) who spent quite some time prospecting the rivers, artesian wells and groundwater tables of the Southern mainland and, finally, the studies on flora and fauna by Gauthier (1928) and Gauthier-Lievre (1931). To these should be added important reviews on malacololgical species that serve as intermediate hosts for parasites that transmit diseases to humans and more specifically *Bulinus*, the vector of bilharzia.

More recent studies concern physico-chemical properties and a complete review of invertebrate and vertebrate faunas of the oueds and seguias (Boumaiza, not yet published), and the taxonomic and ecological analyses of the *Melanopsis praemorsa* (Zaouali et al. 1984) populations.

Briny Thermal Sources in the South

Until recently they have been very little studied, except for an hydrological study carried out by Solignac (1927) and for a biological survey made by Seurat who discovered a new species of Malacostraca *Thermosbaena mirabilis* Monod (1924) in the thermal spring (+47°C) of El Hamma near Gabes. At present, however, they are the target of a research project initiated within the framework of Belgian cooperation with Tunisia undertaken to promote aquaculture of the crustacean *Macrobrachium rosenbergii* since its preliminary experimental introduction has provided encouraging results.

Canals

Soon after its flooding the Mejerda—Cap Bon canal was quickly invaded by *Potamogeton pectinatus* (producing an average biomass of 1,000t) which causes considerable slowing of the water flow. This problem encouraged Canal management to introduce the Chinese Carp *Ctenopharyngodon idella* to clean the canal. To achieve the desired results, a team of researchers of the "Institut National Agronomique" has undertaken follow-up of abiotic and biotic patterns and the experimental introduction of the Carp which seems to adapt rapidly to local conditions (Krichen et al. 1990).

Lakes

Although there are no real lakes in Tunisia, the "Lake" Ichkeul with an average salinity of 13.5% can be qualified as a continental permanent water. Indeed, if in winter it constitutes the outlet for 5 oueds, in the summer, however, losses due to evaporation are offset by inflows of salt water from the lagoon of Bizerte. So, it is characterized by high and abrupt fluctuations of salinity (polytypic water plane) with strong restriction of species. This restriction is felt particularly among benthic organisms and fish which are represented mainly by species living in such briny environment as the Cokle *Cerastoderma glaucum*, the Mullets (*Mugil cephalus* mainly) and the Eel (*Anguilla anguilla*). The presence from winter to the middle of summer time of the pondweed *Potamogeton pectinatus* which constitutes the food of hundreds of thousands of migrating water birds (ducks) made that until recently Lake Ichkeul was the most important meeting place of water avifauna in the whole Mediterranean area.

At present, important dams that are being built on the three major oueds flowing into the lake have considerably altered the low salinity content prevailing during the winter season which has always sustained growth of vegetation. In view of the threat of continuance, and even worse, the exacerbation of plant growth which was mainly dependent upon fresh water inflow (the construction of two other dams is projected), and therefore the risk of inducing a slow-down in the migration of birds which feed on *Potamogeton* (Ducks) and *Scirpus* bubbles (Geese), major studies have been planned to find a solution to the progressive "salinisation" of this environment and to the dwindling of surrounding marshes because major drainage networks set up to reclaim these parts for agricultural use.

Although the area had already been described by naturalists during the Roman era (Pliny), it was only at the beginning of the 20th century that Lake Ichkeul started attracting the attention of biologists. It was visited by Gurney (1909) and Gauthier (1928) who noted a very scant fauna dominated essentially by the Copeooda *Popella guerneri* and the Amphipoda *Gammarus locusta*. During the 1930s ichthyologists started taking an interest in the fishery potential of the lake and hence in commercially exploitable species (Gandolfi-Hornyold 1930, Heldt 1931). During the 1970s, works in other fields increased. At present, our knowledge on the lake may be considered as adequate as studies have been undertaken in several fields such as geology, sedimentology (Ouakad 1982), hydrology (Lemoalle 1983), but also in those relating to primary (Ben Rjeb 1986) and fish productivity (Vidy 1983), as well as ecology (Zaouali 1975) and malacology (Zaouali 1976, Madhioub et al. 1988). Monographs on most fish speices living in the lake have been published (Kraiem 1983, Trabelsi et al. 1985). The migrating avifauna and beds of pond grass (*Potamogeton*) have been fairly extensive studied during the 1980s by researchers from the London College with a view to creating an international wildlife reserve.

Permanent Standing Water Bodies

Ponds of the Northern region

Several ponds were visited by Gauthier (1928) who noted the existence of a rather poor "European" type fauna. He notes the occurrence of several species of which he considered as endemic (which, in fact, they are not) such as *Diaptomus numidicus* and *lilleborgi*.

The Ichkeul Marshes

Although at the beginning of this century marshes were very little studied except for visits by carcinologists and specially gauthier who noted the presence of a rich fauna (21 species of Entomostraca). During the past ten years important multi-disciplinary research work concerning specially the flora and avifauna (Hollis 1978) has been undertaken as the region became classified as wildlife reserve for the protection of water birds. In 1987, Lake Ichkeul with an area of 11,227 ha (including marshes) was designated as an Internationally Important Wetland especially for Waterfowl under the Ramsar Convention.

Reservoirs

Although reservoirs are well monitored from the physico-chemical viewpoint by the Ministry of Agriculture, their biological patterns are not yet well known, despite the fact that most reservoirs have been stocked, in a more or less haphazard manner, with imported fish species. This stocking, made for a large number of species (Zaouali 1981), was able to prove the ease with which pike perch (*Stizostedion lucioperca*) can adapt and sustain the severest climatological constraints and muddy environments.

At present, these results have created awareness that dam sites have potential for pisciculture. Studies have been initiated with this in mind, and more particularly within the framework of German Cooperation (GTZ) which has launched a multi-disciplinary R&D project on the Sidi Salem dam (midstream on the Mejerda). Planktological studies (Solhobji 1992) have been able to demonstrate the presence of stocks which are abudnant in number but reduced in species (20 phytoplankton, 18 zooplankton species, six fish species). During the summer, there are an increase phytoplankton production of *Planctonema lauterboornii* and zooplankton where the cladoceran *Diaphanosoma brachyurum* predominates accompanied by a severe reduction in species (6 phytoplankton, 3 zooplankton species). In the winter, the inflow of river water can be seen in the development of cyanobacteria *Oscillatoria* and *Lyngbya*. And finally, the quasi permanent presence of a Copepoda characteristic of the Western Mediterranean *Copidodiaptomus numidicus* occurs.

Temporary Water Bodies

Ponds in the Northern region

They have never been studied although they seem to shelter an interesting flora (water lilies) and fauna.

R'dirs

Gauthier (1928) was able to show that they were the habitat of numerous temporary forms: *Branchipus stagnalis, Apus cancriformis, Apus numidicus* and a Copepodean fauna of "middle-Eastern" aspect. Since that time, nobody has undertaken the updating of this information.

Sebkhas

Sebkha Sejoumi

It was visited by Gurney in 1909 and Gauthier in 1928 who both noted the presence of the Copepoda *Diaptomus saliens (Arctodiaptomus salinus)*. Since then no other biological studies has been carried out and at present there are only a few geological and sedimentological data available (Pimienta 1959).

Sebkha Kelbia

This sebkha is shallow and drains every ten years, with a salinity ranging between 3% and saturation. During the briny water period it is uniformly overgrown with *Zannichiella palustris* which constitutes the habitat of a planktonic fauna which, although, very plentiful, is excessively destitute in species and dominated by the copepod *Arctodiaptomus wierzejskii* and at the benthic level by a not yet identified Ostracoda. In the 1920s this environment was explored by Gauthier who noted the presence of the copepod *Diaptomus saliens* and by Gauthier-Lievre, but then it was completely abandoned by biologists. The Ministry of Agriculture have continued studies of the hydrological levels, which has evaluated the ten-year cycle of flooding and draining of this sebkha.

Since the 1950s, it has been able to attract interest and has been the subject of numerous biological studies: on the shrimp *Palaemonetes varians* (Heldt 1953), on fish populations and a ecological survey (Zaouali 1976). These studies revealed that during severe floods where an indirect communication is established between the sebkha and the sea, different species of fishes coexist and some come from the sea *Mugil cephalus and Mugil ramada, Anguilla anguilla*, while others are allochtonous fresh-water species coming from dams, the common Carp *Cyprinus carpio*.

Sebkha El Hani

This sebkha may be considered as virtually unknown and has, apparently, been visited a single time by Gauthier who noted the presence of *Artemia salina*.

Sebkha Ariana

Its geology has been well reexamined (Mansouri et al. 1979) and such research revealed an depleted fossil fauna, noteworthy only for the abundance of several euryece species and more particularly of the Foraminifera *Streblus beccarii*. At present, it is the habitat of several Cyanophyceae which make up the food supply of *Artemia salina* colonies.

Cap Bon Sebkhas

Apart from several investigations undertaken by sedimentologists (Sassi 1969) they have raised little interest. However, almost all of them have been visited by members of the Belgian Centre for Artemia Studies, who noted the overall presence of this Phyllopoda whose diminutive size was deemed to be of no commercial value.

Southern Sebkhas

The sebkha El Melah near Zarzis, a "fossil-lagoon", is the only one to have been studied thoroughly from the geochemical viewpoint (Milokhoff 1950). It has briny waters rich in magnesium chloride and bromide ($MgCl_2$: 141g L^{-1}, $MgBr_2$: 5g L^{-1}).

The Great Chotts

Ever since the middle of the 19th century and until today, they have been the object of numerous studies in many fields: hydrochemical (Gueddari 1980), geomorphological (Coque 1962) and more specially geological and paleontological (from Tournouer in 1878 to Zaouali in 1989). A constant interest was pointed out about the enigmatic origin of the fossil populations of the Cockle *Cerastoderma glaucum*. Unfortunately, however, they have attracted little interest from the zoologists, except for Seurat (1938) who noted the presence of *Daphnia magna*. Several recent studies have, however, been made on the flora (Serpett 1947) which comment on the presence of a large numbers of the cyanobacteria *Aphanotheca microps, Spirulina meneghiensis* and *S. subsahara*.

PRESENT STATUS

As we have just seen, research in the mainland environment was very active at the beginning of this century. Beginning towards the end of the 19th century, it reached its peak during the 1920s and 30s to be almost entirely forgotten during the ensuing 50 years. In this framework, it is worthwhile mentioning the bibliographical work edited by O.R.S.T.O.M. in 1987-88 on shallow water expanses in Africa (Burgis and Symoens 1987, Davies and Gasse 1988) has about 100 reference entries for Tunisia between 1880 and 1940 and a little more than 10 between 1940 and 1970.

It was only after 1970 that studies have been taken up again in new unexplored habitats to allow for the updating of knowledge on taxonomy and distribution of Copepoda (Dussart 1967, 1969) which had become outdated. Among others should be mentioned the work of Dumont et al. (1978) pertaining to the exploration of Entomo-straca in 60 sites spread all over Tunisia and which allowed for the identification of 56 species. Among the most frequent groups are the Cladocera (27 species) with *Chyrodus sphaericus* and *Simocephalus vetulus* and the Copepoda (24 species) with *Tropocylops prasinus* and *Copidodiaptomus numidicus* (Table 1).

Except for fish and crustaceans, knowledge of other flora and fauna (30 entries in ORSTOM bibliographical work) remains fragmentary. Physico-chemical data on the streams are very incomplete; there is no significant study on the dynamics of stock and populations. The planktonic fauna and flora of Tunisian rivers may be said to be unknown.

Biological and ecological studies on most marshes (except for those of Ichkeul), temporary water expenses, sebkhas and chotts are yet to be carried out. Reservoirs have been studied from an abiotic standpoint by Ministry of Agriculture departments, but, apart from a few ichthyological explorations, their flora and fauna have not been methodically investigated (part from the sole Sidi Salem dam site). The biotic environment of the Lower Mejerda valley canal remains an unknown factor.

RESEARCH INSTITUTIONS

Tunisia cannot call its own any specialised laboratory in limnology. Research is carried out by a few dispersed groups belonging to the "Faculté des Sciences de Tunis", the "Ecole d'Ingénieurs de Sfax" (ENIS) and the "Institut Scientifique, Technique, Océano-graphique et de Pêches de Tunisie" (INSTOP), the "Institut National Agronomique" (INAT) and Hydraulic Engineering Services of the Ministry of Agriculture. The "Institut Pasteur de Tunis" which had long been very active in the research of endemic parasitic diseases generated by fauna living in the springs and seguias in the oases, has given up this type of work. It is noteworthy, however, that the measures it proposed had been followed and that parasitic concerns have declined and even disappeared.

There is hardly any nationwide research axis. Any multi-disciplinary research work carried to date has been promoted by foreign or international organisations: aquacul-tural trial near the oases of Gabès (Mullet farming) and in the Southern area of Jérid (Kebili and Douz oases, Mullets and *Tilapia nilotica* farming) were started under FAO patronage in 1973 by Pillai (1975) but not continued despite satisfactory preliminary results. In-depth studies on the marshes of Lake Ichkeul were undertaken by the scien-

Table 1. Distribution of Copepoda in Tunisia as indicated by the frequency of reports in published literature. Number of reports for frequent species are in bold, for rare species are in italics.

Species	Fresh Waters			Briny Waters			No. of Reports	Distribution	Ecology
	North	Central	South	North	Central	South			
Calanoida									
Pseudodiaptomidae									
Calanipeda aquaedulcis	3	2	-	-	3	-	8	Mediterranean	Halophilic
Diaptomidae									
Arctodiaptomus wierzejskii	3	3					6	Cosmopolitan	Eurytherm
Copidodiaptomus numidicus	4						4	Mediterranean	Thermophilic
Diaptomus cyaneus	5	1					6	North Africa	Thermophilic
Gigantodiaptomus ingens	2						2	North Africa	Thermophilic
Metadiaptomus chevreuxi	2	2			1		5	North Africa	Thermophilic
Mixodiaptomus incrassatus	6						6	Cosmopolitan	Thermophilic
Mixodiaptomus lilljeborgi	3			1			4	Cosmopolitan	Thermophilic
Rabdodiaptomus salinus	1			1	2	1	5	Cosmopolitan	Euryhaline
No. of reports	**29**	8		2	6	1	**46**		
Cyclopoida									
Eucyclopinae									
Eucyclops enacanthus	1						1	Cosmopolitan	Thermophilic
Eucyclops serrulatus	1						1	Cosmopolitan	Eurytopic
Paracyclops affinis	2	2					4	Cosmopolitan	Eurytopic
Paracyclops fimbriatus	1						1	Cosmopolitan	Eurytopic
Macrocyclops albidus	1	1					2	Cosmopolitan	Eurytopic
Paracyclops poppei	1						1	Cosmopolitan	Thermophilic
Tropocyclops prasinus	**12**	2					**14**	Cosmopolitan	Thermophilic

Cyclopinae

Species							No. of reports		
Acanthocyclops robustus	4	2	1				7	Cosmopolitan	Thermophilic
Acanthocyclops viridis	7	1	1				9	Cosmopolitan	Eurytopic
Cryptocyclops linjaticus			2	1			3	Mediterranean	Thermophilic
Cyclops abyssorum mauritanae	2						2	Cosmopolitan	Thermophilic
Cyclops furcifer (lacunae)	5						5	Cosmopolitan	Eurytopic
Cyclops strenuus	1	1	2				4	Cosmopolitan	Eurytopic
Diacyclops bicuspidatus	1						1	Cosmopolitan	Euryhaline
Mesocyclops leuckarti	1						1	Cosmopolitan	Thermophilic
Metacyclops minutus	3		2				5	Cosmopolitan	Eurytopic
Metacyclops planus	3	1					4	Mediterranean	Thermophilic
Microcyclops rubellus	1						1	Cosmopolitan	Thermophilic
Thermocyclops dybowskii			1				1	Cosmopolitan	Thermophilic
Thermocyclops oblongatus			2				2	Mediterranean	Thermophilic
No. of reports	43	9	16	1			69		

Harpacticoida

Species							No. of reports		
Canthocamptus microstaphylinus	1						4	Cosmopolitan	Eurytopic
Cletocamptus confluens	2						3	Cosmopolitan	Euryhaline
Cletocamptus retrogressus		1	2				4	Mediterranean	Halophilic
Mrazekiella trispinosa	1		2				2	Cosmopolitan	Eurythermic
Number of Reports	4	3	4	2			13		

Total Number of reports	74	19	22	3	8	2	128		
Number of Species	25	11	16	2	4	2			

tists from London College, London, under the patronage of the "Parcs Nationaux Tunisiens". A study on the possibility of stocking dams with fishes was supported by the German Society for Technical Cooperation (GTZ) under the aegis of the "Direction des Pêches". A study on brine thermal waters in Southern Tunisia was carried out by INAT research staff under the patronage of Gent University (Belgium).

In view of the highly positive results obtained recently in the area of limnology by the few teams who are active in this field, it is deemed urgent that official Tunisian organisations become aware of the socio-economic importance of limnology. Against this background and considering the experience gained by research staff at the "Institut National Agronomique", it is deemed that they are the best placed to implement R&D programmes.

Publications

Before 1960, articles in the field of limnology were published by the *"Archives de l' Institut Pasteur"*. At present, the majority of articles are edited by only two Tunisian revues: the *"Bulletin de l'Institut national Scientifique et Technique d'Océanographie et des Pêches"* (INSTOP) for aquacultural items and for fresh and saline waters linked with health problems the *"Archives de l'Institut Pasteur de Tunis"*.

CONCLUSIONS

Confronted with the aridity of climate prevailing in their country, Tunisians have, for thousands of years, practiced a policy of conservation and rational development of their national water resources. A number of specific techniques have been developed in conformity with the need for optimum preservation of the environment. At present, this policy is pursued by the construction of major water reservoirs and irrigation canals which mobilise a significant proportion of the national resources. Water management, in Tunisia, may be considered as satisfactory and, even excellent, as until now it has afforded optimum management of available resources and, this in spite of the periodical droughts.

However, a number of deficiencies are perceptible when it comes to awareness of biological data which are yet based on only rare, and generally incomplete studies. It is therefore in this field that the scientific community should concentrate efforts. By the same token, it appears as most desirable that a national structure for the teaching of limnology be implemented.

REFERENCES

Ben Rjeb, A. 1986. Contribution à l'étude du lac Ichkeul: conditions de milieu et activité photosynthétique du phytoplancton. D.E.A. Université de Tunis. 152 pages. ronéo.

Blanc, E. 1895. Sur les Poissons qui habitent les sources et les puits artésiens du Sahara (Tunisie). Mémoire Societe Zoologique Français 8: 164-172.

Boumaiza, M. 1984. Contribution à la limnologie de la Tunisie: étude physico-chimique. Archives de l'Institut Pasteur de Tunis 61 (2&3): 205-246.

Bourguignat, J.R. 1868. Historie malacologique de la Régence de Tunis. 36 pages.

Bourguignat, J.R. and Letourneux. 1887. Prodrome de la malacologie terrestre et fluviatile de la Tunisie. Imprime Nationale, Paris. 166 pages.

Burgis, M.L. and Symoens, J.J. 1987. Zones humides et lacs peu profonds d'Afrique. Répertoire. Editions ORSTOM, Travaux et Documente 210, 650 pages.

Coque, R. 1962. La Tunisie présaharienne: étude géomorphologique. Armand and Colin Ed., Paris, 488 pages.

Davies, B. and Gasse, F. 1988. Zones humides et lacs peu profonds d'Afrique. Bibliographie. Editions ORSTOM, Travaux et Documente 211, 502 pages.

de Chaignon H. 1904. Contribution à l'histoire naturelle de la Tunisie. Bulletin de la Société d'Histoire Naturelle de Autun 17: 1-162.

Dumont, H.J., Laureys, P., and Pensaert, J. 1978. Anostraca, Conchostraca, Cladocera and Copepoda from Tunisia. Hydrobiologia 66 (3): 259-274.

Dussart, B. 1967. Les Copépods des eaux continentales d'Europe occidentale. Tome I: Calanoïdes et Harpacticoïdes. Edition Boubee et Cie, Paris. 500 pages.

Dussaert, B. 1969. Les Copépods des eaux continentales d'Europe occidentale. Tome I: Cyclopoïdes et biologie quantitative. Editions N. Boubée et Cie, Paris. 292 pages.

El Amami, S. 1984. Les aménagements hydrauliques traditionnels de Tunisie. Centre de Recherches Génie rural, Tunis. 69 pages.

Gandolfi-Hornyold, A. 1930. Recherches sur la taille et le sexe de la petitide anguille du lac de l'Ischkeul. Notes Station Océanographique Salammbô 11. 15 pages.

Gauthier, H. 1928. Recherches sur la fauna des eaux continentales de l'Algerie et de la Tunisie. Imprime Minerva, Alger. 419 pages, 3 plates, 2 color plates.

Gauthier-Lièvre L. 1931. Recherches sur la flore des eaux continentales de l'Afrique du Nord. Bulletin de la Société Histoire Naturelle d'Afrique Noire, Mémoire H.S. 299 pages.

Gervais H., and Jasienski, H. 1879. Les Poissons de Tunisie: énumération et description valeurs alimentaire et commerciale. Saint-Denis Imprime C. Lambert, Paris. 54 pages, 19 pl.

Gueddari, M. 1980. Géochimie des sels et saumures du chott el Jerid. Thèse spec., Universite de Toulouse, Toulouse. 131 pages.

Gurney R. 1909. On the fresh water Crustacea of Algeria and Tunisia. Journal of the Royal Microscopical Society, London: 273-305.

Heldt, H. 1931. Sur le mal dont périssent les muges de l'Ichkeul et sur les remèdes possibles. Notes Station Océanographique, Salammbô 17. 8 pages.

Heldt, J.H. 1953. Palaemonetes varians (Leach) du lac Kelbia. Cas de poeciligonie dans une même nappe d'eau. Bulletin Station Océanographique, Salammbô 44: 1-14.

Hollis, G.E. 1978. Nature conservation projects for the national parks of Ichkeul. Bulletin d'Office National des Pêches, Tunisie 2(1-2): 235-248.

Khallel, M.R. 1974. Monographie de la Mejerda. Publication of the Ministry of Agriculture, Tunis. 427 pages.

Kraiem, M.M. 1983. Les poissons d'eau douce de Tunisie: inventaire, commenté et répartition géographique. Bulletin de la Institut National des Sciences Pêches, Salammbô 10: 107-124.

Krichen, Y., Ben Slama, R., Abdessatar, A., Zaouali, J. and Romdhane, M.S. 1990. Lutte par empoissonnement contre le développment des plantes aquatiques dans le canal Mejerda-Cap Bon. Institut National Agronomique de Tunisie. 105 pages. ronéo.

Laroussi Ch. 1991. L'eau, actualité et devenir en Tunisie. Convergences 19: 24-25.

Lemoalle, J. 1983. L'oued Tinja: observations, éléments de l'hydroclimat. Rapport et Documente, CGP Tunis 1: 3-33.

Lemoalle, J. and Vidy, G. 1983. Exploitation halieutique et conditions du milieu dans le lac Ichkeul. Rapport et Documente, CGP Tunis 1: 46-51.

Madhioub, M.N. and Zaouali, J. 1988. Captage de l,huitre creuse Crassostrea gigas dans le lac Ichkeul. Bulletin de la Institut National des Sciences Pêches, Salammbô 15: 47-60.

Mansouri-Menaouar, R. 1979. Contribution à l'étude de la sédimentation littorale historique et actuelle au voisinage du delta de la Mejerda. Thèse spé. Univrsite de Bordeaux. 172 pages.

Mansouri, R., Carbonnel, P. and Bobier, C. 1979. A propos de l'évolution récente de la sebkha de l,Ariana. Bulletin d'Office National esPêche, Tunisie 3(2): 157-163.

Milokhoff, W. 1950. Rapport géologique et chimique sur la sebkha el Melah de Zarzis. Mines domaniales des Potasses d'Alsace, 200 pages. ronéo.

Monod, T. 1924. Sur un nouveau type de Malacostracé *Thermosbaena mirabilis*, nov. gen. nov. sp. Bulletin de la Société Zoologique de France, Paris 49: 58-68.

Ouakad, M. 1982. Evolution sédimentologique et caractères géochimiques des dépôts récents de la Garaet el Ichkeul (Tunisie septentrionale). Thèse spé. Université de Perpignan, 166 pages. ronéo.

Pallary, P. 1923. Faune malacologique des eaux douces de la Tunisie. Archives de l'Institut Pasteur de Afrique du Nord 3: 22-47.

Paskoff, R. 1981. L'évolution de la lagune littorale de Ghar el Melah, delta de la Mejerda (Tunisie nord orientale). Bulletin de la Société Languedoc Géographique 15: 49-57.

Pellegrin, J. 1921. Les Poissons des eaux douces de l'Afrique nu Nord française. Mémoire de la Société des Sciences Naturelles et Physique du Maroc 1: 216 pages.

Pillai, T.G. 1975. Possibilités de l'aquaculture et développment de la pêche en eau douce et saumâtre en Tunisie. Bulletin Pêche PNUD-FAO, 2: 69-130.

Pimienta, J. 1953. Sur les déplacements de l'embouchure de la Mejerda et les caractères de son delta. Compte Rendu de l'Académie des Sciences, Paris, 236: 2326-2328.

Pimienta, J. 1959. Le cycle Pliocène-actuel dans les bassins paraliques de Tunis. Mémoire de la Société Geologique Français 38 (65): 176 pages.

Sassi, S. 1969. Contribution à l'étude de la sebkha Tedgimane et du chott el Guettar. Notes Service Géologique du Tunis 24: 17 pages.

Saullaud, E. 1927. Les crevettes des eaux supralittorales et continentales de la Berbérie. Association Français Avancement des Sciences No. 51.

Serpette, M. 1947. Observation écologiques et systématiques sur quelques Cyanophycées de Tunisie. Bulletin de la Société Botanique France 94: 306-309.

Seurat, L.G. 1922. Faune des eaux continentales de la Berbérie. Bulletin de la Société d'Histoire Naturelle de Afrique du Nord 13: 45-60.

Seurat, L.G. 1927. L'estuaire de l'Akarit (golfe de Gabès). Bulletin de la Société d'Histoire Naturelle de Afrique du Nord 18: 80-82.

Seurat, L.G. 1934. Formations littorales et estuaires de la Syrte mineure. Bulletin Station Océanographique Salammbô 32: 65 pages, 1 c.

Seurat, L.G. 1938. Faune aquatique de la Tunisie méridionale (sud et extrème sud). Mémoires de la Société de Biogeographie 6: 121-143.

Seurat, L.G. 1940. Peuplement des eaux continentales du Cap Bon et de Zembra (Tunisie septentrionale). Compte Rendu des Séances de la Société de Biogéographie. 27-29.

Seurat, L.G. 1941. Le Cyprinodon rubané en Tunisie. Archives de l'Institut Pasteur de Tunis 30(3-4): 245-265.

Simon, E. 1885. Etude sur les Crustacés terrestres et fluviatiles recuellis en Tunisie. Explor. Sci. Tunisie.

Solhobji, D. 1992. Etude zooplanctonique du barrage de Sidi Salem. DEA. University de Tunis. 140 pages.

Solignac, M. 1927. Etude sur les sources thermo minérales de la Tunisie. Region de Gabès et de Tunis. Serv. Mines, Tunis. 67 pages.

Tournover, M. 1878. Sur quelques coquilles marines recueillies dans la région des chotts sahariens. Association Français Avancement des Sciences No. 7: 608-622.

Trabelsi, M. and Kartas, S. 1985. Contribution à l'étude des caractères numériques de l'Athérine *Atherina boyeri* Risso, 1810, des côtes tunisiennes. Rapport, Commission Internationale pour l'Exploration Scientifique de la Mer Méditerranée 29 (4): 187-189.

Vidy, G. 1983. Organisation de la pêche et statistiques de la production du lac Ichkeul. Rapport et Documente, CGP Tunis 1: 34-45.

Zaouali, J. 1975. Contribution à l'étude écologique du lac Ichkeul (Tunisie septentrionale). Bulletin de la Institut National des Sciences Pêche, Salammbô 4(1): 115-124.

Zaouali, J. 1976. Contribution à la connaissance de la fauna malacologique du lac Ichkeul. Etude du Bivalve *Cerastoderma glaucum* Poiret. Archives de l'Institut Pasteur de Tunis 53 (1-2): 113-126.

Zaouali, J. 1976. Contribution à l'étude écologique de la sebkha Kelbia (Tunisie centrale). Archives de l'Institut Pasteur de Tunis 53 (3): 261-269.

Zaouali, J. 1981. Problèmes d'aquaculture: eaux saumâtres et potentiel aquacole. Archives de l'Institut Pasteur de Tunis 58 (1-2): 93-103.

Zaouali, J. 1989. Ecologie des milieux à *Cerastoderma glaucum* du sud tunisien, périodes actuelle et quaternaire. Rapport Congrès Jerba. (in press).

Zaouali, J. and Baeten, S. 1984. Contribution à l'étude des *Mélanopsis* (Gastropoda, Prosobranchia, Thiaridae) tunisiens. Haliotis 18: 33-41.

Gopal, B. and Wetzel, R.G. (Editors) **Limnology in Developing Countries**: 63-103
© 1995, International Association for Limnology

Limnological Research and Training in Sri Lanka: State of the Art and Future Needs

H.H. Costa
Department of Zoology, University of Kelaniya, Kelaniya, Sri Lanka

P.K. de Silva
Department of Zoology, University of Peradeniya, Peradeniya, Sri Lanka

ABSTRACT

The island of Sri Lanka covers an area of 65,525 km² with a maximum north-south length of 452 km. The major features of the landscape are the abundance of perennial rivers and a multitude of man-made lakes.

Geologically, Sri Lanka is an extension of the peninsular India. Rainfall is the most seasonal climatic factor with slight seasonal variation in temperature, humidity and daylength.

A considerable amount of limnological research has been carried out to date both by local and foreign scientists and these are reviewed here. These cover taxonomic studies of aquatic flora and fauna, ecological studies of organisms in lentic and lotic waterbodies, physico-chemical studies of rivers, man-made lakes and estuaries, primary production, pollution of aquatic bodies, conservation of aquatic fauna, fish production and fisheries management. However, there are still significant gaps specially with reference to the effects of increasing human activities on water quality of lotic and lentic waterbodies.

External funding received has been mostly for the department of fishery resources in inland reservoirs. The assistance received exceeded US\$ 2.7 million.

The major constraints on limnological teaching and research in universities and research institutions in Sri Lanka are the lack of qualified limnologists, the scarcity of analytical and experimental equipment and inadequate funds.

INTRODUCTION

The island of Sri Lanka (0—10° N Latitude, 80—82° E Longitude) situated to the south of the Indian sub-continent and separated from it by the narrow Palk Strait, has been described as one of the most beautiful tropical islands of the world. It covers a land area of 65,525 km² with a maximum north-south length of 452 km.

The island is drained by 103 river systems but there are no natural lakes. Nevertheless a multitude of man-made lakes, both ancient and recent, are present.

Limnology has evolved in Sri Lanka through descriptive analysis. For many years limnological research was confined to taxonomical studies of aquatic flora and fauna. It was only in the late nineteen sixties that adequate attention was paid to functional relationships of the flora and fauna of the inland waters and to the dynamics of their environment. Remarkable progress in the understanding of physical, chemical and biological processes of Sri Lankan inland waters has been achieved in the last two decades through the combined efforts of local and foreign scientists.

This progress reflects interest in the maintenance of water quality, understanding of biodiversity and the need for conservation of flora and fauna, and develop fisheries resources, especially in lentic environments.

Physiography

Cooray (1984) and Erb (1984) have described the physiography of Sri Lanka in detail. The island consists of a central mountain mass, the central highlands, rising in a series of tiers from a low flat plain surrounding it on all sides and extending to the sea. The highland is surrounded by two peneplains the lowest of which extends from the coast inland from sea level to about 100-150 m and is usually described as the low land. The second peneplain, the upland, extends from the lowland to about 500—700 m which in some places is irregular and eroded. The third peneplain extending up to about 2500 m and usually termed the highland consists of the Knuckles group to the north, Central massifs and the Sabaragamuwa ridges to the South West and consists of a complex of plateaux, mountain chains and basins all at the same general level. Because of these topographical features of well marked ridges and valleys, when a stream descends from one elevation to another there is a waterfall. There are over fifty such waterfalls in the island.

Geology

The island is essentially an extension of the peninsular India which formed a part of the Gondwana shield. The most recent account of the geology of the island is given by Cooray (1984). The summary of various geological formations and their distribution in the country is given in Table 1. The precambrian rocks cover about 90 percent of the

Table 1. Geological formations and their distribution in Sri Lanka.

Geological formation	Composition	Distribution
Precambrian	a. Highland series Charnockite, metamorphosed sediments, Quartzites, Quartz-schists, etc.	Hill country and Northern plain
	b. South Western group metasediments	Coastal belt of the South-West sector
	c. Vijayan series Granites, granitic Gneisses, etc.	Lowlands to the North-West and South-East highland series
Jurassic	Sandstones, shales etc.	Tabbowa beds
Miocene	Limestone	Jaffna
Pleistocene	Red earth laterites	Ratnapura bed
Recent	Alluvium beach and dune sands	Coastal belts

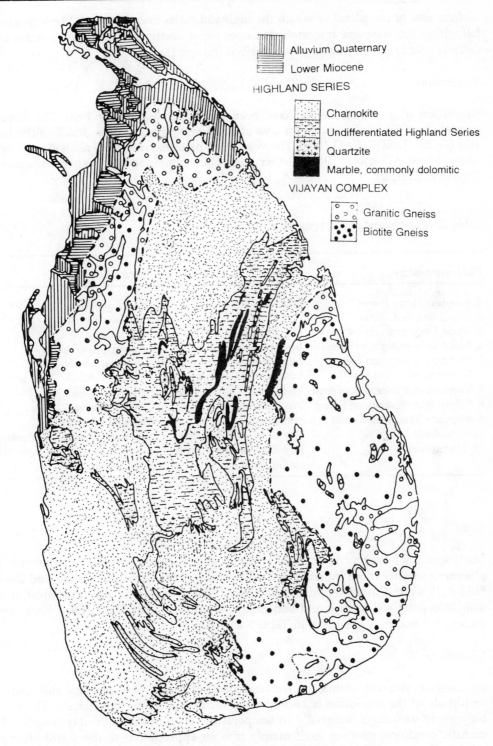

Alluvium Quaternary

Lower Miocene

HIGHLAND SERIES

Charnokite

Undifferentiated Highland Series

Quartzite

Marble, commonly dolomitic

VIJAYAN COMPLEX

Granitic Gneiss

Biotite Gneiss

Figure 1. Geological map of Sri Lanka

surface area of the island of which the highland series and the South Western group fall within the West and Intermediate Zones (see Climate) and the Vijayan series falls entirely within the Dry Zone (Cooray 1984) (Figure 1).

Vegetation

Vegetation maps of Sri Lanka have been published since early 1930. The natural vegetation of Sri Lanka covers an area of 2.375 million hectares or 36.5% of the land area (GOSL/UNDP/FAO 1986). The vegetation patterns have been related to climatic zones (Mueller-Dombois 1968). Eleven major plant communities have been recognized (Figure 2, Table 2).

Table 2. Major vegetation types of Sri Lanka

Plant community	Climatic zone	Common species
1. Tropical Thorn Forest	Dry Zone	*Carissa spinarum*
2. Dry Evergreen Forest	Dry Zone	*Manilkara hexandra*
3. Moist Deciduous Forest	Dry Zone	*Vitex pinnata*
4. Moist Semi-evergreen Forest	Intermediate zone	*Chlorozylon sweeteenia*
5. Wet Semi-evergreen Forest	Intermediate zone	*Artocarpus nobilis*
6. Tropical Savannah Forest	Intermediate and Dry zone	*Terminalia chebula, Vitex pinnata*
7. Tropical Wet Evergreen Forest	Wet Zone	*Dipterus zeylanica*
8. Submontane Evergreen Forest	Wet Zone	*Corallia caracina*
9. Montane Temperate Forest	Wet Zone	*Michaelia nilagirica*
10. Grassland	Dry Zone and Wet zone	*Limonia acidisima, Chrysopogon* sp.
11. Mangroves	Dry Zone and Wet zone (saline habitat)	*Avicennia* sp.

Soils

Studies on soil have received special attention as a result of various land development schemes specially those initiated in the Dry Zone of Sri Lanka. Moorman and Pana-bokke (1961) and more recently Panabokke (1984) presented a new classification of soils into great soil groups and sub groups. Fourteen Great Soil Groups have been recognized and they are given in Table 3 and Figure 3.

Climate

Sri Lanka is situated within the equatorial belt of calms. The intensity and narrow amplitude of the insolation is an important factor controlling the climate. There are only slight variations seasonally in temperature, air humidity and day length. The climatic condition resolves itself mainly into an appreciation of the distribution of rainfall, the seasonal changes in temperature being slight.

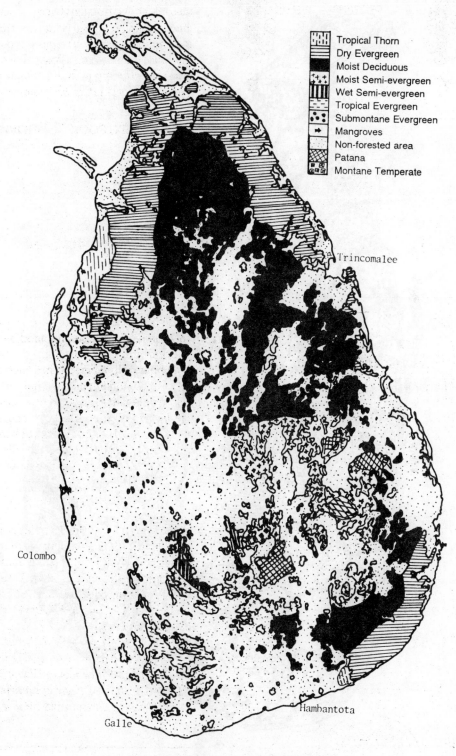

Figure 2. Vegetation map of Sri Lanka

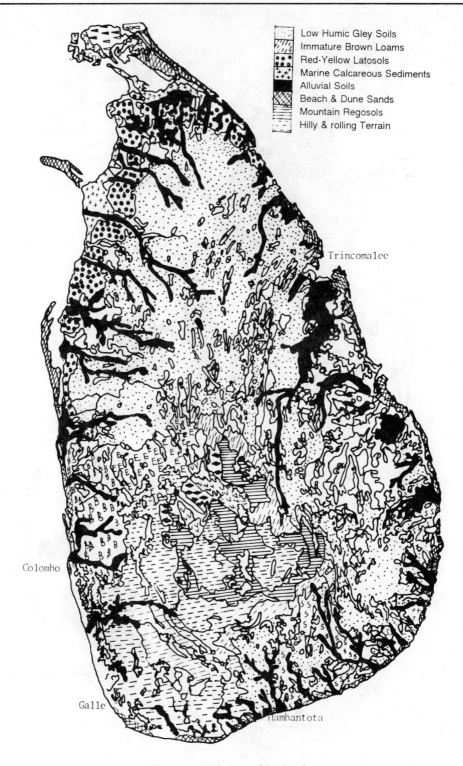

Figure 3. Soil map of Sri Lanka

Table 3. The Great Soil Groups of Sri Lanka

Soil group	Characteristics	Terrain
Reddish brown earths	Fine textured reddish brown soils	Crests upper & midslopes of undulating landscape
Low humid grey soils	Moderately textured	Undulating landscape
Solodized Solonetz	Coarse textured brown to dark brown	Flat bottomed land
Non-calcic brown soils	Medium textured	Upper and midslopes of undulating landscape
Immature brown loams	Well drained dark brown soils	Eroded slopes of hills
Soils on old alluvium	Coarse textured brown	Mid slopes of undulating landscape
Red yellow latosols	Very deep excessively drained	Occupy Crests, Mid slopes and Lower fine textured slopes
Caleo Red-Yellow latosols	Underlain big limestone	Lower slopes
Grumusols	Dark grey brown to black clayey soils	Flat landscapes
Alluvial soils	White, reddish brown black in colour, well to poorly drained	Flood plains, rivers
Rugosols	Whitish excessively drained soils	Beaches and sand dunes
Red-Yellow Podzolic soils	Reddish or yellowish moderately drained	Steep slopes of mountains
Reddish-brown Latosolic soils	Reddish brown, moderately fine textured	Valley bottoms and hilly landscapes
Bog and half Bog soils	Very poorly drained soils, rich in brown to black organic matter	Flat coastal land

Temperature

The temperature of the island is equitable (Figure 4) and in the low country averages about 27 °C with a mean daily range of 6 °C. In the central highlands with altitudes upto 2400 m a cooler climate is experienced. At Nuwara Eliya (altitude 1800 m) the mean annual temperature is 15 °C and the mean daily range is 10 °C.

The mean temperature of the months varies only slightly (Table 4). The narrow amplitude of the temperature is a result of the influence of the sea and the cloudiness which is often greatest during the day.

Table 4. Average monthly and yearly temperatures (°C) (average of 20 years)

	Colombo	Ratnapura	Nuwara Eliya
Altitude (m above MSL)	7	27	1800
January	26.1	26.7	21.4
February	27.6	27.5	24.6
March	27.5	28.0	24.5
April	28.0	28.1	21.4
May	28.1	27.7	17.3
June	27.5	26.9	10.1
July	27.2	26.6	10.6
August	27.3	26.9	10.6
September	27.3	26.7	13.7
October	26.9	26.6	15.7
November	26.5	26.6	16.3
December	26.3	25.9	26.4
Yearly average	27.1	27.0	17.7

Table 5. The rainfall pattern of Sri Lanka

Wind regime	Period	Distribution
South West Monsoon	May to September	South West quarter
2nd Intermonsoonal period	October to November	Widespread
North East Monsoon	December to February	Eastern half of the island including Rakwana hills
1st Intermonsoonal period	March to April	South East and North West

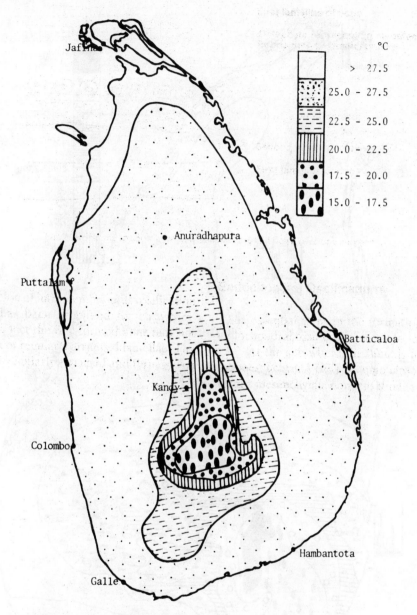

Figure 4. The annual average temperature pattern of Sri Lanka

Rainfall

Rainfall is the most obvious climatic factor in Sri Lanka. The annual rainfall varies from 900 mm to 6000 mm. The central massif plays an important part in the distribution of rainfall (Figure 5).

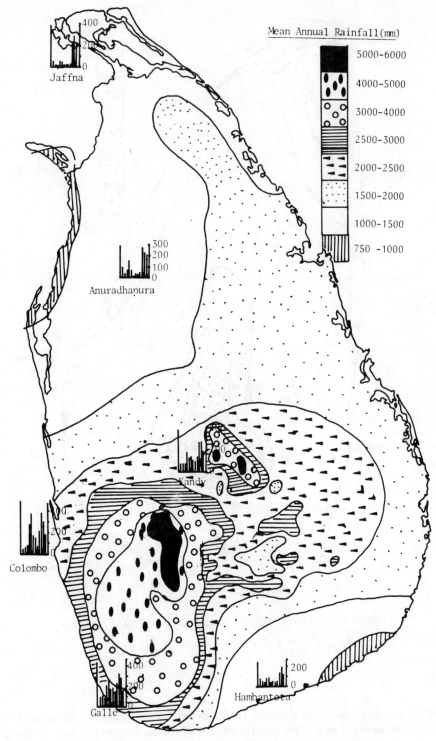

Figure 5. The mean annual rainfall pattern of Sri Lanka

The island is influenced by two important wind regimes, the South West monsoon and North East monsoon. The rainfall during the two intermonsoonal months is mainly convectional (Table 5).

On the basis of amount of rainfall received, one could separate a "Wet Zone" (with 2000 mm rainfall) with rain all the year around from a "Dry Zone" with a marked dry season, which lasts several months.

Humidity

The mean relative humidity varies only slightly. 30 year annual amplitude values show that for lowland (Colombo) it was 68—79% RH in the day time, 87—93% RH at night; in the upland (Kandy) 60—76% RH in the day time 87—94% at night and in the highland (Nuwara Eliya) 60—84% in the day time and 83—93% RH at night.

Climatic Zones

Presently, on the basis of altitude, annual temperature range and mean annual rainfall, three climatic zones are recognized in Sri Lanka (Table 6). These are further sudivided into sub-zones based mainly on altitude.

Table 6. Climatic zones of Sri Lanka

Zone	Altitude (m)	Temperature (°C)	Rainfall (mm)
WET ZONE Lowland Wet Zone Upland Wet Zone Highland Wet Zone	0-1500	15-34	>250
INTERMEDIATE ZONE Lowland Intermediate Zone Upland Intermediate Zone	1000-1500	25-28	175-250
DRY ZONE Arid Zone Semi Arid Zone Lowland Dry Zone	0-200	26-38	<125

FRESHWATER RESOURCES

The inland water resources of Sri Lanka are considerable and are made up of river systems, man-made perennial reservoirs, man-made seasonal reservoirs, irrigation reservoirs and the marshes. To this may be added the brackish water resources comprising lagoons, estuaries and salt marshes.

Running Water (Lotic) Systems

The major rivers arise in the central highland located in the southern part of the country and flow more or less in a radial fashion through the low country. Some of these rivers produce shallow flood plains in their lower reaches. These may be short-lived lasting only during the floods or they may be permanent as in the lower reaches of Mahaweli river. Most of the rivers in the Dry Zone may be reduced to a series of pools during the period of drought.

The rivers are remarkable for their number than for their size. There are 103 perennial rivers. All these rivers have flow characteristics which are dependent on their geographical position, physical characteristics of the terrain and the regional climatic parameters (Erb 1984). Table 7 gives the major characteristics of the 16 principal rivers.

The rivers of Sri Lanka fall under four categories (Erb 1984).
1. Rivers with headwaters in the mountain plateaux and plains of the inner region of the Central massif flowing outwards to the coastal plain and sea.
2. Rivers with headwaters in the marginal hills, plateaux of Central massif flowing down to the coastal plain and sea.
3. Rivers with headwaters in the mountain hills and plateaux of Sabaragamuwa hills and Elahera ridges traversing down to the coastal plain and sea.
4. Rivers with headwaters on the circum island peneplains traversing the coastal plain and sea.

Table 7. Major characteristics of the sixteen principal rivers of Sri Lanka.
        (Data from Somasekaram 1988).

River	Length (km)	Catchment area (km^2)	Precipitation (m^3 x 10^6)	Discharge to sea (m^3 x 10^6)	Discharge % of precipitation
Mahaweli Ganga	329	10327	26804	11016	41
Aruvi Aru	166	3246	4592	568	12
Kala Oya	155	2772	4424	587	13
Kelani Ganga	144	2278	8692	5474	62
Yan Oya	150	1520	2269	300	19
Deduru Oya	139	2616	4794	1608	34
Maduru Oya	138	1541	2476	805	32
Walawe Ganga	133	2442	9843	2165	22
Menik Ganga	130	1272	1472	486	33
Maha Oya	125	1510	4132	1608	39
Kirindi Oya	117	1165	1606	476	30
Kalu Ganga	112	2688	10122	7862	77
Gin Ganga	112	922	3039	1903	62
Kumbukkan Oya	112	1218	2140	774	36
Mi Oya	107	90	144	28	19
Gal Oya	99	1792	4031	1250	31

Precipitation, Run-off and Water Budget

The total annual precipitation over Sri Lanka is about $123,000 \times 10^6$ m³ of water (Costa 1986). The surface water resources in terms of total mean annual escape to the sea and lagoons from 103 river basins have been estimated to be $56,281 \times 10^6$. The total ground water resoruces available in the island have been estimated by Fernando (1973) to be around 7380×10^6 m³ per annum which is about one-sixth of the water resources of the country (Figure 6). Most of the residual precipitation is lost by evapotranspiration through the luxuriant vegetation.

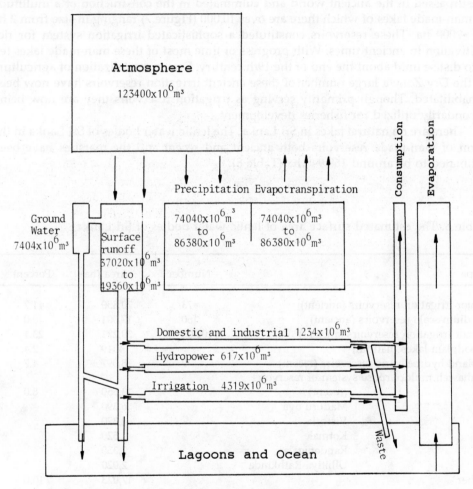

Figure 6. Water budget of Sri Lanka based on data from many sources

The major uses of surface water resources are for domestic, industrial, irrigation and hydro-power generation. Approximately 1230×10^6 m³ of water are presently utilized for domestic and indusdtrial purposes while the irrigation and hydroworks consume around 4920×10^6 m³ of water. The installed reservoirs such as Laxapana,

Norton, etc. together have a storage capacity of around 246×10^6 m^3 while the reservoirs constructed under Multipurpose Mahaweli Development Scheme will hold around 2000×10^6 m^3 of water.

Standing (Lentic) Waterbodies

The ancient civilization of Sri Lanka was centered in the Dry Zone of Sri Lanka. This necessitated the conservation of water that falls during the restricted rainy season (November to February) which initiated a hydraulic engineering civilization that was unsurpassed in the ancient world and culminated in the construction of a multitude of man-made lakes of which there are over 10,000 (Figure 7) ranging in size from 2 ha to >2000 ha. These reservoirs constituted a sophisticated irrigation system for rice cultivation in ancient times. With progress of time most of these man-made lakes fell into disuse until about the end of the 19th century. Due to revitalization of agriculture in the Dry Zone a large number of these ancient irrigation reservoirs have now been rehabilitated. Though primarily serving as irrigation reservoirs they are now being secondarily utilized for fisheries development.

There are no natural lakes in Sri Lanka. The lentic water bodies of Sri Lanka in the form of man-made reservoirs both ancient and recent and the marshes have been estimated to be around 169,940 ha (Table 8).

Table 8. The estimated surface area of lentic water bodies of Sri Lanka

Type	Number	Area (ha)	Percent
Major irrigation reservoirs (ancient)	73	70,850	41.7
Medium-scale reservoirs (ancient)	160	17,001	10.0
Minor irrigation reservoirs (ancient)	>10,000	39,271	23.1
Floodplain lakes (natural)	-	4049	2.4
Upland hydroelectric reservoirs (recent)	7	8,097	4.7
Mahaweli multipurpose system of reservoirs			
(recent)		13,650	8.0
Maduru oya		6,390	
Victoria		2,370	
Kotmale		520	
Randenigala		2,350	
Ulhitiya-Rathkinda		2,020	
Other		17,023	10.0
Total		169,941	100.0

PHYSICO-CHEMICAL CHARACTERISTICS OF LOTIC WATER BODIES

In contrast to lentic water bodies little information is available on physico-chemical characteristics of lotic water bodies.

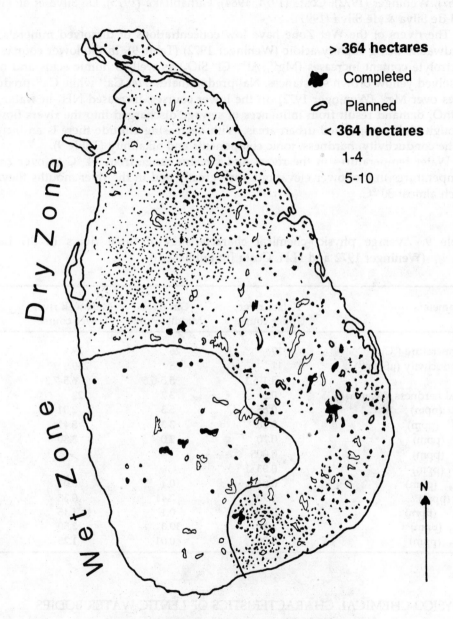

> **364 hectares**

🐾 Completed

⌒ Planned

< **364 hectares**

1-4

5-10

Figure 7. Lentic water resources of Sri Lanka.

Water chemistry of rivers is largely a product of geological structure. Under tropical conditions of heavy rainfall and high temperatures, chemical weathering is very intense and so is leaching (Weninger 1972). Most of the information that is available is of the running waters of central highlands and coastal areas in the south west.

Physico-chemical characteristics of lotic water bodies have been studied by Geisler (1967), Weninger (1972), Costa (1974, 1984), Gunatillaka (1975), De Silva et al. (1984) and de Silva & de Silva (1991).

The rivers of the Wet Zone have low concentrations of dissolved minerals, the headwaters being slightly acidic (Weninger 1972) (Table 9). In the lower courses the electrolyte content increases (Mg^{2+}, Al^{3+}, Cl^- SiO_2) as well as humic acids and other dissolved yellow brown substances. Na^+ predominates over Ca^{2+} while Ca^{2+} predominates over Mg^{2+} (Weninger 1972). In the lower courses, increased NH_3 in water and $KMnO_4$ demand result from influences of sewage discharged into the rivers flowing through highly populated urban areas. With decreasing altitude there is an increase in the conductivity, hardness, ionic components and alkalinity (Table 9).

Water temperatures in the rivers and streams range from 14 °C to over 25 °C. Temperatures in the lower elevations vary greatly and in the river mouths they can reach almost 30 °C.

Table 9. Average physico-chemical characteristics of three rivers in Sri Lanka (Weninger 1972 and H.H. Costa [unpublished]).

Parameters	Kelani river Upper course	Gin river Middle course	Mahaweli river Lower course
Temperature (°C)	19	26	29
Conductivity (μS cm^{-1})	11	36	280
pH	5.1-6.1	5.5-6.6	6.5-7.3
Total hardness (° German)	0.5	3.2	22
Ca^{2+} (ppm)	0.65	5.3	2.01
Mg^{2+} (ppm)	0.26	3.3	5.41
Na^+ (ppm)	0.70	2.0	3.80
Fe^{2+} (ppm)	0.005		
Al^{3+} (ppm)	0.03		
NH_4^+ (ppm)	0.04	0.1	0.01
Cl^- (ppm)	1.70	2.41	0.38
PO_4^{3-} (ppm)	0.00	0.1	1.15
SiO_2 (ppm)	3.15	10.3	3.50
NO_3^- (ppm)	0.05	0.01	1.25

PHYSICO-CHEMICAL CHARACTERISTICS OF LENTIC WATER BODIES

Perennial Reservoirs

These basins retain water throughout the year. The perennial reservoirs in the Dry Zone are both ancient and may be subclassified as major reservoirs and medium scale reser-voirs. The medium scale reservoirs may sometimes dry up to form pools during severe dry weather. However, in all these the levels fluctuate during the wet season and the dry season. The water bodies in the Wet Zone are of minor scale and may

Table 10. Physico-chemical characteristics of some important perennial reservoirs in the Dry Zone and Wet Zone of Sri Lanka.

Reservoir	Surface Area (ha)	Temp. (°C)	pH	Total Alkalinity (ppm)	Conductivity ($\mu S\ cm^{-1}$)	Secchi depth (cm)	PO_4 (ppb)	NO_3 (ppm)	O_2 (mg L^{-1})	Author(s)
Dry Zone										
Parakrama Samudra	2262	28-30	8.3-9.6	1.8-3.2	218-243	-	70-167	-	6.1-9.0	10
Hurulu wewa	2195	20-34	7.0-8.5	59-164	140-300	40-111	-	-	6.0-10.5	1
Kala wewa	2598	27-32	7.4-8.4	50-119	82-400	41-94	8.4-15.7	-	7.9-9.4	1,11
Mahakandara wewa	1457	23-32	7.9-8.5	107-189	403-910	40-95	-	-	7.1-13.0	1
Mahavilachchiya wewa	1784	28-34	7.5-8.5	81-147	400-800	42-78	-	-	7.6-9.3	1
Nachchaduwa wewa	1748	29-33	7.5-8.5	45-150	350-570	40-90	-	-	7.7-9.8	1
Nuwara wewa	1196	28-31	8.2-8.6	8-143	300-850	22-54	-	-	6.7-10.1	1
Rajangana wewa	1599	26-32	7.5-8.6	124-191	455-650	65-151	-	-	4.8-9.0	1
Badagiriya wewa	482	26-34	7.9-8.8	-	360-1110	20-75	-	-	5.6-8.4	12,8,5
Ridiyagama wewa	888	26-33	7.6-8.6	4.4	400-1050	50-100	-	-	5.8-8.4	12,9,5
Wirawila wewa	567	28-34	7.5-9.5	-	540-920	20-100	-	-	7.1-10.1	12,5
Tissa wewa	233	27-31	7.6-9.5	-	360-830	100-300	-	-	5.2-12.5	12,9,6
Udawalawe wewa	3282	28-36	7.1-9.1	53-105	112-260	-	-	-	6.0-9.6	3
Yodakandiya wewa	488	29-32	7.8-8.7	-	400-1050	25-100	-	-	5.2-9.0	12,9,6
Pimburattewa wewa	834	28-32	7.5-8.3	8.4*	450-650	7.5	-	-	-	2,13
Wet Zone										
Colombo Lake	65	29-31	7.0-9.1	52-108	2200	-	-	0.0-0.2	0.5-12.6	4
Kandy Lake	18	25-30	7.0-7.8	0.2*	150-155	-	5.0-16.2	-	7.0-8.1	7

* m.eq. L^{-1}

Authors: 1. Amarasinghe et al. (1983); 2. Amarasinghe (1987); 3. Chandrasoma et al. (1989); 4. Costa and De Silva (1978); 5. Daniel et al. (1988); 6. Daniel et al. (1989); 7. De Silva and De Silva (1984); 8. De Silva and Sirisena (1985); 9. De Silva and Sirisena, 1987); 10. Gunatillaka (1983); 11. Gunawardene and Adikari (1981); 12. Wijeyaratne and Costa (1991); 13. H.H. Costa (personal observations) contain water throughout the year. With change of weather the reservoirs in the Dry Zone get enriched with the washing in of domestic and cattle wastes.

The physico-chemical characteristics of the perennial major and medium scale reservoirs in the Dry Zone and the minor "lakes" of the Wet Zone have been comprehensively studied, since most of these reservoirs have been subsequently used to develop inland fisheries.

The physico-chemical characteristics of perennial man-made reservoirs in the Dry Zone have been studied by Mendis (1965), Amarasiri (1972), Gunawardene and Adikari (1981), Gunatillaka (1983), Amarasinghe et al. (1983), Wijeyaratne and Amarasinghe (1984), DeSilva and Sirisena (1987) and Daniel et al. (1988) (Table 10). In the Wet Zone the variation of physico-chemical parameters of minor reservoirs have been studied by Costa and de Silva (1969, 1978a); de Silva and de Silva 1984) and Costa et al. (1991).

Seasonal Reservoirs

Seasonal "tanks" or reservoirs, as the name indicates, are small, shallow water bodies and retain water for only 6-8 months of the year. Generally they are located in the Dry Zone and receive rain during the North East monsoon. Filling occurs around October and maximum level is reached around January/February. They dry completely by about July/August.

Although this type of reservoir is numerous in the Dry Zone, there exist only a few studies on physico-chemical charateristics (Table 11) (Chandrasoma 1986, Wijeyaratne and Wanninayake 1994).

Table 11. Physico-chemical characteristics of some seasonal reservoirs in the Dry Zone of Sri Lanka (data from Chandrasoma 1986)

Reservoir	Area (ha)	pH	Secchi disc visibility (cm)	Hardness (CaCO$_3$ mg L^{-1})	Conductivity (μS cm^{-1})	O$_2$ (mg L^{-1})
Tunkama	4.0	7.2-8.7	40-75	130-220	530-750	2.5-6.4
Mahawewa	6.0	7.1-7.8	33-75	55-120	640-950	3.0-6.4
Epitagoda	3.5	7.1-7.9	22-40	20-31	90-120	4.2-5.2
Maduranwela	3.5	7.0-7.7	70-110	52-67	135-250	5.0-8.7
Benthis wewa	2.0	7.3-8.1	40-70	50-65	210-390	3.7-10.0
Nika wewa	0.6	7.2-8.3	30-70	40-70	155-540	4.1-4.7
Welapahale	2.5	6.9-7.4	80-110	58-64	110-250	4.4-5.8
Komaligama	3.0	7.0-7.5	80-110	50-72	200-240	4.3-5.8
Angunakola pelassa	4.0	7.1-7.6	30-35	30-60	80-105	4.3-10.2
Kalwelgala	4.0	7.0-8.0	30-70	28-40	50-92	4.6-10.3

Multipurpose Irrigation Reservoirs

The development of new irrigation works by the government, some of which will also be used for generation of hydroelectricity, is expected to create a large number of reservoirs of which the multipurpose Mahaweli river system is expected to cover over 20,000 ha. Under this project five major reservoirs have been constructed. These reservoirs have the potential for both capture and culture fisheries. As these reservoirs have been newly filled, these provide excellent opportunities for study of water characteristics in relation to ageing. Limnological studies and studies on fish yield have been already initiated in some reservoirs (Table 12) (Silva 1991, de Silva 1993, Piyasiri 1991).

BIOLOGICAL CHARACTERISTICS

Freshwater Macrophytes

A rich and a luxuriant aquatic vegetation, some of which are important as ornamental plants, is encountered in the streams, reservoirs and marshes. Abeywickrama (1956) gives a brief account of some of the aquatic plants. In irrigation reservoirs, species tend to occur in zones roughly along isobeths. In the rivers and streams, where rocks are covered by flowing water, various members of the Podostemaceae may occur. Species such as *Podostemum subulatus* occur on the quieter part of the rapids. Along the margin attached macrophytes with floating or submerged leaves such as *Aponogeton crispum* may occur. In the lentic water bodies different communities may occur in the deep water and the shallow water. However, there is a general paucity of data concerning the distribution and ecology of aquatic macrophytes.

Two noxious exotic aquatic plants *Eichhornia crassipes* and *Salvinia molesta* recently introduced into Sri Lankan waters have rapidly invaded reservoirs, irrigation channels and ponds. Presently these two species cover respectively 5,000 and 20,000 ha. In the last few years successful control of *S. molesta* has been achieved by releasing the insect *Cyrtobagous salviniae* (Order Coleoptera) (Room and Fernando 1992).

Phytoplankton

The species composition and ecology of freshwater phytoplankton have been fairly well studied in Sri Lanka. Interest in the study of the phytoplankton arose mainly because it is, in turn, directly or indirectly the source of food of the fish species, specially *Oreochromis mossambicus*, which form the secondary level of productivity. Seasonal variations, species composition, distribution and ecology of the major phytoplankton groups have now been worked out for Wet Zone and Dry Zone water bodies (Holsinger 1955, Costa and de Silva 1978b, de Silva and Somaratne 1991, Rott 1983, Daniel et al. 1988). A comprehensive study has been done on the phytoplankton biomass of Para-krama Samudra, a lentic perennial waterbody in the Dry Zone, by Dokulil et al. (1983).

Cyanophyceae forms the dominant phytoplankton group in the ancient lentic water bodies. In the newly impounded Mahaweli reservoirs it is the Chlorophyceae that dominates the phytoplankton group. The phytoplankton numbers in the Dry Zone reservoirs vary from 2,000 to 45,000 litre^{-1} (Table 13). The numbers and taxa vary during the different seasons of the year and with the location of the reservoirs. The phytoplankton densities decrease during rainy months and rapidly increase in numbers during the dry season.

Table 12. Some physico-chemical characteristics of irrigation reservoirs of the Mahaweli system

Mahaweli reservoir	Temperature (°C)	pH	Total alkalinity	Conductivity (μS cm^{-1})	Secchi disc transparency (cm)	Oxygen (mg L^{-1})	Author
Kotmale	21.0	6.70		68			Silva (1989)
	24.0-27.6	6.8-7.2	0.23-43	40-55	200-230	7.5 - 8.9	de Silva (1990)
	21.5-28.8			30-90	136-226	7.5 ± 1.76	Piyasiri (1991)
Victoria	26.2	7.20		127			Silva (1989)
	24.8-26.9	6.7-7.8	0.45-0.82	53-92	121-161	6.0 - 8.0	de Silva (1990)
	24.0-32.0			85-140	134-302	6.5 ± 1.06	Piyasiri (1991)
Randenigala	27.0	7.34		143			Silva (1989)
	26.2-30.6	7.0-7.2	0.68-0.97	78-100	251-301	6.4 - 8.8	de Silva (1990)
	25.3-31.0			110-190	176-330	6.4 ± 1.03	Piyasiri (1991)

Table 13. Variations in the number of phytoplankton and primary productivity in some important reservoirs in Sri Lanka.

Reservoir	Number of organisms (10^4 L^{-1})	Primary productivity (g m^{-2}day^{-1})	Author(s)
Hurulu wewa	60-110	2.20-5.40	Amarasinghe et al. 1983
Kala wewa	70-120	1.42-4.16	Amarasinghe et al. 1983
Mahakanadara wewa	50-60	1.42-4.85	Amarasinghe et al. 1983
Mahavilachchiya wewa	30-90	1.98-4.20	Amarasinghe et al. 1983
Nachchaduwa wewa	25-100	1.73-3.67	Amarasinghe et al. 1983
Nuwara wewa	125-510	2.25-5.63	Amarasinghe et al. 1983
Rajangana wewa	20-250	1.35-4.36	Amarasinghe et al. 1983
Parakrama Samudra	0.02-0.6	3.80-14.70	Dokulil et al. 1983
Udukiriwela wewa	0.005-1.1	0.64-3.68	Daniel et al. 1988
Muruthawela wewa	0.01-11	0.38-1.24	Daniel et al. 1988
Ridiyagama wewa	0.01-45	0.38-2.85	Daniel et al. 1988
Badagiriya wewa	0.02-30	0.15-1.2	Daniel et al. 1988
Wirawila wewa	0.01-0.85	0.23-1.43	Daniel et al. 1988
Tissa wewa	0.01-0.4		Daniel et al. 1988
Beira Lake	20-300	2.32-4.95	Costa and De Silva 1978
Tunkana wewa	3.21		Chandrasoma 1986
Kalawelagala wewa	4.25		Chandrasoma 1986
Nika wewa	2.82		Chandrasoma 1986
Elpitagoda wewa	1.57		Chandrasoma 1986

Faunal Characteristics

The systematics of the zooplankton groups Rotifera, Cladocera and Copepoda are better known for Sri Lanka than any other country in the Asian region (Fernando 1980; Chengalath and Fernando 1973; Chengalath et al. 1984). The zooplankton species found in Sri Lanka are either cosmopolitan or tropicopolitan (Rajapakse and Fernando 1984). 138 species of Rotifers, 58 species of Cladocera and 23 species of free-living Cyclopoida and Calanoida are known from Sri Lanka.

The zooplankton composition, density, distribution and seasonal variation have been studied for Wet Zone reservoirs by Costa and de Silva (1978b) and for Dry Zone reservoirs by Jayatunga (1982), Rajapakse and Fernando 1983, Duncan 1983 and by Duncan and Gulati (1983) (Table 14). The lowest numbers of zooplankton occur in streams, rivers and flood lakes. Ponds and reservoirs have the richest fauna. Large reservoirs have fewer species than small reservoirs (Fernando 1984). Uniform high temperatures, flushing rates and predation are the major factors that regulate the densities of zooplankton.

The zooplankton consists of typcial tropical assembly and possess a small number of typically limnetic species. Rotifera are dominated by *Brachionus* and *Keratella* species. Cladocera are fewer in number, only three species are known from the limnetic zone. On the other hand Cyclopoid copepods dominate the limnetic zone (Fernando 1980).

Table 14. Studies conducted on zooplankton in Sri Lanka

Reservoir	Topics studied	Author(s)
Beira lake	Composition	Apstein (1907)
Lake Gregory	Composition	Apstein (1910)
Lake Gregory	Composition	Chengalath and Fernando (1973)
Lake Gregory	Composition, distribution	Chengalath and Koste (1973)
Lake Gregory	Composition, distribution	Fernando (1980)
Beira lake	Diurnal variation	Costa and De Silva (1969)
Kalawewa	Composition, distribution and seasonal variation	Jayatunga (1982)
Parakrama samudra	Seasonal changes	Rajapakse and Fernando (1984)
Parakrama samudra	Composition, density and distribution	Duncan (1983)
Parakrama samudra	Dynamics of zooplankton	Duncan and Gulati (1983)
Udukiriwela	Seasonal variation	Daniel et al. (1986)
Muruthawela	Seasonal variation	Daniel et al. (1986)
Ridiyagama	Seasonal variation	Daniel et al. (1986)
Badagiriya	Seasonal variation	Daniel et al. (1986)
Wirawila	Seasonal variation	Daniel et al. (1986)
Tissa wewa	Seasonal variation	Daniel et al. (1986)
Yodakandiya	Seasonal variation	Daniel et al. (1986)
Udawalawe	Density of zooplankton with depth	Chandrasoma et al. 1986

The data on the ecology and production of zooplankton in Sri Lanka, however, are very meagre.

Littoral Fauna, Periphyton and Benthos

Most of the water bodies in the Dry Zone and Wet Zone are shallow, sometimes with low water levels during part of the year. The knowledge of the littoral fauna is scanty and has been documented by Fernando (1965), Fernando and Ellepoda (1969) for Dry Zone reservoirs and by Costa and De Silva (1978b) for Wet Zone reservoirs. Little is known of the seasonal abundance and the factors controlling such abundance or the ecology of the constituent species; this is specially true in relation to insect and mollusc species and their correlation with the production of fish species feeding on them.

The dynamics of the aquatic fauna living on plants are known only for one Wet Zone lake (Costa and De Silva 1978b). Similar studies for Dry Zone lakes are desirable for comparative purposes as macrophytes form an important component of the biota of the Dry Zone reservoirs. An assessment of the periphyton is of value in the context of studying the biological productivity and the food and feeding habits of fish. As has been mentioned earlier, the low country water bodies have been invaded by two exotic plant pests namely *Eichhornia crassipes* and *Salvinia molesta*. These plants form important and interesting niches for the successful existence of some species of animals.

The benthic fauna of the streams and large rivers have not yet been qualitatively and quantitatively studied except for some groups such as Mollusca (Starmuhlner 1974). The benthic biomass of lentic water bodies determined for a limited number of samples for some Dry Zone reservoirs is however known (Mendis 1964, 1965) and ranges from 4.5 to 41.0 kg ha^{-1}. Recently comprehensive studies on the benthos have been carried out in Colombo (Beira) lake (Wigneswaran and Costa [in preparation]). They found that the biomass of benthos ranged from 0.05 to 8.70 g m^{-2} wet weight for different parts of the lake.

Faunal Groups Recorded from Sri Lanka

The taxonomy of freshwater fauna and flora (mainly phytoplankton) has been studied to a fair extent to enable ecological and environmental studies to be carried out with more accuracy. The aquatic fauna is about the best documented for any tropical Asian country. Some of the groups have been studied recently through joint ventures of Sri Lankan and foreign scientists (Brinck et al. 1971, Costa and Starmuhlner 1972, Schiemer 1983). However, many freshwater invertebrate groups such as Protozoa, Nematoda etc. have yet to be studied taxonomically. The invertebrate aquatic faunal groups that have been studied are given in Table 15.

Table 15. The invertebrate aquatic fauna described from Sri Lanka

Taxon	Author(s)
Turbellaria	De Beauchamp (1973)
Oligocheata	Costa (1967)
Hirudinea	Costa (1978)
Ostracoda	Neale (1984)
Decapoda: Caridea: Atyidae	Arudpragasam and Costa (1962), de Silva (1983)
Decapoda: Caridea: Palaemonidae	Costa (1979)
Decapoda: Reptantia: Potamonidae	Bott (1970)
Coleoptera	Jaech (1982), Wewalka (1973), Bertrand (1973)
Diptera	Davis (1984)
Ephemeroptera	Hubbard and Peters (1984)
Heteroptera	Polhemus (1979)
Plecoptera	Zwick (1980)
Trichoptera	Schmidt (1958), Malicky (1973)
Gastropoda, Bivalvia	Starmuhlner (1984)

Fish

The ecology of streams, rivers and reservoirs has a close bearing on the ecology of fish. About sixty species of fish are native to Sri Lanka. Although 50% of the fish inhabiting fresh waters belong to Family Cyprinidae only a few of them such as *Labeo dussumieri*,

Barbus (=*Puntius*) *sarana* and *Barbus dorsalis* are economically important as food fish. Some small cyprinids such as *Barbus cumingi, Barbus nigrofasciatus* and *Barbus titteya* are important as aquarium fish.

Twenty-four species of exotic fish had been introduced between 1882 and 1969 (Table 16). Five of them are African cichlids while six are major carps, three from mainland China and three from India. Of the exotic fish introduced only *Oreochromis mossambicus* has an impact on the commercial freshwater fishery having successfully established itself in the reservoirs of the Dry Zone. Its success appears to be mostly due to its food habits specially the utilization of phytoplankton, which is abundant in the reservoirs as food. Recent fishery statistics indicate that *Oreochromis niloticus* is replacing *O. mossambicus* in certain reservoirs (Chandrasoma 1986).

Table 16. Exotic species that have been introduced into Sri Lankan waters and their present status (from De Silva 1991).
[- breeding populations not established;   ± a few instances of breeding reported;   + small scattered breeding populations present;   ++ breeding populations estab-lished in some parts of the country;   +++ breeding populations common in most parts of the country]

Species	Year of introduction	Purpose	Present status	Possible future population changes
Aristichthys nobilis	1948/75	food	-	extinction
Barbus gonionotus	1951?	food	-	extinction
Carassius auratus	1915	food	-	extinction
Catla catla	1942/82	food	-	extinction
Cirrhinus mrigala	1981	food	-	extinction
Ctenopharyngodon idella	1948/75	food	-	extinction
Cyprinus carpio	1915	food	±	reduction
Hypophthalmichthus molitrix	1948/81	food	-	extinction
Labeo rohita	1981	food	-	extinction
Osphronemus gorami	1939	food	+	reduction
Helostoma temmincki	1951	food	+	reduction
Trichogaster pectoralis	1951	food	++	stabilization
T. trichpterus	1951?	accidental	±	extinction
Oreochromis mossambicus	1952	food	+++	stabilization
O. niloticus	1956/75	food	++	stabilization
O. urolepis	1969	food	-	extinction
Tilapia rendalli	1969	food	+	stabilization
T. zillii	1969	food	-	extinction
Onchorhynchus mykiss	1889-93	recreation	±	stabilization
Salmo trutta	1882-93	recreation	-	extinction
Gambusia affinis	1980?	mosquito control	±	extinction
Poecilia reticulata	1928/45	mosquito control	+	expansion
Xiphophorus helleri	1958	accidental	+	expansion
X. maculatus	1965?	accidental?	+	expansion

Food Habits of Fish

The food habits of most of the freshwater fish are now known. Most of the indigenous food fish are carnivorous (Fernando 1956, 1965, Costa and Fernando 1966, Costa 1980). These include *Channa* (= *Ophicephalus*) sp., *Anguilla* sp., *Mystus* sp., *Wallago attu*, and *Ompok bimaculatus*. Most of the *Barbus* spp. are omnivorous (S. De Silva et al. 1977) some acquiring a herbivorous habit later. Because of their particular food habits, *Aplocheilus* species have been evaluated as suitable mosquito larvivores (Costa and Fernando 1977).

Predation of Fish

The role of predators in relation to fish productivity has become an important consideration specially with the present accent on fish propagation and fish culture in the major and minor reservoirs. Details of predation of fish have been given by Fernando (1965) and Winkler (1983). In Parakrama Samudra reservoir the annual consumption of fish by cormorants has been estimated to be around 254 MT which is higher than the total commercial fish catch from this reservoir. The detailed role of the predators still remains to be assessed.

Fisheries

Limnological studies have played an important role in the development of fisheries in Sri Lanka.

The inland fisheries of Sri Lanka is mainly a capture fishery confined to large and medium scale reservoirs and culture fishery confined to minor reservoirs (S. De Silva 1988). The Sri Lankan reservoirs are shallow and small in surface area and can be highly productive. Limnological studies carried out on physico-chemical charateristics, plankton, primary productivity, rates of nutrient flux, food of fish and benthic production have helped considerably the developmental and management aspects of the fishery. Before 1950s the low catch of indigenous food fish, which are mainly carnivorous, indicated that the phytoplankton of the reservoirs available through high primary production was not utilized by fish because of the absence of truly lacustrine herbivorous fish in the reservoirs. The introduction of exotic *Oreochromis mossambicus* led to a dramatic increase in fish production through natural recruitment.

The inland fishery contributes to about 30,000 MT year^{-1} which is about 20% of the total fish production for the island. The yield of *O. mossambicus* presently accounts up to 90% of the total yield from individual reservoirs.

Limnological studies carried out in seasonal reservoirs (Chandrasoma 1986, Wijeyaratne and Wanninayake 1994) have contributed to the understanding of potential fish yields from these reservoirs, which are being developed for culture fisheries. In seasonal reservoirs the fish culture period is limited to 6-8 months. There are more than 10,000 seasonal reservoirs with a command area of 100,000 ha. These reservoirs are generally stocked with Chinese and Indian carp fingerlings. The fingerling requirement is around 20 million of which about 8 million are now produced in the country.

Experimental polyculture trials with fertilization have shown the possibility of raising good fish crops from ponds in Sri Lanka with a production of 4.0-6.5 MT ha^{-1}

(Chakrabarty and Hettiarachchi 1982). However, the pond culture programme has proved to be an unmitigated failure even though Chinese and Indian carps have been used for stocking these ponds. Perhaps the indifference of fish farmers and the inability of the Ministry of Fisheries to provide fish seed at appropriate times may have contributed to this failure.

Limnological studies have been used to provide models for the management of reservoir fisheries based on yield data and morphoedaphic index (MEI) (Wijeyaratne and Costa 1981) and yield data and maximum sustainable yield (MSY) (Wijeyaratne and Amarasinghe 1984).

None of these models developed appear to be perfect as conditions in Sri Lankan reservoirs vary from one reservoir to another. These models however, provide useful although approximate information on the sustainable yields from these reservoirs.

POLLUTION

Rapid industrialization, increased agricultural production and large scale destruction of forest cover coupled with rapid expansion in population and urbanization during the last few decades have adversely affected the aquatic environment of Sri Lanka. Even domestic solid wastes which are relatively inert have become a public health hazard.

The major environmental concerns are from three groups:
1. Pollution due to the discharge of untreated effluents from industries,
2. Pollution caused by agrochemicals, and
3. Pollution by human settlements.

Only a few investigations have been made regarding pollution of freshwaters in the island (Tabel 17). Water quality of most of the lotic systems in their lower courses has deteriorated due to discharge of effluents from industries or due to contamination with sewage (Gunatillaka 1973, De Silva et al. 1984).

Table 17. Water quality and pollution studies in Sri Lanka

Water bodies	Subjects studied	Author(s)
Kelani River	Industrial effluents	Gunatillaka (1975) (unpublished)
Kelani River	Industrial effluents	De Silva et al. (1984) (unpublished)
Katunayake streams	BOD	De Alwis et al. (1988)
Coastal domestic sewers	BOD	Costa (1989)
	Insecticides: Effects on shrimps	Costa (1970)
	Pesticides: Effects on fish	Shafiei and Costa (1990)
Colombo Lake	Bacterial ecology	Costa and Gunatillaka (1978)
Nuwara Eliya Lake	Agrochemicals	Dassanayake et al. (unpublished)

The government has recently begun to establish industrial zones. This has led to the pollution of ground and surface waters in the vicinity due to discharge of untreated industrial wastes. Recent studies (De Alwis et al. 1988) in the treatment of domestic and industrial wastes by biological oxidation processes have been effective in reducing BOD levels to a degree at which these wastes could be released on to surface waters.

Most of the lentic water bodies show increased signs of eutrophication due to organic pollution. The largest amount of organic pollution is due to human settlements (Costa and Gunatilleka 1978). The estimated value of BOD_5 from domestic sewers in the coastal zone is around 8,000,000 MT per annum (Costa 1989).

The use of pesticides in agriculture and in the control of vectors has increased dramatically in Sri Lanka in the last two decades. It is known that in 1984 alone 2075 MT of pesticides were imported to Sri Lanka. Investigations on the effects of these pesticides on aquatic fauna have been few (Costa 1970, Shafiei and Costa 1990).

ENDEMICITY OF FRESHWATER FAUNA

Sri Lanka, although is a small island, has a relatively high endemicity of animal species, which is also reflected in its aquatic fauna (Table 18). However, the endemicity at the generic level is rare. For instance, among aquatic vertebrates, there are only two genera of teleosts (both monotypic) and one genus of Anura with three species, viz. *Malpulutta kretseri* (Family Belontidae), *Horadandiya atukorali* (Family Cyprinidae) and *Nannophrys ceylonensis*, *N. guentheri* and *N. marmorata* (Family Ranidae). There are no endemic families or higher taxa of freshwater fauna.

Most of the endemic fish species are cyprinids. Out of 32 indigenous cyprinid species 17 are endemic. *Barbus* species predominates the cyprinids having 16 species which include 9 endemic species. Among Anura, there are three endemic *Rana* species, in addition to which, beside the three *Nannophrys* species mentioned, there are 2 *Bufo* spp., 3 *Rhacophorus* spp., one species of *Philautus*, 2 species of *Ramanella* and one species of *Microphyla*, which are endemic (and have aquatic larval stages). (The endemic tree frog *R. microtympanum* does not have an aquatic larval stage). All the 3 species of *Gymnophiona* present in the island, namely, *Ichthyophis glutinosus*, *I. pseudoangularis* and *I. orthoplicatus* are endemic and have aquatic larval stages.

Of the two species of crocodiles in the island one is considered to be an endemic subspecies, *Crocodylus palustris kimbula*. The Large Monitor lizard (*Varanus monitor kabaragoya*) is also considered as a subspecies peculiar to Sri Lanka. Although there are 80 water-associated bird species only 3 subspecies, namely, *Vanellus inducus lankae* (Redwattled lapwing), *Himantopus himantopus ceylonensis* (Sri Lankan Blackwinged stilt) and *Charadrius alexandrinus seebohmi* (Sri Lanka Kentish plover) are peculiar to the island.

As has been reported earlier only a few freshwater invertebrate groups, mostly the inhabitants of lotic waters, have been investigated in sufficient taxonomic details and therefore warrant comment on their endemism. In addition to this incomplete knowledge of fauna, these taxa are very inadequately investigated in neighbouring countries such as India. However, the endemicity of the few taxa that have been fairly well studied island-wide is considered in Table 18.

Out of the 31 species of freshwater gastropods described (Starmuhlner 1974) 10 *Paludomus* species (Family Thiaridae) and *Bulimus* (= *Bithynia*) *inconspicua* (Family Buliminidae) are endemic to Sri Lanka. Of the 12 species of Atyid shrimps found in the island, 6 *Caridinia* species (one with 2 subspecies) are endemic (de Silva 1991). Of 11 Palaemonid species recorded only one appears to be endemic (Costa 1984). Seven potamonid species have been recorded from the island of which 4 species are endemic and appear to be peculiar to Sri Lanka (Bott 1970).

Table 18. Endemicity of freshwater fauna in Sri Lanka

Taxonomic Group	Endemic genera	Endemic species	Endemic subspecies	Non-endemic indigenous species
Vertebrata				
Teleostei	2	30	-	42
Amphibia				
Anura	1	14	-	18
Apoda	-	3	-	-
Reptilia				
Chelonia	-	-	-	2
Crocodilia	-	-	1	2
Lacertilia	-	-	3*	80*
Invertebrata				
Gastropoda	-	10	1	20
Decapoda				
Atyidae	-	6	2	5
Palaemonidae	-	1	-	10
Potamonidae	1	3	1	3

* water-associated birds

Distribution of Endemic Aquatic Fauna

The aquatic fauna of Sri Lanka is mainly lotic; 96% of fish species (95% of indigenous and 97% of endemic), 74% of snail species (63% indigenous and 92% endemic) and 75% of atyid (60% indigenous and 86% endemic) are found in lotic habitats. The major lentic habitat of irrigation reservoirs, which are man-made and not older than 2500 years, appears to be inhabited by the lotic species, marshy species and a few estuarine species. All endemic fish species except *Horadandia atukorali* are recorded from the lotic waters and 22 of these are confined to the latter habitats. Only 4 endemic species, *Barbus bimaculatus*, *Esomus thermoicos*, *Clarias brachysoma* and *Belontia signata*, are recorded from the irrigation reservoirs. Eight endemic species (*Horadandia atukorali*, *Heteropneustes microps*, *Aplocheilus dayi*, *Channa orientalis* (and the four species present in the reservoirs) are found in marshy habitats. *H. atukorali* is found only in swamps and marshes.

All endemic snail species are recorded from the lotic waters except *Paludomus palustris*, which is recorded from a Dry Zone reservoir (Starmuhlner 1974). In addition to the latter species, two other endemic species, *Bellamya dissimilis* and *P. palustris* have been recorded from irrigation reservoirs; the former species is common and found in marshy habitats as well.

Of the endemic atyids, only *C. fernandoi* has been recorded from the littoral region of the reservoirs. *C. zeylanica* is found in low-salinity estuaries and marshes. Most of the endemic freshwater fauna (and also land fauna) are found in the lowland Wet Zone (first peneplain of the Wet Zone) of the island.

In the freshwaters above 1,500 m (*i.e.*, in the third peneplain or montane zone), only three endemic fish species (the carplets *Barbus bimaculatus* and *Garra ceylonensis* and the hill stream loach *Schistura notostigma*) have been recorded. One endemic gastropod (*Paludomus nigricans*) and one endemic atyid species (*Caridina singhalensis*), which is confined to the region, have also been recorded in this zone. In the sub-montane zone also the endemic fish species present in the montane zone were present. This region contains two additional endemic snail taxa (*P. decussatus* and *P. tanshauricus nasutus*) and one atyid species, *Caridina kumariae*), which is confined to the region.

The lowland wet zone contains all endemic fish species except *Barbus srilankensis*, of which there appears to be only a small population in the type locality in the tributary of the river Mahaweli in the Intermediate Zone. 20 of the 30 endemic fish species are confined to the lowland wet zone. All endemic gastropod species except *Paludomus palustris*, which is recorded only from a single location in the Dry Zone, are present in the lowland Wet Zone. All atyid species except the endemic *C. kumariae* and *C. singhalensis* are found in this zone. The endemic *C. pristis pristis* is distributed in slow flowing streams in the elevation range of 300 to 1000 m; the other subspecies, *C. p. cruszi*, also an endemic, is recorded only from the forest streams of Singharaja forest at 425 m (De Silva 1991).

Dry Zone contains only 13% of the endemic fish species. Same pattern is observed with respect to other groups as well (Table 19).

Table 19. Frequency of occurrence of endemic freshwater faunal groups in different regions (D: dry zone; I: intermediate zone; W_1: lowland wet zone; W_2: sub montane wet zone; W_3: montane wet zone; n: number of species). (Data from De Silva 1991)

Class	D	I	W_1	W_2	W_3	n
Teleostei	4	10	29	3	3	30
Amphibia	1	3	10	11	8	18
Gastropoda	4	7	1	3	1	11
Atyidae	2	1	4	1	1	6

It must be pointed out that freshwaters, especially the headwaters of rivers, of some parts of the island have not been surveyed intensively. This is reflected by the fact that during 1991 three new species of fish have been described from the southern and central parts of the island.

CONSERVATION OF FRESHWATERS

Human Interference with Lentic Waters

At present, the human interference is with the lentic habitats and this is largely a result of increase in human population. This has caused a significant disturbance on the freshwater vertebrate fauna of wetlands, especially those of marshes. The teleost diversity in the Wet Zone marshes is quite high. At least 30 non-endemic indigenous freshwater fish species (out of 42) and 8 endemic species (out of 30) are found in the Wet Zone marshes as well as in the Dry Zone of Sri Lanka. It may be that this is the same for several other faunal groups also, although there is no data available on these groups at present.

The few reservoirs (and also the marshes) located in the vicinity of cities are grossly polluted by the activities of the high human population in the nearby cities. For instance, Gregory Lake (elevation 1800 m above MSL), Kandy Lake (elevation 510 m), and Beira Lake (elevation <5 m) situated within the townships of Nuwara Eliya, Kandy and Colombo, respectively are polluted to different degrees. Eutrophication during rainy season followed by mass mortality of fish is well documented in Beira Lake (Costa and Gunatilleka 1978).

Human Interference with Lotic Waters

During the last few decades man has been interfering with the lotic habitats of the island very significantly. The interference with freshwater fauna has been due to many sources, namely, (a) overexploitation and introduction of species new to various areas, and (b) habitat changes. Activities of the first category include fishing, introduction of exotic species and translocation of local species. Important changes in the lotic habitats 22are indirectly caused by river impoundment and diversion, deforestation, gem and sand mining and water pollution.

Fishing

Among freshwater fauna, only fish are being harvested to any significant degree. The effect of capture fishery of food fish has no significant effect on the fish in lotic waters. However, the exploitation of natural populations for aquarium purposes, both foreign and local, could affect the endemic fish species quite significantly. Of the 30 endemic species, at least 24 are exported in aquarium trade including those that have a restricted distribution. Most heavily exported endemic fish species are *Barbus nigrofasciatus*, *B. titteya*, *Belontia signata* and *Rasbora vaterifloris*, and at present, their populations are dwindling.

Fish Introductions

24 exotic species, have been introduced to Sri Lankan waters as mostly food fish (Costa 1986). There is no doubt that the exotic species exert pressure on the indigenous fauna. There are instances in which the exotic species have affected the size and distribution of indigenous fish populations. For instance, *Labeo dussumieri* and *L. porcellus*, both non-

endemic indigenous species, are now quite scarce in Sri Lanka (De Silva 1991). It is likely that the pressure in this instance came from the exotic carps than from tilapia. It will be interesting to note whether the populations of *L. dussumieri* and *L. porcellus* would recover as the stocking of carps is stopped now.

Translocations

There are few instances where fish translocations have been carried out in the island. *Chanos chanos, Etroplus suratensis* and *Mugil cephalus* had been translocated from the estuaries to irrigation reservoirs for food fishery purposes; out of these *E. suratensis* is now well established in the lowland reservoirs (Costa 1982). However, being sea spawners, the other two species have not been successful in translocations. *B. cumingi, B. nigrofasciatus, B. titteya* and *R. vaterifloris* have been translocated from Kelani basin to the Mahaweli basin (Wickramanayake 1990) and all four species are now well established in the area. Although there appears to be no detrimental effect of these translocations on the other aquatic fauna, inter-basin translocations should be carried out only after careful study of the biota of the area to which the translocations will be made.

Indirect Interference by Habitat Changes

Habitat modification seems to be the main threat to the endemic freshwater fauna of Sri Lanka today and this is mainly brought about by (a) the river impoundment and diversion and (b) deforestation of the catchment areas.

Several major rivers in Sri Lanka have been impounded and diverted for the production of hydroelectricity for irrigation, while some others are under consideration for future impoundment. Mahaweli river diversion is one of the largest impoundment efforts that has been carried out in Asia (Silva 1991). There is strong evidence that the creation of one of these hydroelectric reservoirs, the Victoria reservoir, has endangered the fast water-dwelling, endemic *Labeo* fishery which is restricted to the reservoir area.

Deforestation is perhaps the most important cause in the degradation of stream habitats in Sri Lanka. The main effect of deforestation is the siltation of marshes, headwaters and streams which will obviously change the habitats (Costa 1974). Also, this will cause lowering of water table, reduction of precipitation, change of flow regime and under-mining the river and stream banks. As many fish species of forest streams are habitat specialists, a change of habitat would affect them severely. Breeding of many species, which mainly occurs in small streams, also could be affected due to loss of spawning grounds due to siltation. Loss of shady areas is another factor which may affect some of the shade loving fish species (Pethiyagoda 1991).

Gem mining, a high foreign exchange earner in the island, affect the lotic habitats in the respective areas, mostly in the Wet Zone. Increase in turbidity created by the disturbance caused by sand mining in rivers is also important in this regard. Both processes may affect the fauna in the lotic habitat of the area (de Silva and de Silva 1991).

Conservation of Freshwater Habitats

Most developing countries have to develop their natural resources in order to maintain a viable economy. The demand of the ever increasing human population places a great pressure for the rapid development of natural resources. For instance, Sri Lanka has a population of 17 million today with an annual growth rate of 1.7%. Hence it is important to develop natural resources for human use. However, it is of prime importance at the same time to conserve as much as possible of the biodiversity and endemism of wildlife resources including the inland waters (De Silva 1991).

Most efforts of conserving biodiversity and endemism in Sri Lanka today seemed to be focussed on to the Dry Zone, mainly because of the importance laid on the large mammals, mostly distributed in the monsoon forests of the Dry Zone. Of the 11 national parks with a total area of 466,000 ha and five nature reserves with a total area of 64,124 ha, only one national park (Horton plains) with an area of 1142 ha are in the Wet Zone, and these too are situated in the montane zone. 40 wildlife sanctuaries (area 221,432 ha) are in the Dry Zone whereas only nine (area 23,268 ha) in the lowland Wet Zone. Therefore, in view of the high biodiversity and endemism in the Wet Zone and the endangered nature of the several aquatic species including some fish species in the zone, demarcation of critical Wet Zone areas for strict conservation is urgently required.

INSTITUTIONAL INVOLVEMENT IN LIMNOLOGICAL STUDIES

External Assistance for the Development of Inland Fisheries and Training Programmes

Fish is the major source of protein in the Sri Lankan diet contributing about 60% of the animal protein. The inland fishery accounts for about 20% of the total fish production of 150,000 MT. Since fish is the source of animal protein and considering that the island's inland waters are substantial, the government (until 1990) through the Ministry of Fisheries devoted a considerable amount of attention to the development of inland fisheries and aquaculture.

A concerted effort to develop inland fisheries through research and experimental work was started in 1978. A new organisation called National Aquatic Resources Agency (NARA) was created in 1981 for the purpose of conducting research on aquatic resources.

Sri Lanka being a developing country requires substantial financial aid for the implementation of the developmental programmes. External assistance has been received from multilateral sources like UNDP, FAO, ADB, SEAFDEC or from bilateral sources like India, IDRC, CIDA etc.

Total external assistance for inland fisheries sector amounted (until end of 1990) to about US $ 22.97 million (Table 20). However, all the programmes lacked limnological research components and any research that has been carried out has been towards the development of the fishery resource of the reservoirs.

Institutions Associated with Studies in Limnology, Fisheries and Aquaculture

The development of limnology in Sri Lanka has been mainly through the interest in development of fishery resources. Much of the limnological research effort in the past have been contributed by scientists from the developed countries while considerable research work has been done recently by scientists trained abroad and locally. The major constraint in the understanding of our freshwaters more extensively is the derth of trained limnologists. Since post-graduate facilities in some fields are not available locally, it has become neessary to send our young scientists abroad or to bring down foreign experts to train them locally.

Table 20. External assistance received for inland fisheries from international organisations. (Limnological surveys, fish and fisheries studies, aquaculture).

Name of project/activity	Source	Terms	Year	Amount (US$)
Inland fisheries development	FAO/TCP	Grant	1962	41,500
Training limnologists/fishery biologists/aquaculturists	FAO/UNDP	Grant	1975	75,600
Fish breeding station for training	P.R.China	Grant	1975/6	1,200,000
Training of Sri Lankans in aquatic sciences	FAO/UNDP	Grant	1977	7,800
Development of fisheries in man-made lakes and reservoirs	FAO/TCN	Grant	1979/80	40,000
Technical equipment	UNICEP	Grant	1981/84	25,000
Aquaculture development projects and training	FAO/UNDP/ADB	Grant	1981/84	1,775,000
Cage culture	IDRC	Grant	1982/85	290,000
Aquaculture development (seasonal reservoirs)	ADB	Grant	1984/87	17,270,000
Mollusc culture	IDRC	Grant	1984/86	140,000
Inland fisheries	CIDA	Grant	1985/89	2,000,000
Inland fish nutrition	IDRC	Grant	1985/87	110,000
Total				22,974,900

None of the Sri Lankan universities teaches limnology as a subject. Generally courses in limnology are offered as course units in the departments of Zoology. Postgraduate courses are however offered in all the universities to M.Sc., M.Phil and Ph.D. degrees associated with fields such as limnology, fish biology, fisheries biology and aquaculture.

NARA, which was created as an arm of the Ministry of Fisheries to conduct research on aquatic resources, has one of its divisions, the Inland Fishery Resources Division, exclusively devoted to research on limnology and other applied aspects related to Inland Fishery resources.

The Inland Fisheries Division of the Ministry of Fisheries had about 40 trained personnel involved in the applied limnological studies most of which are related to increasing fish production. Since the closing down of the Inland Fisheries Division, most of them have joined private enterprises involved in shrimp production.

Table 21 gives the list of the universities, institutions and number of scientists associated with teaching or research in limnology.

Scientific Societies

There are no societies in Sri Lanka concerned exclusively with limnology or other related subjects although several societies, which deal with the environment, have been inaugurated recently.

There are no journals devoted exclusively for publication of limnological reseaerch in Sri Lanka. However, research in Limnology and other related subjects both by foreign and local scientists are published in the following local journals, which also publish articles on other subjects.

a. *Journal of Inland Fisheries* (abolished in effect from 31.12.1991)
b. *Ceylon Journal of Science* (Bio Science)
c. *Journal of National Science Council of Sri Lanka*
d. *Journal of the National Aquatic Resources Agency*
e. *Spolia Zeylanica*

However, most of the papers written by local scientists are still published abroad.

Constraints to Development of Limnological Research

Shortage of trained limnologists and technical personnel has been the biggest constraint in the development of limnological research in the country (Table 21). However, this inadequacy has been ameliorated to a great extent by conducting joint projects with the limnologists and limnological institutes of developed countries (Brinck et al. 1971, Costa and Starmuhlner 1972, Schiemer 1983).

Research in limnology has been also hindered by the shortage of funds. Out of US $ 23 million given as assistance to fisheries research by foreign agencies and organisations no funds have been allocated for pure limnological research. Sometimes meagre funds have been made available by national funding authorities to the scientists in the universities for study of inland waters.

Analytical and sampling equipment used in limnological research are unavailable in most universities and even in government sponsored institutes. Even the few pieces of equipment available are sometimes not in use due to unavailability of qualified service personnel. Lack of literature and pertinent reference works and shortage of senior limnologists for guidance and advice have been the major constraints.

The greatest constraint to future development of limnological studies will be the recent decision by the Government of Sri Lanka to abolish the Inland Fisheries Division of the Ministry of Fisheries. This will effectively stop the government patronage in terms of government subsidies and aid programmes to inland fisheries and aqua-culture projects carried out in Sri Lanka.

Table 21. Universities and research institutes engaged in limnological/fisheries research.

University/ Organisation/ Division	Number of scientists trained at M.Sc./Ph.D. level engaged in limnological/fish & fishery biological/aquacultural studies	Scientists trained at Ph.D. level in limnology/ freshwater	Institutions conducting courses/ course units in limnology biology
University of Colombo	2	1	+
University of Peredeniya	3	1	+
University of Kelaniya	5	1	+
University of Sri Jayawardanapura	3	1	+
University of Ruhuna	2	1	+
Eastern University Sri Lanka	2	1	+
University of Jaffna	1	0	+
National Aquatic Resources Agency	14	1	-
Inland Fisheries Division, Ministry of Fisheries (abolished w.e.f. 31.12.1991)	40	1	-
Total	72	8	

LIMNOLOGICAL STUDIES IN FUTURE

The present state of limnological knowledge of the Sri Lankan waters, although not impressive by comparison with that of the temperate regions, is nevertheless quite substantial. However, there exist many areas where there are significant gaps in the understanding of the dynamics of the freshwaters of Sri Lanka.

The entire ecological spectrum of rivers and reservoirs has to be studied to evaluate productivity. Very little is known of the dynamics of lotic environments. Aspects such as interactions at land-water interface, running water ecology, watershed management and conservation have yet to be studied. Considering lentic habitats many studies need to be done on seasonal, diurnal and vertical variations of thermal features, oxygen regimes, nutrient cycling, organic inputs and dissolved solids. No work has yet been done on microbial ecology, abundance of autochthonous detritus in relation to fish production and on the metabolic activities of the littoral zone and sediments.

Large gaps of knowledge exist as to the quantities of domestic sewage, agro-chemicals and industrial effluents that are discharged into the water bodies, and their effect on aquatic organisms and health. Studies on biological monitoring have yet to be carried on.

The assortment of planktonic and benthic organisms have to be evaluated to guide fish stocking programmes in reservoirs. Furthermore, basic biological research on indigenous fish and other aquatic organisms have to be carried out in order to work out the ecological energetics of aquatic bodies.

Further work has to be done to develop predictive models using limnological data for effective management of diverse reservoirs that exist in Sri Lanka.

Furthering of Limnological Research and Training

The development of limnology, manpower and infrastructure in Sri Lanka should be combined with the identification of national research programmes to form the basis of strengthening of limnological research and training.

The needs and priorities to promote scientific management and conservation of water bodies and their living resources could be summarized as follows.

1. Establishment or strengthening of university infrastructure in a few universities for undergraduate training and for post graduate training in specialized fields necessary to conduct identified research programmes.
2. Establishment and/or strengthening of research laboratories of institutes carrying out limnological research with qualified personnel and research equipment.
3. Short term training and long term fellowships in foreign limnological institutes/ departments at regional level to upgrade individuals' scientific capabilities.
4. Strenghening of library facilities with essential reference works and monographs in limnology.
5. Providing mechanisms for scientific cooperation with internationally known limno- logists at research level.
6. Providing travel grants to young limnologists to attend conferences and workshops held in countries in the region.
7. Organisation of periodic local workshops, seminars, etc. to review and evaluate the current limnological research projects in progress in different parts of the island.

REFERENCES

Abeywickrama, B.A. 1956. The origin and the affinities of the flora of Ceylon. Proceedings Ceylon Association Advancement of Science: 99-121.

Amarasinghe, U.S. 1987. Status of the fishery of Pimburettewa wewa, a man-made lake in Sri Lanka. Aquaculture and Fisheries Management 18: 375-385.

Amarasinghe, U.S. and Pitcher, J. 1986. Assessment of fishing effort in Parakrama samudra, an ancient man-made lake in Sri Lanka. Fisheries Research 4: 271-282.

Amarasinghe, U.S., Costa, H.H. and Wijeyaratne, M.J.S. 1983. Limnology and fish production potential of some reservoirs in Anuradhapura district, Sri Lanka. Journal of Inland Fisheries 2: 14-29.

Amarasiri, S.L. 1973. Water quality of major irrigation tanks in Sri Lanka. Tropical Agriculture 79: 19-25.

Apstein, C. 1907. Das Plankton in Colombo See auf Ceylon. Zoologische Jahrbücher 25: 210-244.

Apstein, C. 1910. Das Plankton des Gregory See auf Ceylon. Zoologische Jahrbücher 29: 661-680.

Arudpragasam, K.D. and Costa, H.H. 1961. The Atyidae of Ceylon I. Crustaceana 4: 7-24.

Bertrand, H.P.I. 1973. Results of the Austrian-Ceylonese Hydrobiological Mission 1970. Part XI. Larvae and pupae of water beetles collected in the island of Ceylon. Bulletin of the Fisheries Research Station, Sri Lanka 24: 95-112.

Bott, R. 1970. Die Süsswasser Krabben von Ceylon (Crustacea, Decapoda). Arkives Zoologie 22: 627-640.

Brinck, P., Anderson, H. and Cederholm, L. 1971. Report No.1 from the Lund University, Ceylon Expedition in 1962, Introduction. Entomological Science and Supplements 1: i-xxxvi.

Chakrabarty, R.D. and Hettiarachchi, A. 1982. Preliminary observations on fish polyculture cum duck raising in a farm pond in Sri Lanka. Journal of Inland Fisheries, Sri Lanka 1: 54-63.

Chandrasoma, J. 1986. Preliminary productivity and fish yields in ten seasonal tanks in Sri Lanka. Journal of Inland Fisheries, Sri Lanka 3: 56-63.

Chandrasoma, J. and De Silva, S.S. 1981. Reproductive biology of Puntius sarana, an indigenous species and Tilapia rendalli an exotic in an ancient man-made lake in Sri Lanka. Fish Management 12: 17-28.

Chandrasoma, J., Muthukumarana, G., Pushpakumara, U. and Sreenivasan, A. 1986. Limnology and fish production in Udawalawe reservoir. Journal of Inland Fisheries, Sri Lanka 3: 68-88.

Chengalath, R. and Fernando, C.H. 1973. Rotifera from Ceylon. I. The genus Lecanae with description of two new species. Bulletin of the Fisheries Research Station, Sri Lanka 24: 13-27.

Chengalath, R., Fernando, C.H. and Koste, W. 1973. The Rotifera from Sri Lanka. 2. Further studies on the Eurotatoria including new records. Bulletin of the Fisheries Research Station, Sri Lanka 24: 29-62.

Chengalath, R., Fernando, C.H. and Koste, W. 1974. The Rotifera from Sri Lanka. 3. New species and records with a list of Rotifera recorded and their distribution in different habitats from Sri Lanka. Bulletin of the Fisheries Research Station, Sri Lanka 25: 83-96.

Cooray, P.G. 1984. An introduction to the geology of Ceylon. Ceylon National Museum Publication. 324 pages. Colombo, Sri Lanka.

Costa, H.H. 1967. A taxonomic study of the freshwater Oligochaeta of Sri Lanka. Ceylon Journal of Science (Biological Science) 7: 37-51.

Costa, H.H. 1970. Effects of some common insecticides and other environmental factors on the heart beat of Caridina pristis. Hydrobiologia 35: 469-480.

Costa, H.H. 1974. Limnology and fishery biology of the streams at Horton Plains, Sri Lanka. Bulletin of the Fisheries Research Station, Sri Lanka 25: 15-26.

Costa, H.H. 1978. The freshwater Hirudinea of Sri Lanka. Bulletin of the Fisheries Research Station, Sri Lanka 32: 326-341.

Costa, H.H. 1979. The Palaemonidae of the inland waters of Sri Lanka. Ceylon Journal of Science (Biological Sciences) 13: 39-64.

Costa, H.H. 1982. Biological studies on the Pearl Spot Etroplus suratensis Bloch (Pisces, Cichlidae) from 3 habitats in Sri Lanka. Internationale Revue der gesamten Hydrobiologie 68: 565-580.

Costa, H.H. 1984. The ecology and distribution of free-living meso- and macro-crustacea of inland waters. pp. 195-213. In: Fernando, C.H. (Editor) Ecology and Biogeography in Sri Lanka. Dr W. Junk bv. Publishers, The Hague.

Costa, H.H. 1986. The physical, chemical and biological characteristics of the freshwater bodies of the lowlands of Sri Lanka. Spolia Zeylanica 35: 43-99.

Costa, H.H. 1989. Land based marine pollution in Sri Lanka. Paper presented at the Workshop on Land-based Marine Pollution, Bangkok, Thailand.

Costa, H.H. and Abeyasiri, R. 1978. The hydrobiology of Colombo (Beira) lake. VII. The food and feeding ecology of Tilapia mossambica. Spolia Zeylanica 32: 94-110.

Costa, H.H. and De Silva, S.S. 1969. Hydrobiology of Colombo (Beira) lake. I. Diurnal variations in temperature, hydrochemical factors and zooplankton. Bulletin of the Fisheries Research Station, Sri Lanka 20: 141-149.

Costa, H.H. and De Silva, S.S. 1978a. Hydrobiology of Colombo lake. II. Seasonal variation in chemical factors. Spolia Zeylanica 32: 26-41.

Costa, H.H. and De Silva, S.S. 1978b. Hydrobiology of Colombo lake. IV. Seasonal fluctuations in aquatic fauna living on water plants. Spolia Zeylanica 32: 60-75.

Costa, H.H. and Fernando, E.F.W. 1977. Evaluation of three indigenous species of fish as mosquito larvivores of Sri Lanka. WHO/VBC/77,665. World Health Organization, Geneva.

Costa, H.H. and Gunatilleka, W.D.A. 1978. Hydrobiology of Colombo lake VIII. Bacterial Ecology. Spolia Zeylanica 32: 115-132.

Costa, H.H. and Liyanage, H. 1978. Hydrobiology of Colombo lake. IX. Productivity of *Tilapia mossambica*. Spolia Zeylanica 32: 133-152.

Costa, H.H. and Starmuhlner, F. 1972. Results of the Austrian hydrobiological mission 1970 of the 1st Zoological Institute of the University of Vienna and the Department of Zoology of the Vidyalankara University of Ceylon, Kelaniya 1. Introduction and the description of the stations. Bulletin of the Fisheries Research Station, Sri Lanka 23: 43-76.

Costa, H.H., Wanninayake, T.B. and Wijeyaratne, M.J.S. 1994. The hydrobiology of Ihalagama wewa, Ragama. Spolia Zeylanica (in press).

Daniel, D.J., Costa, H.H. and Wijeyaratna, M.J.S. 1988. The hydrobiology and fish production potential of major freshwater reservoirs in Hambantota district. Journal of Inalnd Fisheries, Sri Lanka 4: 95-121.

Davis, D.M. 1984. Notes on Simuliidae (Diptera) in Sri Lanka. pp. 275-381. In: Fernando, C.H. (Editor). Ecology and Biogeography in Sri Lanka. Dr W. Junk bv. Publishers, The Hague.

De Alwis, D.P. 1987. Hazardous waste management in Sri Lanka. pp. 22-26. In: Proceedings Hazardous Waste Management. UNIDO, Vienna.

De Alwis, P. 1990. Investigation of reported mass fish mortality in Beira lake. National Aquatic Research Agency, Colombo, Sri Lanka (unpublished). 6 pages.

De Alwis, P., Yatapana, H., Dassanayake, W.H. and Pereira, R. 1988. Monitoring of industrial effluents with a view to pollution control. Paper presented at the 43rd annual session of the Sri Lanka Association for the Advancement of Science, Colombo, Sri Lanka (unpublished).

De Beauchamp, P. 1973. Freshwater triclads (Turbellaria, Tricladida) from Ceylon. Bulletin of the Fisheries Research Station, Ceylon 24: 95-112.

De Silva, K.H.G.M. 1983. Studies on Atyidae (Decapoda, Caridea) of Sri Lanka. II. Distribution of atyid shrimps. Crustaceana. 44: 205-215.

De Silva, K.H.G.M. 1991. Diversity and endemism of three major freshwater faunal groups, Atyidae (Decapoda), Gastropoda and Teleostei, in Sri Lanka. Proceedings of the Conference on Conservation and Management of Tropical Inland Waters: Problems, Solutions and Prospects, September 5-9, Hongkong: 1-30.

De Silva, K.H.G.M. and De Silva, P.K. 1991. Stream fauna in Horton Plains and Peak Wilderness areas. Proceedings, Seminar on Conservation/Management of Ritigala Kanda, Horton Plains and Peak Wilderness Wildlife Reserves and the adjoining areas. Colombo 9-10 August 1990.

De Silva, M.K.W., Nandani, C. and Jayaweera, V. 1984. Mass mortality of fish in Kelani river. National Aquatic Research Agency, Colombo, Sri Lanka (unpublished). 5 pages.

De Silva, P.K. 1993. Some aspects of the limnology and the fishery biology of Kotmale and Randenigala reservoirs in Sri Lanka. Sri Lankan Agriculture Science 30: 71-85.

De Silva, P.K. 1993. Physico-chemical characteristics, phytoplankton and the fishery of Victoria reservoir. Ceylon Journal of Science (Biological Science) 34: 29-39.

De Silva, P.K. and De Silva, K.H.G.M. 1984. An ecological study of the meso- and macrofauna of the littoral regional of the Lake Kandy in Sri Lanka. Archiv für Hydrobiologie 102: 53-72.

De Silva, P.K. and Somaratna, R.M.D. 1994. Ecological studies of phytoplankton in Victoria reservoir. Proceedings in Stream Ecology and Reservoir Production. Institute of Fundamental Studies, Kandy, Sri Lanka (in press).

De Silva, S.S. 1988. Reservoirs of Sri Lanka and their fisheries. FAO Fisheries Technical Paper 298. 128 pages.

De Silva, S.S. and Sirisena, H.K.G. 1987. New fish resources of reservoirs of Sri Lanka; feasibility of introduction of a subsidiary gill net fishery. Fisheries Research 6: 17-34.

De Silva, S.S., Kortmulder, K. and Wijeyaratne, M.J.S. 1977. A comparative study of the food and feeding habits of *Puntius bimaculatus* and *P. titteya* (Pisces, Cyprinidae). Netherland Journal of Zoology 27: 253-263.

Dissanayake, N.H., De Alwis, P. and Pereira, R. 1990. Preliminary results of an environmental survey. National Aquatic Research Agency, Colombo, Sri Lanka (unpublished). 6 pages.

Dokulil, M., Bauer, K. and Silva, I. 1983. An assessment of the phytoplankton biomass and primary productivity of Parakrama Samudra, a shallow man-made lake in Sri Lanka. pp. 49-76. In: Schiemer, F. (Editor). Limnology of Parakrama Samudra, Sri Lanka. Dr W. Junk bv. Publishers, The Hague.

Duncan, A. 1983. The composition, density and distribution of the zooplankton of Parakrama Samudra. pp. 85-94. In: Schiemer, F. (Editor) Limnology of Parakrama Samudra, Sri Lanka. Dr W. Junk bv. Publishers, The Hague.

Duncan, A. and Gulati, R.D. 1983. A diurnal study of the planktonic rotifer populations in Karakrama Samudra reservoir, Sri Lanka. pp. 95-106. In: Schiemer, F. (Editor). Limnology of Parakrama Samudra. Dr W. Junk bv. Publishers, The Hague.

Erb, D.K. 1984. Land forms and drainage. pp. 35-63. In: Fernando, C.H. (Editor). Ecology and Biogeography in Sri Lanka. Dr W. Junk bv. Publishers, The Hague.

Fernando, A.D.N. 1973. The ground water resources of Sri Lanka, Ministry of Irrigation, Power and Highways, Colombo. 21 pages.

Fernando, C.H. 1956. On the food of four common freshwater fishes of Ceylon. Ceylon Journal of Science 1: 201-207.

Fernando, C.H. 1965. A preliminary survey of 21 Ceylon lakes 3. Parasites and predators. Bulletin of the Fisheries Research Station, Sri Lanka 18: 17-28.

Fernando, C.H. 1980. The freshwater zooplankton of Sri Lanka with discussion of tropical zooplankton composition. Internationale Revue der gesamten Hydrobiologie 65: 85-125.

Fernando, C.H. and De Silva, S.S. 1984. Man made lakes, ancient heritage and modern biological resources. pp. 431-451, In: Fernando, C.H. (Editor). Ecology and Biogeography in Sri Lanka. W. Junk bv., The Hague.

Fernando, C.H. Ellepola, W.B. 1969. A preliminary study of two village tanks in the Polonnaruwa area with biological notes on these reservoirs in Ceylon. Bulletin of the Fisheries Research Station, Sri Lanka. 20: 3-13.

Geisler, R. 1962. Limnologisch-ichthyologische Beobachtungen in S.W. Ceylon. Internationale Revue der gesamten Hydrobiologie 2: 559-572.

GOSL/UNDP/FAO. 1986. National Inventory of Sri Lanka. SRL/79/014. Colombo, Sri Lanka.

Gunatillaka, A. 1975. Pollution aspects of the lower reaches of Kelani river. Unpublished report, CISIR, Sri Lanka.

Gunatillaka, A. 1983. Phosphorus and phosphatase dynamics in Parakrama Samudra based on diurnal observations. pp. 35-47. In: Schiemer, F. (Editor). Limnology of Parakrama Samudra. Dr W. Junk bv. Publishers, The Hague.

Gunawardene, H.D. and Adikari, A.M.K.R. 1981. Studies on the quality of irrigation waters in Kalawewa area. Journal of the National Science Council Sri Lanka. 9: 121-148.

Holsinger, E.C.T. 1955. The planktonic algae of three Ceylon lakes. Hydrobiologia 7:8-24.

Hubbard, M.D. and Peters, W.L. 1984. Ephemeroptera of Sri Lanka, an introduction to their ecology and biogeography. pp. 257-274. In: Fernando, C.H. (Editor). Ecology and Biogeography in Sri Lanka. Dr W. Junk bv. Publishers, The Hague.

Jeach, M. 1982. Neue Dryopidae und Hydracaenidae aus Ceylon Nepal, New Guinea und der Turkei (Coleoptera). Koleopteran Rundschau 56: 89-114.

Jayatunga, Y.N.A. 1982. Studies on the hydrobiology and zooplankton in the Kalawewa area. M.Phil thesis. University of Colombo, Sri Lanka (unpublished). 257 pages.

Maitepe, P. and De Silva, S.S. 1985. Switches between zoophagy, phytophagy and detritivory in adult Sarotherodon mossambicus populations of twelve man-made lakes in Sri Lanka. Journal of Fisheries Biology, Sri Lanka 26: 49-61.

Malicky, H. 1973. The Ceylonese Trichoptera. Bulletin of the Fisheries Research Station, Sri Lanka 24: 153-157.

Mendis, A.S. 1964. A contribution to the limnology of Colombo lake. Bulletin of the Fisheries Research Station, Sri Lanka 17: 213- 220.

Mendis, A.S. 1965. Preliminary study of twenty one Ceylon lakes. 2. Limnology and fish production. Bulletin of the Fisheries Research Station, Sri Lanka 18: 7-16.

Moorman, F.R. and Panabokke, C.R. 1961. Soils of Ceylon; a new approach to the identification and classification of the soils of Ceylon. Tropical Agriculture 117.

Muller-Dombois, D. 1968. Climatic maps of Ceylon. Survey Department, Sri Lanka.

Neale, J.W. 1984. The freshwater Ostracoda. pp. 171-194. In: Fernando, C.H. (Editor). Ecology and Biogeography in Sri Lanka. Dr W.Junk bv. Publishers, The Hague.

Newrkla, P. and Duncan, A. 1984. The biology and density of *Ehirava fluviatilis* in Parakrama Samudra. Verhandlungen der internationale Vereinigung für theoretische und angewandte Limnologie 22: 1572-1578.

Panabokke, C.R. 1984. Sri Lanka showing the approximate distribution of great soil groups. Survey Department, Colombo. 16 pages.

Pethiyagoda, R. 1991. Freshwater fishes of Sri Lanka. Wildlife Heritage Trust of Sri Lanka, Colombo. 362 pages.

Piyasiri, S. 1991. Limnology project of Mahaweli reservoirs. 1. Some physical properties of Kotmale, Victoria and Randenigala reservoirs. Vidyodaya Journal of Science 3: 44-63.

Polhemus, J.J. 1979. Aquatic and semi aquatic Hemiptera of Sri Lanka. Bulletin of the Fisheries Research Station, Sri Lanka 29: 89-113.

Rajapakse, R. and Fernando, C.H. 1984. Freshwater zooplankton. pp. 155-166. In: Fernando, C.H. (Editor). Ecology and Biogeography in Sri Lanka. W. Junk bv., The Hague.

Room, P.M. and Fernando, I.V.S. 1992. Weed invasions countered by biological control: *Salvinia molesta* and *Eichhornia crassipes*. Aquatic Botany 42: 99-107.

Rott, E. 1983. A contribution to the phytoplankton species composition at Parakrama Samudra. pp. 209-226, In: Schiemer, F. (Editor). Limnology of Parakrama Samudra. W. Junk bv., The Hague.

Schiemer, F. (Editor). 1983. Limnology of Parakrama Samudra. Dr W. Junk bv., The Hague. 292 pages.

Schmidt, F. 1958. Trichoptera de Ceylon. Archiv für Hydrobiologie 54: 1-193.

Shafiei,T.M. and Costa, H.H.1990. The susceptibility and resistance of fry and fingerlings of *Oreochromis mossambicus* Peters to some pesticides commonly used in Sri Lanka. Journal of Applied Ichthyology 6: 73-80.

Silva, E.I.L. 1991. Limnology and fish yields of newly built standing water bodies in the Mahaweli river basin, Sri Lanka. Verhandlungen der internationale Vereinigung für theoretische und angewandte Limnologie 24: 1425-1429.

Silva, E.I.L. and Davies, R.W. 1986. Primary productivity and related parameters in three different types of inland waters in Sri Lanka. Hydrobiologia 137: 239-249.

Somasekaram, T. (Editor). 1988. The National Atlas of Sri Lanka. Survey Department, Sri Lanka, Colombo. 142 pages.

Sreenivasan, A. and Thayaparan, K. 1983. Fisheries development in the Mahaweli system. Journal of Inland Fisheries, Sri Lanka 1: 89-96.

Starmuhlner, F. 1974. The freshwater gastropods of Ceylon. Bulletin of the Fisheries Research Station, Sri Lanka. 25: 97-181.

Weninger,G. 1972. Hydrochemical studies on mountain rivers in Ceylon. Bulletin of the Fisheries Research Station, Sri Lanka 23: 77-100.

Wewalka, G. 1973. Results of the Austrian-Ceylonese Hydrobiological Mission Part 9 Dytiscidae (Coleoptera). Bulletin of the Fisheries Research Station, Sri Lanka 24: 83-87.

Wickramanayake, E.D. 1990. Conservation of endemic rain forest fishes of Sri Lanka: Results of a translocation experiment. Conservation Biology 4: 32-37.

Wijeyaratne, M.J.S. and Amarasinghe, U.S. 1984. Estimations of maximum sustainable fish yields and stocking densities of inland reservoirs of Sri Lanka. Journal of National Aquatic Resources Agency, Sri Lanka. 31: 65-72.

Wijeyaratne, M.J.S. and Costa, H.H. 1981. Stocking rate estimation of Tilapia mossambica fingerlings for some reservoirs of Sri Lanka. Internationale Revue der gesamten Hydrobiologie 66: 327- 333.

Wijeyaratne, M.J.S. and Wanninayake, T.B. 1994. Limnology and fish production potential of Anamaduwa wewa. Internationale Revue der gesamten Hydrobiologie (in press).

Winkler, H. 1983. The ecology of cormorants (Genus Phalacrocorax). pp. 193-200. In: Schiemer, F. (Editor). Limnology of Parakrama Samudra. W.Junk bv. Publishers, The Hague.

Zwick, P. 1980. The genus Neoperla (Plecoptera, Perlidae) from Sri Lanka. Oriental Insects 14: 263-269.

Note: This review is an expanded and updated version of a similar review published by the first author in *Mitteilungen der internationale Vereinigung für theoretische und angewandte Limnologie* 24: 73-85, 1994.

Gopal, B. and Wetzel, R.G. (Editors) **Limnology in Developing Countries**: 105-120

Limnological Research in Bangladesh

Moniruzzaman Khondker

Department of Botany, University of Dhaka, Dhaka 1000, Bangladesh

ABSTRACT

Limnological research which is practiced for more than a quarter of a century in Bangladesh has been reviewed briefly. The nature of the country's rich aquatic resources such as rivers, beels, haors, baors, reservoirs, ponds etc. are described. A number of research works on physicochemical limnology, phytoplankton quality, quantity, seasonality and primary productivity are discussed showing the range of measured variables in many cases. Some works of hydrobiological nature ranging from algae to angiosperms with their qualitative aspect, biomass, biochemical contents and the associated limnological factors of the habitats have been discussed. In the present review attempts have been made to assess the facilities existing in the field of limnological research, education and training together with the identification of major limnological problems of the country and possible solutions.

INTRODUCTION

The ancient community of people called Vangas, Pundras[1] as mentioned in the Aitareya Aranyaka, Mahabharata; Marco Polo's Bengala (1250 A.D. – 1323 A.D.); Mughal Emperor Akbar's Subha-Bangla (1542-1605) and the former East Pakistan (1947-1971) all represent the same ancestor for Bangladesh (Rashid 1977, Miah 1981). The country got independence from Pakistan in 1971 with its present boundary.

Bangladesh is a South Asiatic country situated in the humid tropics. The geoclimatic condition of the country is presented in Table 1. Except a part of the south eastern border (Arakan province of Burma) and the southern Bay of Bengal the country is bounded by Indian territory on all sides (Figure 1). Geologically the land mass of Bangladesh can be divided into three broad categories of physiographic regions namely: Pleistocene uplands (highest peak 46 m), Tertiary hills (highest peak 1004 m) and Recent plains (ca. 80% of the total area and some places having very low elevation). Majority of the Recent plains consists of floodplains and deltaic plains confluenced by Ganges, Brahmaputra and Meghna system. The Sunderbans in the southwestern estuarine part of Bangladesh is one of the largest mangrove forests of the world.

Bangladesh enjoys monsoonal climate characterized by hot, rainy, humid, summers and dry mild winters. Heavy monsoonal rainfall (duration 4-5 months) and the

---

1. Pundranagara (present day Mahasthangarh of Bogra district) capital city of the Mauryan empire from the fourth to the second century B.C.

flooding effect of large rivers have helped Bangladesh to support a large number of aquatic habitats of varying dimensions. On the other hand due to the unique geo-climatic condition (Table 1) the country has been converted to a densely populated area. So, to speak about limnology Bangladesh has a vast resource to explore. Part of its 36663 km^2 aquatic habitats is perturbed causing hazards and declining productivity. On the contrary there is a great demand for cheaper protein supply to this huge mass of population in order to avoid malnutritional problem. Therefore, the importance of limnological research in Bangladesh is more than casual. The present review describes the limnological potentiality of the country together with the task completed so far and the tasks to be undertaken in the future.

Table 1. Geoclimatic condition of Bangladesh*

Latitude	20° 34′ N and 26° 38′ N
Longitude	88° 01′ E and 92° 41′ E
Area	143,988 km^2
Population (1991)	111,455,185
Rural	90.05%
Urban	9.95%
Population density	755 perons km^{-2}
Literacy	24.19%
Mean air temperature (1983)	11.14 - 34.76 °C
Total mean annual rainfall (1984)	2569.47 mm
Mean humidity (1983)	79.64%

* Rahman, pers. comm. Department of Geography, University of Dhaka.

FRESHWATER RESOURCES

The types of water bodies present in Bangladesh conform with the very deltaic nature of the land mass. Many seasonal and perennial water bodies were created due to the fluviatile activity of large rivers along their courses and by the accumulation of rain water in shallow tectonic depressions. Table 2 shows the area shared by each type of habitats. A brief description of water bodies characteristic to Bangladesh is provided below.

River systems

The river systems comprise large rivers like Ganges, Jamuna (known as River Brahma-putra in India), Padma and Meghna (Figure 1) which pass their pool zone stage through the land i.e., with reduced current, increased siltation and having a tendency to change the main course.

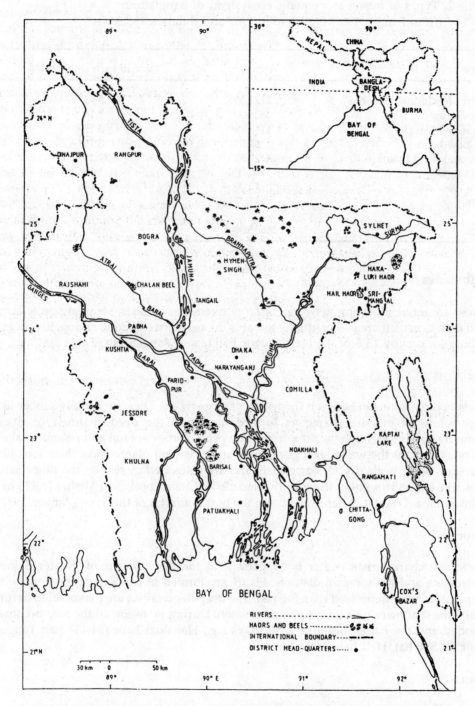

Figure 1.: Map of Bangladesh showing major rivers, haors, beels and Kaptai lake.
Inset shows the geographical locations of the country in the Indian sub-continent.

Table 2. Types of freshwater aquatic ecosystems of Bangladesh
(from Ameen 1987, Duijvendijk 1987 and Rahman 1988).

Type	Area (km^2)	Share of each category (%)
Rivers (excluding estuaries)	2171.35	5.92
Tributaries	2626.00	7.16
Beels and Haors	1147.93	3.13
Ox-bow lakes	54.88	0.15
Seasonal flood plains	28327.92	77.27
Kaptai lake	688.00	1.88
Feni reservoir	12.00	0.03
Ponds	1634.92	4.46
Total	36663.00	100.0

Tributaries

These are interconnecting networks of large rivers by channels, some are quite large and their density increases gradually towards the southern estuarine region. Rivers and tributaries occupy 13% of the total aquatic habitats of Bangladesh (Table 2).

Beels

Beels occupy basins in between the leeves of large rivers. They are usually saucer-like depressions of marshy characters formed mostly in the dead channels of rivers formerly passing through the area. In the rainy season they are full and resemble lakes. At other seasons the water level goes down and emergent plants make them look like marshes. Some beels dry up completely and are cultivated. A few on the other hand look like lakes throughout the year (Rashid 1977). Chalan beel, Beel Mishra (6,475 ha), Kamaladaha, Dakatia, Arial beel etc. are the best examples of this type (Ameen 1987).

Haors

These are characteristic water body present in the Haor Basins of greater Sylhet, Netrokona and Kishoreganj districts. Haors are formed in tectonic depressions with some parts more depressed than the rest. The deep depressions are perennial in nature while the shallower part dries up in dry season. During monsoon all the area becomes flooded and the haors look like large lakes e.g., Hakaluki haor (34,437 ha); Tangua haor (25,506 ha), Hail haor etc.

Baors

Baors are essentially ox-bow lakes formed by the cut off loop of meandering rivers. They are shallow in nature, more stagnant, occasionally perennial, derelict lakes where rooted vegetation is very common. All the baors are situated in the moribund delta in south-west Bangladesh (greater Jessore district). The main baors of these area are: Baluhar (282 ha), Marjat (253 ha), and Gabindapur baor (217 ha).

Reservoirs

There are two reservoirs in Bangladesh namely: Kaptai reservoir and Feni reservoir. Kaptai is a H-shaped, deep water discharge, water body created by damming the river Karnaphuli in the Chittagong Hill Tracts for a hydro-electric power plant in the year of 1961. Whereas Feni reservoir was commissioned in 1986 for flood control and irrigation by the construction of a cross-dam and regulator at the mouth of the Feni River in the Feni district. It is a surface di1xharge water body (Ameen 1987, Duijvendijk 1987).

Ponds

The rural life of Bangladesh is very familiar with the pond system. It plays a greater socio-economic role in the village community. Ponds are usually dug out for storage of water for domestic use and fish culture or are formed when water accumulates in the burrow pits excavated for earth for house construction in lower floodplain area. Pond basins are usually constructed deeply to reach the subsoil water level so, they become perennial. Large ponds called Dighi, a traditionally created water body, are mostly present in the recreational grounds of residential palaces of old Zamindars.

Seasonal Floodplains

These are low lying areas close to the banks of large rivers which remain submerged from June to early November. Floodplains of Ganges, Meghna and Jamuna are the main category. Deep water rice plant (physiological race of *Oryza sativa* L.) is invariably cultivated in these places.

Lakes

In Bangladesh, strictly speaking there are only three natural lakes. They are Rainkhyongkine (ca. 1.6 km long, 0.40 km wide and Z_{max}=26 m) and Bogakine lake (altitude 372 m) of Chittagong Hill tracts and Ashula beel of Eastern Barind Tract (Islam 1969, Rashid 1977, Ameen 1987).

PAST AND CONTEMPORARY TRENDS OF LIMNOLOGICAL RESEARCH

Pioneered by the phycological research wing of the Department of Botany, Dhaka University and under the guidance of Professor A.K.M. Nurul Islam, the first work of limnological nature in Bangladesh was published in 1966. In that work (Islam and Khatun 1966) few organically polluted permanent ponds situated in and around Dhaka University Campus were studied. Luxuriant growth of water blooms largely consisting of blue-green algae, bacteria etc. were noticed under a limnological condi-tion of: water temperature 28-34 °C; pH 7.5-8.5; NO_3-N 5 mg L^{-1} and average P_2O_5 concentration 43.8

mg L^{-1}. Islam and Nahar (1967) simultaneously carried out research in the above mentioned ponds giving particular emphasis on the blue-greens. They recorded a pH range of 8.2 and 8.5 during bloom formation by *Microcystis* sp. Oldest systematic study on the plankton of freshwater ponds of Dhaka dates back to 1958 when Begum (1958) provided an excellent qualitative account of phyto- and zooplankton from three ponds but the study did lack the physico-chemical data of the habitats. By studying algal flora indicative of water quality, Islam (1969) described lake Rainkhyongkine as a semi-hard, drainage lake, with kettle hole type depression and may be passing into meso-trophy. Islam and Begum (1970) described 110 species of phytoplankton (mainly Chlorococcales) with notes on seasonal changes of water temperature and pH from Dhaka district. Islam (1991) cited about 100 research works related to taxonomy and ecology of freshwater planktonic and non-planktonic algae from British Indian and pre-independence period of Bangladesh.

In between 1971 and 1980 a large number of limnological works were carried out in the country. Islam et al. (1974) studied the river Buriganga at 8 stations along a 5 km stretch from Parzoar to Postgola. The water condition according to their results were: DO: 2.4–9.5 mg L^{-1}; total nitrogen: 26–440 μg L^{-1}; PO_4-P: 4–126 μg L^{-1}; pH 6.9–7.8. Phytoplankton showed their highest abundance from March to May and depleted in winter months. During the year 1969-1971 Freshwater Fisheries Research Station (FERS) of Chandpur conducted a limnological survey (though few parameters were considered only) in rivers, baors, ponds and Dighis in different districts of Bangladesh (Anonymous 1971, Anonymous 1973). Two lentic habitats of Dhaka city Ramna lake and Shere-bangla Nagar jheel were studied by Islam and Saha (1975) and Islam and Mendes (1976) respectively. The ecology of *Wolffia arrhiza* (L.) Wimm. growing profusely in a shallow pond of Faridpur district was studied in 1976 and 1977. The biomass was harvested and the biochemical contents e.g., protein, lipid, ash, pentosans etc. of *W. arrhiza* were determined (Islam and Paul 1977). Oppenheimer et al. (1978) conducted a detail study of physiocochemical characteristics and total plankton density of 3 ponds of Dhaka city. A survey of aquatic macrophytes and phytoplankton with limnological notes was made by Islam and Paul (1978), Islam et al. (1979) and Islam and Chowdhury (1979) in Hakaluki haor and Dhanmondi lake respectively. Islam et al. (1992) carried out a comparative hydrobiological study of two habitats near Dhaka metropolis and reported the occurrence of 29 aquatic macrophytes. An excellent account of aquatic angiosperms from Bangladesh has been contributed by Khan and Halim (1987).

Chowdhury and Mazumdar (1981) studied the seasonal, vertical, horizontal and diurnal fluctuations of water temperature, Secchi depth, pH, DO, CO_2, hardness, phosphate and nitrate of Kaptai reservoir. They considered the lake as oligotrophic in nature. A brood holding tank situated in the ground of FFRS Chandpur was studied by Ali et al. (1982). With the diurnal variations in physicochemical factors the population dynamics of *Cyclops*, *Daphnia*, *Diaphanosoma*, rotifers and *Diaptomus* were also studied. Safiullah et al. (1985) and Ittekot et al. (1985) determined the amount of DO, alkalinity, total hardness, total suspended solids, analytical fractions of various organic carbon compounds, sugars and amino acids of Ganges and Brahmaputra rivers in Bangladesh. Inverse relationship between the abundance of macro-inverteb-rates and ceratopogonids with water depth was recorded in a fish pond by Ali et al. (1985). Comparative limnological studies between semi-intensive and extensive fish culturing ponds from South Eastern districts of Bangladesh were carried out by Ameen et al. (1986) and Begum and Alam (1987). Concentrating more on the pond ecosystems many studies have dealt mainly with the interactions of plankton, fish and the prevailing physico-chemical and environmental factors (Alam et al. 1985, 1987a,b, Ali et al. 1980, 1989, Ameen et al. 1988, Banu et al. 1992, Begum et al. 1992, 1989, Khaleque and Islam 1983, Khondker and Chowdhury 1993a,b, Miah et al. 1983, Mumtazuddin et al. 1982, Sufi and Farooque 1983). Besides, several books have also appeared on general limnology, pollution, freshwater invertebrates, insects and fishes, based on the work done in the country (Ali 1992, Ali and Chakraborty 1992, Rahman 1989, Rahman and Hossain 1988, Shafi and Quddus 1982).

Works on primary productivity are meagre in Bangladesh. First report on this particular field came out in 1978 and some studies were made on the fish ponds of a village in Mymensingh district (Hussain et al. 1978 a,b, Rab et al. 1978). Later studies on primary productivity were carried out by Bhouyain and Das (2985) and Mahmood (1986). Mahmood (1986) reported the yearly average of daily primary productivity for Kaptai lake as 2.39 g O_2 m^{-2} day^{-1} but the report did not provide details of measurement technique and area integration procedure. Khondker et al. (1988) determined the rate of primary productivity (at 0.50 m depth) in Dhanmondi lake, Dhaka. A detailed study on the determination of primary productivity by applying Talling's 1957 model was carried out in the same lake (Khondker and Parveen 1993). In Dhanmondi lake the yearly average primary productivity was calculated as 26.19 g O_2 m^{-2} day^{-1}. A comparative limnology of three different habitats is provided in Table 3.

The floodplain ecosystem in Bangladesh (water retention time is ca. 4-5 months) where deepwater rice cultivation is done, is an interesting aquatic habitat. The area covered by them accounts 77% of the total aquatic resources of Bangladesh. A part of the country's open water capture fishery depends on this particular ecosystem. During the years of 1981-1983, 1985 and 1986 this environment was investigated by Whitton and his co-workers. This was a very elaborative study on the key physical, chemical and biological features covering a wide range of parameters like: light climate, temperature, pH, conductivity, biogenic gases, ionic species, heavy metals, epiphytic algae on rice plants, types, biomass, chemical composition of aquatic macrophytes and finally the nitrogen fixation rate by the heterocystous blue-green algae colonizing on rice plants (Whitton et al. 1988 a,b,c, Whitton and Rother 1988, Rother et al. 1988; Rother and Whitton 1988, Aziz and Ahmed 1992).

Human influence on small water bodies like small ponds, ditches, road side canals etc. are tremendous in Bangladesh. But these aquatic grounds could be served as growing places for many valuable aquatic species ranging from algae to angiosperms, microzooplankton to aquatic birds, fish culturing etc. Recently Khondker et al. (1990) studied four polluted ponds in and around Dhaka city with reference to indicator species. Most of the ponds were seen organically enriched dominated by *Euglena* population. In another study Khondker and Rahim (1991, 1992) studied the effect of contamination by sewage water in Dhanmondi lake, in which 14 limnological parameters together with seasonality and diversity of plankton and periphytic algae were determined. Islam and Khondker (1991) studied the limnology of 8 polluted habitats in Dhaka where profuse growth of *Lemna perpusilla* Torrey and *Spirodela polyrhiza* (L.) Schleid were observed.

Table 3. Comparative limnological features (average value) of three lentic habitats of Bangladesh.

Parameters	Kaptai lake (Mahmood 1986) (n=12)	Dhanmondi lake (Khondker and Parveen 1992 a,b, 1993) (n=22)	Shahidullah Hall Pond (Khondker and Kabir 1994) (n=22)
Daily average aerial PAR input ($\mu E\ m^{-2}\ s^{-1}$)	-	834	675
Z_{max} (m)	36	4.77	4.76
Z_e (m)	2.03	0.40	1.17
Water temperature (°C)	27	27.93	27.7
pH	7.2	7.43	7.45
Alkalinity (meq L^{-1})	0.88	3.70	1.74
Conductivity ($\mu S\ cm^{-1}$)	114	579	340
DO (mg L^{-1})	5.3	7.77	4.37
DO % sat.	67	99	55
Silicate (mg L^{-1})	7.67	30.55*	11.8
SRP (mg L^{-1})	0.53	0.88	0.02
NO_3-N (mg L^{-1})	1.63	0.16	0.08
Chl. a (mg m^{-3})	-	265	13
Primary productivity (g C m^{-2} day^{-1})	0.89	8.87	3.85

* Data from Khondker and Rahim (1991)

IMPACT OF LIMNOLOGICAL RESEARCH ON SCIENCE, ENVIRONMENT AND SOCIO-ECONOMIC CONDITION OF BANGLADESH·

The science of limnology arose as a separate discipline in the Northern Temperate zone of the world and is still biased to that zone. Many generalizations used by the limnologists are based on data collected from the lakes belonging to the same area. Although it is assumed that tropical lakes are generally similar, if not in thermal relations, at least in faunal composition and other features (Fernando 1980). However, in the geo-climatic perspective of Bangladesh various limnological questions related to the thermal mixing pattern and response of biological populations adapted to this particular habitat towards various metabolic activities could be of much interest. The theories and models developed so far in 'temperate limnology' could be applied and their validity should be tested in this limnologically interesting area of the world. Such comparisons these could contribute to the science of limnology.

The demophoric growth principle imposed upon the freshwater resources of Bangladesh is increasing the problems of water pollution and eutrophication day by day. Coupled with high temperature, uncontrolled nutrient supply in many shallow basins favours obnoxious bloom formation by coccoid cyanobacteria and euglenoid algae. Water bodies quickly get chocked with pest-like aquatic weeds such as

Eichhornia crassipes (Mart.) Solms, *Pistia stratiotes* L., *Lemna perpusilla, Spirodela polyrhiza, Salvinia* spp., *Azolla pinnata* R.Br., etc. Recently it has been reported that many of the aquatic plants act as carrier for dangerous water-borne diseases. Of concern are aquatic bacterial and viral diseases such as typhoid fever, cholera, diarrhoea, bacterial dysentry, virus A hepatitis and polio. Diarrhoea claims many lives every year through the contamination of drinking water. Besides, skin rashes and irritations have been reported by many peoples as they are used to take bath in water with algal blooms. Occasional reports on fish kill from rivers contaminated with industrial discharge and from man made lakes are also noticed.

Another menacing threat has emerged through intensive agriculturization. The recent 'green revolution' program (particularly monoculture of rice) to increase food production has intensified the use of urea, potash, phosphate and pesticides by a factor of 14, 7, 10 and 44 fold respectively, in the agricultural lands between 1970 and 1984 (Safiullah and Huq 1986). Flushing of monsoonal rain helps in bringing the residue of agricultural fields into the water body. Whitton et al. (1988a) studied the load of heavy metals in deep-water rice fields of Bangladesh which ranged Co 0.76–24.9 mg m^{-2}; Ni 1.47–36.2 mg m^{-2}; Cu 0.79–42 mg m^{-2}; Zn 5.07–133 mg m^{-2}; Cd 0.012–0.795 mg m^{-2} and Pb 1.64–20.2 mg m^{-2}. High nitrate concentration in drinking water can have detrimental health effects, especially on small children (methenoglobinemia) but also on adults when nitrosamines are formed. The latter compounds are known to be potentially carcinogenic. In Bangladesh nitrate concentration in ground water aquifer near Chalan beel area has been reported as 27 mg L^{-1} whereas safe level recommended by WHO is 11 mg L^{-1} (Safiullah and Huq 1986).

Bangladesh though industrially least developed has some common industries like jute, textile, leather, fertilizer, cane sugar, pulp and paper, cement and ceramics. Many of these industries are old fashioned and lack pollution control system. Mostly the effluents are discharged without pretreatment. Until now scant attention has been paid to the damage of the environment and ecology created by these industries. Absence of any public awareness about the issues involved are the main reasons for that. The tannery waste effluent which is discharged in the nearby river Buriganga of Dhaka city contains BOD: 800–3300 mg L^{-1}, COD: 1870–31,200 mg L^{-1} and chromium more than 5 mg L^{-1} (Reazuddin 1991). Organic nitrogen ranging from 50–400 mg L^{-1} in the effluent discharged by the fertilizer factory in the river Sitalakhya has posed threat to the aquatic ecology of the river (Reazuddin 1991). The river water is claimed to be devoid of fish life along the stressed stretch. These are only a few of the many examples set forth about the degradation of water quality by industrial sector. Nonetheless, the range of consequences is sufficiently clear and the magnitude of the resources at stake so enormous that policy action is required sooner rather than later. Once a crisis has been reached it will be too late to act. An overview of the problem can be obtained from Rahman et al. (1990) and Haider (1984, 1988). Recently Zahangir (1992) studied the limnology of a pond receiving textile effluents.

In Bangladesh fisheries is second to agriculture and earns more than 9% of the nation's foreign exchange earnings. Fish accounts for about 6% of the per capita protein intake and about 80% of the animal protein intake of the people (Rahman 1988). The maximum fish production in semi-intensively managed pond fisheries in Bangladesh is about 7 times lesser than the production rate obtained in Israel and Taiwan (Ameen 1987, Hepher and Pruginin 1981). On the other hand a 40% decrease in the per capita fish protein consumption has been observed during the last three decades. The present rate of intake (21 g caput^{-1} day $^{-1}$) is about 2.7 times less than the recommended value. So, much effort is needed to promote aquacultural production in Bangladesh. Though, aquaculture is multidisciplinary subject but the importance of limnological knowledge and research for an effective management processes can not be overruled.

Running Water Habitats and Related Problems

In Bangladesh, about 90 percent of the total inland aquatic ecosystems are dependent on the flow of three major rivers namely, Padma (Ganga), Jamuna (Brahmaputra) and Meghna. These ecosystems support nearly 50-56% of the total aquatic flora of the country and 80% of the total inland freshwater capture fishery (61% of the contry's total fisheries), and thereby support the livelihoods of 10 million people. Besides, the river systems also act as a carrier and consumer of organic matter, pollutants and solid wastes generated by the dense population and industries of the country. The constant flow of the rivers safeguards the land against the intrusion of saline water from the Bay of Bengal. Several irrigation projects are also linked with the flow of major rivers. Thus, the maintenance of water flow in the major rivers together with the proper functioning of the floodplain, beel and haor ecosystems are of extreme importance to the socio-economic and environmental perspective of Bangladesh.

For the past two decades Bangladesh has suffered seriously due to the problems of water flow in the Ganga-Padma river system. India built the Farakka barrage (18 km from the border of Bangladesh) on the river Ganga to divert 40,000 cusecs of Ganga water into the Bhagirathi-Hooghly system in order to clear the silt and to improve the navigability of Hooghly river on which the post of Calcutta is located. The diversion of Ganga water through Frakka barrage was considered necessary by India during the dry season when Bangladesh also needs water. Though some early agreements on the sharing of Ganga water had been reached between the two countries in 1975 and 1977, the spirit of the agreement was lost with the political changes in both the countries. The situation has only turned worse since then. Due to the withdrawal of water at Farakka, the discharge of Ganga at Hardinge Bridge (Bangladesh) reached a record low (9218 cusec on 3 March 1993 compared to normal flow of 65,000 cusecs) during the dry season. This causes excessive siltation, elevation of the river bed, shifting of channel courses, blockage of flow of other rivers, drop in water depth at the mouth of irrigation channel, lowering of groundwater level, increase in salinity and alkalinity in the Sundarban mangrove forest, and even favours intrusion of salinity in the surface water from the Bay of Bengal (Anwar 1992).

No doubt, Ganga water is needed by the people of both the countries, India and Bangladesh. Recognising the concept of "One Earth" and the common interest of people for a safe environment, it is time to resolve the problem in a non-partisan manner, and take appropriate steps ensuring the welfare of the common people and environment in the region.

CENTRES FOR LIMNOLOGICAL RESEARCH AND EDUCATION

There is no independent limnological research institute in Bangladesh. The discipline has been so far developed in the country as side sproutings of other subjects of Biological Sciences e.g., Zoology, Botany, Ecology etc. At present Department of Botany, Dhaka University is offering courses on limnology in undergraduate and postgraduate levels. The department has also a well organized research team for carrying out researches in the field of hydrobiology and limnology. The neighbouring Zoology Department of the same University has also a good potentiality of conducting research in zooplankton, bottom fauna, fish and aquatic wildlife. Besides, limnological researches (in some cases with Ph.D. programme) are being carried out in the Department of Zoology and Marine Science Institute of Chittagong University, Department of Botany in Rajshahi University and Life Science Institute of Jahangir Nagar University. In the Bangladesh Agriculture University, Mymensingh two departments namely Department of Limnology and Fisheries Biology and the Department of Aquaculture and Management are also carrying out researches on phytoplankton, zooplankton, bottom fauna and fish. Limited researches of limnological nature are being conducted by River Research Institute, Faridapur; Environmental Pollution Control Board, Government of Bangladesh and Civil Engineering Department of Bangladesh University of Engineering and Technology, Dhaka. Moreover, a number of government fisheries institutes carry out various training programmes on fish culture in inland waters.

Societies and Journals

A national society of limnologists has not yet been founded in Bangladesh. Around 20 limnologists are now actively working in different parts of the country and they belong to different scientific societies such as Bangladesh Botanical Society, Zoological Society of Bangladesh, Fisheries Society of Bangladesh, The Bangladesh Association for the Advancement of Science, and Bangladesh Society of Microbiologists. The journals published by these societies and other University journals often include limnological papers. These are: *Bangladesh Journal of Botany, Bangladesh Journal of Zoology, Bangladesh Journal of Fisheries, Bangladesh Journal of Scientific Research, Bangladesh Journal of Microbiology, Journal of the Asiatic Society of Bangladesh (Science), Dhaka University Journal of Biological Sciences, Bangladesh Journal of Agriculture, Bangladesh Journal of Aquaculture, Journal of Bangladesh Academy of Sciences, Chittagong University Studies*, Part II, and *University Journal of Zoology, Rajshahi University*.

CONCLUSIONS

As reviewed in the previous sections, in Bangladesh till now few fundamental works on physico-chemical limnology and production biology have been carried out and for the purpose mostly some easily reachable habitats were chosen. Vast majority of the country's natural haors, baors, beels etc. remain limnologically untouched. Unique geoclimatic conditions together with shallow eutrophicated nature of the water bodies present in Bangladesh provides attraction for the limnologists to carry out research. However, at this stage three important sectors could be mentioned for promotion of limnological research in Bangladesh: (1) nutrient cycling and productivity; (2) pollution and eutrophication, and (3) aquaculture. In this decade of environmentally conscious world scientific reports rich in field data are very essential to convince the policy makers. But in case of Bangladesh such reports are exceptionally inadequate in the field of limnology. So, there is a strong need of conducting hydrobiological and limnological survey type of works in our natural water bodies. The effect of increasing use of chemical fertilizer and pesticides in the agricultural field upon the open water capture fishery (61.4% of the country's total fish catch) should be assessed. Besides fish, fruits, seeds, rhizome, peduncle and young shoots of many aquatic plants (*Nelumbo nucifera* Gaertn., *Euryale ferox* Salisb., *Trapa bispinosa* Roxb., *Nymphaea nouchali* Burm., *Telanthera philoxeroides* Moq., *Alternanthera philoxeroides* (Mart.) Grisco., *Ipomoea aquatica* Forsk. etc.) are commonly eaten by the local peoples. Many of these are rich in vitamins and essential minerals which can remove malnutrition problems particularly for the children. So, to bring these species under aquacultural practice is also needed. Application of biotechnological principle for recycling waste, production of compost, cattle and poultry fodder should be taken into consideration by utilizing fast growing macrophytes.

The country has already gained a sustainable expertise in the field of limnology and the new comers are also being added to this 'think tank'. So it is now desirable that a research institute with proper facilities should be established. Water is a part of our environment and the aspect of environmental degradation has been given priority by the government. But since the economy of Bangladesh is poor it is difficult for the Government to channelize funds for researches or for buying equipment. So international communities should extend their support in promoting research in limnological sector of Bangladesh.

REFERENCES

Alam, M.J., Habib, M.A.B. and Islam, M.A. 1985. Multiple and linear correlations of some physico-chemical properties of water with abundant genera of zooplankton in nursery ponds. Bangladesh Journal of Aquaculture 6-7: 59-64.

Alam, A.K.M.N., Islam, M.A., Mollah, M.I.A. and Haq, M.S. 1987a. Status of zooplankton in newly constructed ponds and their relation to some meteorological and limnological factors. Bangladesh Journal of Fisheries 10: 83-88.

Alam, A.K.M.N., Mollah, M.F.A., Islam, M.A., Haq, M.S. and Haque, M.M. 1987b. Status of phytoplankton in newly constructed ponds and their relation to some meteorological and limnological factors. Bangladesh Journal of Fisheries 10: 75-81.

Ali, S. 1992. Chingri: Bangladeshe chingri utpadan o chash. Bangla Academy, Dhaka. 98 pages. (Book on shrimp culture, in Bengali).

Ali, S. and Chakraborty, T. 1992. Bangladesher mitha panir amerudandi prani. (Freshwater invertebrates of Bangladesh). (in Bengali). Bangla Academy, Dhaka. 207 pages.

Ali, S., Chowdhury, A. and Ray, A.R. 1980. Ecology and Seasonal abundance of zooplankton in a pond in Tongi, Dacca. Bangladesh Journal of Zoology 8: 44-49.

Ali, S., Chowdhury, A.N., Chowdhury, D.R. and Begum, S. 1989. Studies on seasonal variations of physico-chemical and biological conditions in a pond. Dhaka University Studies, part E (Biological Sciences) 4: 113-123.

Ali, S., Majid, A. and Chowdhury, A.Q. 1985. Studies on the benthic macroinvertebrates in freshwater pond, Bangladesh. Pakistan Journal of Zoology 17: 301-306.

Ali, S., Rahman, A.K.A., Patwary, A.R. and Islam, K.R. 1982. Studies on the diurnal variations in physico-chemical factors and zooplankton in a freshwater pond. Bangladesh Journal of Fisheries 2-5: 15-24.

Ameen, M.U. 1987. Fisheries resources and opportunities in freshwater fish culture in Bangladesh. NRD-II Project/DANIDA, Noakhali, Bangladesh. 244 pages.

Ameen, M.U., Begum, Z.N.T., Ali, S., Rahman, M.M. and Roy, T.K. 1986. A comparative limnological study of two fish ponds in Raipur. Dhaka University Studies, Part E 1: 25-34.

Ameen, M.U., Begum, Z.N.T., Mustafa, A.N. and Ali, S. 1988. Seasonal and diel profile of temperature, light penetration, dissolved oxygen and free carbon dioxide of a fish pond from south of Bangladesh. Bangladesh Journal of Zoology 16: 1-8.

Anonymous. 1973. Annual report of the Freshwater Fisheries Research Station at Chandpur, Comilla (FFRS), for the year ending 30th June 1969. Government of the People's Republic of Bangladesh, Directorate of Fisheries, Dhaka.

Anonymous. 1971. Annual report of the Freshwater Fisheries Research Station at Chandpur, Comilla (FERS), for the year 1969-1970 and 1970-1971. Government of the People's Republic of Bangladesh, Directorate of Fisheries, Dhaka.

Anwar, J. 1992. The Ganges-Brahmaputra delta plain: a challenge. The Bangladesh Observer, Dhaka. 17 July 1992.

Aziz, A. and Ahmed, Q.A. 1992. Occurrence and biomass of algae epiphytic on deepwater rice plants near Sonargaon, Bangladesh. Archiv für Hydrobiologie 125: 479-486.

Banu, N., Khan, S., Ali, S. and Alam, S.M.N. 1992. Studies on the fecundity of *Mystus tengra* (Ham.) of Agargaon region, Dhaka. Dhaka University Journal of Biological Sciences 1: 49-51.

Begum, A. 1958. A short note on plankton of freshwater ponds of Dacca. Agriculture Pakistan 9: 370-391.

Begum, A., Mustafa, G., Ali, S. and Ahmed, K. 1989. Studies on limnology in a mini pond and growth of *Tilapia* (= *Oreochromis*) *nilotica*. Bangladesh Journal of Zoology 17: 35-45.

Begum, S., Chowdhury, A.N., Sufi, G.B. and Sultana, N. 1992. Rotifers in a fish pond: their occurrence and seasonal variation. Dhaka University Journal of Biological Sciences 1: 15-18.

Begum, Z.N.T. and Alam, M.J. 1987. Plankton abundance in relation to physico-chemical variables in two ponds in Maijdee Court, Noakhali. Journal of the Asiatic Society of Bangladesh (Science) 13: 55-63.

Bhouyain, A.M. and Das, D.K. 1985. Primary production of a fish pond. University Journal of Zoology, Rajshahi University 4: 55-58.

Chowdhury, S.H. and Mazumdar, A. 1981. Limnology of lake Kaptai: I. Physico-chemical features. Bangladesh Journal of Zoology 9: 59-72.

Duijvendijk, H.V. 1987. They stopped the sea. National Geographic 172: 92-100.

Fernando, C.H. 1980. Some important implications for tropical limnology. pp. 103-107. In: Mori, S. and Ikusima, I. (Editors) Proceedings of the First Workshop on the Promotion of Limnology in the Developing Countries. SIL Congress, Kyoto.

Haider, S.Z. (Editor). 1984. Economic Utilization of Water Hyacinth. Department of Chemistry, Dhaka University, Dhaka. 101 pages.

Haider, S.Z. (Editor) 1988. Proceedings of the National symposium on Monitoring of Environmental systems of Chemical Industries of Bangladesh. Bose Centre for Advanced Study and Research, Dhaka University, Dhaka. 250 pages.

Hepher, B. and Pruginin, Y. 1981. Commercial fish farming with special reference to fish culture in Israel. John Wiley and Sons, N.Y. 261 pages.

Hoq, M.F. 1977. Jalashayatatva o samudratatva: Part I (Limnology and Oceanography). Bangla Academy, Dhaka. 361 pages. (in Bengali).

Hussain, M.G., Islam, M.A. and Chowdhury, M.Y. 1978a. Primary productivity and growth of major carps (*Catla catla, Labeo rohita, Cirrhina mrigala*) in two man-made ponds of village Boyra, Mymensingh. Bangladesh Journal of Aquaculture 1: 21-32.

Hussain, M.G., Islam, M.A. and Chowdhury, M.Y. 1978b. A study on the relationship between primary productivity and some limnological parameters in a local pond in Mymensingh. Bangladesh Journal of Fisheries 1: 113-119.

Islam, A.K.M. Nurul 1991. Phycology. In: Islam, A.K.M.Nurul (Editor) Two Centuries of Plant Sciences in Bangladesh and Adjacent Regions. Asiatic Society of Bangladesh, Dhaka. 299 pages.

Islam, A.K.M. Nurul and Khondker, M. 1991. Preliminary limnological investigations on some polluted waters covered by duckweeds. Bangladesh Journal of Botany 20: 73-75.

Islam, A.K.M.N., Khondker, M., Begum, A. and Akter, N. 1992. Hydrobiological studies in two habitats at Dhaka. Journal of the Asiatic Society of Bangladesh 18: 47-52.

Islam, A.K.M. Nurul and Chowdhury, A.R. 1979. Hydrobiological studies of Dhanmondi lake, Dacca. II. Phytoplankton. Journal of the Asiatic Society Bangladesh (Science) 5: 47-57.

Islam, A.K.M.N., Rahman, M. and Chowdhury, A.R. 1979. Hydrobiological studies of Dhanmondi lake, Dacca. I. Macrophytes and benthic flora. Journal of the Asiatic Society Bangladesh (Science) 5: 59-75.

Islam, A.K.M. Nurul and Paul, N. 1978. Hydrobiological study of the Haor Hakaluki in Sylhet. Journal of the Asiatic Society Bangladesh (Science) 3: 89-91.

Islam, A.K.M. Nurul and Paul, S.N. 1977. Limnological studies on *Wolffia arrhiza* (L.) Wimm. Journal of the Asiatic Society Bangladesh (Science) 3: 111-123.

Islam, A.K.M. Nurul and Mendes, F. 1976. Limnological studies of a jheel in Sher-e-Bangla Nagar. Dacca University Studies, Part B 24: 63-71.

Islam, A.K.M. Nurul and Saha, J.K. 1975. Limnological studies of the Ramna lake at Dacca. Dacca University Studies, Part B 23: 39-46.

Islam, A.K.M.N., Haroon, A.K.Y. and Zaman, K.M. 1974. Limnological studies of the river Buriganga. Dacca University Studies, Part B 22: 99-111.

Islam, A.K.M. Nurul and Begum, Z.N.T. 1970. Studies on the phytoplankton of Dacca district. Journal of Asiatic Society Pakistan 15: 227-271.

Islam, A.K.M. Nurul 1969. A preliminary report on the phytoplanktons and other algal flora of Chittagong Hill-Tracts. Journal of Asiatic Society Pakistan 14: 343-363.

Islam, A.K.M. Nurul and Nahar, L. 1967. Preliminary studies on the phytoplanktons of polluted waters. Part II. Blue-green algae. Science and Research 4: 141-149.

Islam, A.K.M. Nurul and Khatun, M. 1966. Preliminary studies on the phytoplanktons of polluted waters. Science and Research 3: 94-109.

Islam, M.A. 1992a. Paribesh proshongo o Bangladesher paribesh (Environment and the Environment of Bangladesh). Bangla Academy, Dhaka, 167 pages (in Bengali).

Islam, M.A. 1992b. Macher pukurer pani (Water Quality in Fish Ponds). Bangla Academy, Dhaka, 229 pages (in Bengali).

Islam, M.A. 1993. Bahaman panir paribeshtatta (Ecology of Lotic water). Bangla Academy, Dhaka, 230 pages (in Bengali).

Ittekot, V., Safiullah, S., Mycke, B. and Seifert, R. 1985. Seasonal variability and geochemical significance of organic matter in the river Ganges, Bangladesh. Nature 317: 800-802.

Khaleque, M.A. and Islam, M.A. 1983. A comparative study on the effect of some physico-chemical parameters on the growth of major carps in two ponds. Bangladesh Journal of Aquaculture 2-5: 74-81.

Khan, M.S. and Halim, M. 1987. Aquatic Angiosperms of Bangladesh. Bangladesh Agricultural Rresearch Council, Dhaka. 120 pages.

Khondker, M. 1994. Limnology. Dhaka University, Dhaka (in press) (In Bengali).

Khondker, M. and Chowdhury, S.A. 1993a. Pelagic phytoplankton: its vertical distribution in a pond. Journal of the Asiatic Society of Bangladesh (Science) 19: 9-11.

Khondker, M. and Chowdhury, S.A. 1993b. Relationships of phytoplankton biomass to some water quality parameters in a mesotrophic pond. Dhaka University Journal of Biological Sciences 2: 87-92.

Khondker, M. and Parveen, L. 1992a. Species composition, standing crop and seasonality of phytoplankton in a hypertrophic lake. Dhaka University Studies, Part E 7: 49-55.

Khondker, M. and Parveen, L. 1992b. Study of the physical and chemical limnology of a shallow, hypertrophic artificial lake. Bangladesh Journal of Scientific Research 10: 9-16.

Khondker, M. and Parveen, L. 1992. Daily rate of primary productivity in hypertrophic Dhanmondi lake. pp. 181-191, In: Tilzer, M.M., Khondker, M., Eckman, R., Gibson, C.E., Marchand, H., Martinez, R. and Martens, J. (Editors) Hypertrophic and Polluted Freshwater Ecosystems: Ecological Bases for Water Resources Management. Department of Botany, Dhaka University, Dhaka.

Khondker, M., Islam, A.K.M. Nurul, Begum, Z.N.T. and Haque, S. 1990. Limnological studies of four polluted ponds in and around Dhaka city with reference to indicator species. Bangladesh Journal of Botany 19: 51-63.

Khondker, M., Islam, A.K.M. Nurul, and Islam, R. 1988. Studies on the primary productivity of Dhanmondi lake. Dhaka University Studies, Part E 1: 15-21.

Khondker, M. and Kabir, M.A. 1994. Phytoplankton primary production in a mesotrophic pond of sub-tropical climate. Hydrobiologia (in press).

Khondker, M. and Rahim, S. 1991. Investigation on the water quality of Dhanmondi Lake. I. Physico-chemical features. Bangladesh Journal of Botany 20: 183-191.

Khondker, M. and Rahim, S. 1992. On the water quality of Dhanmondi lake.II. Periphytic and planktonic algae as indicators. Bangladesh Journal of Botany 22: 57-61.

Mahmood, N. 1986. Hydrobiology of the Kaptai reservoir studies programme. FAO/UNDP Aquaculture Development and Coordination Programmes, Rome, Italy. Contract No. DP/BGD/79/615-4/FI. 190 pages.

Miah, M.M. 1981. The physical environment: physiography, rivers and floods. In: Islam, M.A. and Miah, M.M. (Editors), Bangladesh in maps. University of Dhaka: 77 pages.

Miah, M.I., Islam, B.N. and Dewan, S. 1983. Studies on the ecology of two ponds in Bangladesh Agricultural University Campus, Mymensingh. Bangladesh Journal of Aquaculture 2-5: 34-41.

Mumtazuddin, M., Rahman, M.S. and Mostafa, G. 1982. Limnological studies of four selected rearing ponds at the aquaculture experiment station, Mymensingh. Bangladesh Journal of Fisheries 2-5: 83-90.

Oppenheimer, J.R., Ahmed, M.G., Huq, A, Haque, K.A., Alam, A.K.A.U., Aziz, K.M.S., Ali, S. and Haque, A.S.M.M. 1978. Limnological studies of three ponds in Dacca, Bangladesh. Bangladesh Journal of Fisheries 1: 1-26.

Rahman, A.K.A. 1989. Frsshwater Fisheries of Bangladesh. Zoological Society of Bangladesh, Dhaka. 364 pages.

Rahman, M.A. 1988. The need for reservoir fishery management in Bangladesh. In: De Silva,S.S. (Editor), Reservoir Fishery Management and Development in Asia. International Development Research Centre, Ottawa, Canada. 246 pages.

Rahman, R. and Hossain, M. 1988. Jalochar keetpatanga. (Aquatic Insects). (in Bengali). Bangla Academy, Dhaka. 328 pages.

Rahman, A.A., Huq, S. and Conway, G.R. (Editors) 1990. Environmental Aspects of Surface Water Systems of Bangladesh. University Press Ltd., Dhaka. 261 pages.

Rashid, H.E.R. 1977. Geography of Bangladesh. University Press Limited, Dhaka. 579 pages.

Reazuddin, M. 1991. Levels and trends of industrial pollution in Bangladesh. The Bangladesh Observer, Dhaka. 7 April 1991.

Rob, M.A., Islam, M.A., Yakub, M. and Idris, M.M. 1978. Studies on soil, primary productivity and growth rates of major carps (Catla catla, Labeo rohita, Cirrhina mrigala) in an artificial pond of village Boyra, Mymensingh. Bangladesh Journal of Aquaculture 1: 42-60.

Rother, J.A., Aziz, A., Karim, N.H. and Whitton, B.A. 1988. Ecology of deepwater rice-fields in Bangladesh. 4. Nitrogen fixation by blue-green algal communities. Hydrobiologia 169: 43-56.

Rother, J.A. and Whitton, B.A. 1988. Ecology of deepwater rice-fields in Bangladesh. 5. Mineral composition of the rice plant and other aquatic macrophytes. Hydrobiologia 169:57-67.

Safiullah, S. and Huq, S. 1986. Environmental studies in Bangladesh - a perspective for the less developed countries. The Science of the Total Environment 55:165-173.

Safiullah, S., Chowdhury, M.I., Mafizuddin, M., Ali, I. and Karim, M. 1985. Monitoring of the Padma (Ganges), the Jamuna (Brahmaputra) and the Baral in Bangladesh. Mitteilungen der Geologische Palaeontologische Institut der Universität Hamburg, SCOPE/UNEP Sonderband 58: 519-524.

Shafi, M. and Quddus, M.M.A. 1982. Bangladesher matsho shampad. (Fish wealth of Bangladesh) (in Bengali). Bangla Academy, Dhaka. 144 pages.

Sufim G.B. and Farooque, D. 1983. Water quality of fish ponds in Dhaka city in relation to fish production. Dhaka University Studies, Part B., 31: 61-66.

Whitton, B.A., Aziz, A, Francis, P., Rother, J.A., Simson, J.W. and Tahmida, Z.N. 1988a. Ecology of deepwater rice-fields in Bangladesh. 1. Physical and chemical environment. Hydrobiologia 169: 3-22.

Whitton, B.A., Aziz, A., Kawecka, B. and Rother, J.A. 1988b. Ecology of deep water rice fields in Bangladesh. 3. Associated algae and macrophytes. Hydrobiologia 169:31-42.

Whitton, B.A. and Rother, J.A. 1988. Diel changes in the environment of a deepwater rice-field in Bangladesh. Verhandlungen der internationale Vereinigung für Limnologie 23: 1074-1079.

Whitton, B.A., Rother, J.A. and Paul, A.R. 1988c. Ecology of deepwater rice- fields in Bangladesh. 2. Chemistry of sites at Manikganj and Sonargaon. Hydrobiologia 169:23-30.

Zahangir, H. 1992. Limnological studies on the effluents from the textile industries at demra, Dhaka. M.Sc. thesis, Department of Botany, University of Dhaka, Dhaka. 127 pages.

Note: This review was presented first at a Conference held in HongKong during September 1991, and hence, its earlier version has been published in *Mitteilungen der internationale Vereinigung für theoretische und angewandte Limnologie* 24: 147-154, 1994.

Gopal, B. and Wetzel, R.G. (Editors) **Limnology in Developing Countries**: 121-160
© 1995, International Association for Limnology

Limnology in the Wet Tropics: Papua New Guinea

Patrick L. Osborne
*School of Science, University of Western Sydney, Bourke Street, Richmond 2753,
New South Wales, Australia*

ABSTRACT

Papua New Guinea occupies the eastern half of the island of New Guinea (the second largest in the world) and includes the islands of the Bismarck Archipelago and the northernmost island in the Solomon chain: Bougainville. Located near the equator, Papua New Guinea is a mountainous country with a land area of 462,000 km^2. The climate is dominated by the sub-tropical high pressure system and the inter-tropical convergence zone but tempered by oceanic influences. Most of the country receives rainfall in excess of 2500 mm per year, some as much as 10,000 mm per year but there are areas which have a prolonged dry season and low rainfall. There are some 5000 lakes, most associated with two very large rivers: the Sepik and Fly. Both these rivers have mean annual discharges in excess of 6000 m^3 sec^{-1}. Lakes range in size up to 647 km^2 and are found from near sea-level to over 4000 m. Most are situated below 40 m altitude and are shallow but one caldera lake has a depth of 360 m. One lake is oligomictic but most are probably polymictic. Most limnological work has been applied and includes studies on fish introductions, aquatic weed control and the impacts of reservoir construction and the disposal of sewage effluents and mine tailings. The taxonomy and distribution of freshwater organisms are generally poorly known. There are, however, taxonomic guides to the freshwater fishes and plants. The University of Papua New Guinea offers courses in limnology as part of a general science undergraduate degree. Two institutes have facilities for limnological research.

INTRODUCTION

Papua New Guinea occupies the eastern half of the island of New Guinea (the second largest in the world) and includes the islands of the Bismarck Archipelago and the northernmost island in the Solomon chain: Bougainville (Figure 1). New Guinea is the second largest island in the world and is topographically diverse and geologically both young and complex. The island is situated between the stable Australian continent to the south and the deep ocean basin of the Pacific to the north. Most of the north coast of Papua New Guinea is undergoing rapid uplift, whilst in contrast, the southern shore, particularly around the Gulf of Papua is sinking slightly (Löffler 1977). The rugged and faulted mountain chains, which, in Papua New Guinea attain 4500 m, are characterised by steeply-sloping, narrow ridges separated by deeply-incised V-shaped valleys. Recent volcanic and seismic activity have resulted in large areas being covered with volcanic deposits and weathering and erosion of the steeply-sloping mountains has created extensive alluvial plains. The main geomorphologic regions and altitudinal zones are shown in Figures 1 and 2 respectively.

The southern fold mountains, the highlands and the northern and eastern metamorphic ranges are often referred to as the central cordillera (Figures 1 and 2). On the border with Irian Jaya, the main mountain range is about 100 km wide, but it increases

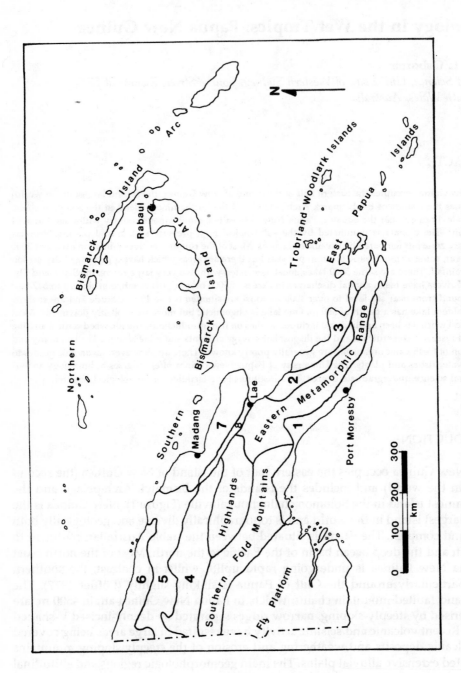

Figure 1. The major geomorphic regions of Papua New Guinea.

(1) Southern Plains and Lowlands; (2) Ultrabasic Range; (3) Cape Vogel Basin; (4) Northern Metamorphic Range; (5) Central Intermontane Trough; (6) Northern Coastal Range (West); (7) Northern Coastal Range (East); (8) Ramu-Markham Trough (adapted from Löffler 1977).

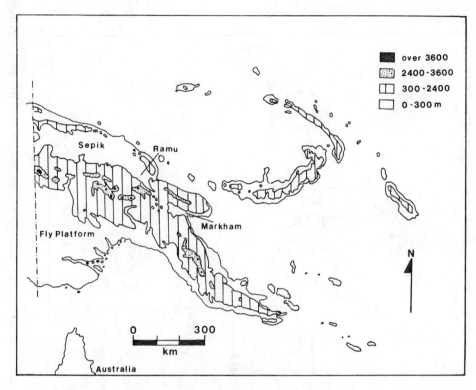

Figure 2. Altitudinal zones of Papua New Guinea (redrawn from Löffler 1977).

in width in the central highlands region to 300 km. From here, the cordillera narrows towards Milne Bay. These highlands are a complex system of ranges and valleys with several huge strato-volcanoes. The main ranges from west to east are the Star Mountains, Hindenburg, Muller, Kubor, Schrader, Bismarck and Owen-Stanley Ranges. The highest peaks are Mt Wilhelm (4509 m), Mt Giluwe (4368 m), Mt Albert-Edward (3990 m) and Mt Victoria (4035 m) (see Figure 3). All these mountains were covered by glaciers during the Pleistocene. Much of this central area is relatively densely populated and anthropogenic grassland is the dominant vegetation. Only a small part of the country is below 300 m altitude and the most extensive lowlands are associated with the Fly and Strickland Rivers.

Numerous islands ranging in area from about 30,000 km² to a few square kilometres lie off the north coast of Papua New Guinea and its eásternmost tip. The Bismarck Archipelago comprises all the larger islands which form an oval ring about the Bismarck Sea (Figure 1). The southern Bismarck Island Arc includes New Britain and the chain of volcanic islands off the north coast of New Guinea. It is a typical island arc with a deep ocean trench and a belt of volcanoes along its concave northern coast. Most of these are active or potentially so.

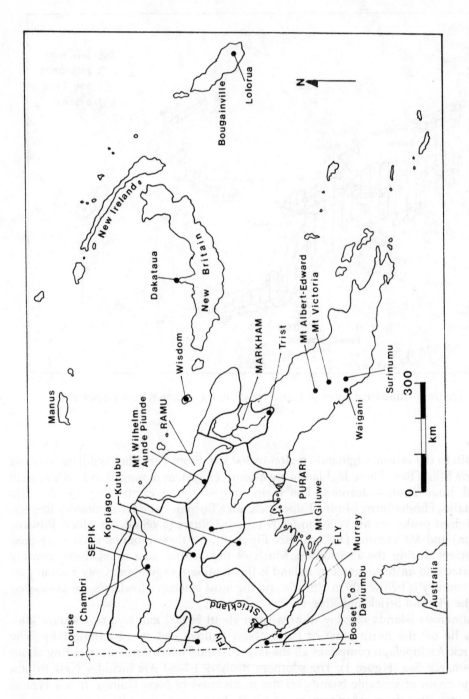

Figure 3. Map of the major river catchments of Papua New Guinea and geographical position of mountains and lakes mentioned in the text.

Climate

The combination of Papua New Guinea's equatorial position and oceanic influences results in a generally warm and wet climate. The larger part of the country experiences high annual rainfall between 2500-3500 mm. Some small lowland areas are drier, but annual falls of less than 1000 mm are unknown except around the national capital, Port Moresby. Areas of uplands to the north and south of the main central range have annual rainfall in excess of 4000 mm and in some locations these can rise to over 10,000 mm per year. This wetness contrasts markedly with the dryness of Papua New Guinea's southern neighbour: Australia. Rainfall in Papua New Guinea varies seasonally in most areas, but the degree of seasonality is not great and McAlpine et al. (1983) described the rainfall over Papua New Guinea as varying from 'fairly wet' to 'very wet'. Nevertheless, minor droughts can occur from time to time even in moderately wet areas.

Seasonal temperature regimes are equable. Daily mean maximum temperatures on the coast are around 30-32°C with the mean minima around 23°C. The most marked characteristic of temperature is the drop associated with increasing altitude. Between 1500 m and 2000 m altitude mean daily maxima and night minima vary between 22-25°C and 11-15°C respectively. Above 2200 m, frost can occur and snow may fall and settle above 4000 m. The combination of relatively high rainfall and temperature results in high humidity and cloudiness.

Papua New Guinea has a very rich flora, with extensive areas covered in pristine rain forest. This high biodiversity is largely attributed to the country's geographical position and the intermingling of the Indo-Malesian and Australian-Pacific Island floras. In addition to its phytogeographical position, altitudinal range, climate and complex geology combine to provide a wide variety of habitats.

Historical Development of Limnology in Papua New Guinea

Limnology is in its infancy in Papua New Guinea. Exploration of the country by Europeans was hampered by rugged terrain, climate and malaria. Coastal areas and the navigable reaches of the large rivers were the first to be explored and naturalists on early expeditions made significant collections of aquatic plants and animals. From the mid-nineteenth to the mid-twentieth century most biological work in Papua New Guinea was taxonomic. Early collections are mostly housed in herbaria and museums outside Papua New Guinea but more recent collections are stored in the country's National Museum and National Herbarium. Taxonomic guides to the freshwater fish and freshwater plants have been compiled (Allen 1991, Leach and Osborne 1985).

Contact between Europeans and the people inhabiting the central highlands was only established in the 1930s. Even today there is only one arterial highway from the north coast to the central highlands and the capital city, Port Moresby, on the south coast, is accessible from most of the country only by sea or air. Access to many lakes is difficult and the first significant, purely limnological studies were only undertaken in the late 1960s. Fortunately there is now an excellent system of air transport but this still imposes limits on the amount of equipment that can be taken into the field. Consequently, most limnological research has had an expeditionary flavour. For example, Ball and Glucksman (1975, 1978) had to construct a raft from forest materials in order to study Lake Wisdom and the biological colonization of volcanic Motmot Island in the middle of lake (Figures 3 and 4). The raft was inadequate to support all personnel and equipment and two members of the expedition swam to the island propelling the raft. Other studies have been carried out using dug-out canoes as research vessels (Chambers 1988, Osborne and Totome 1991, 1992a).

The study coordinated by Petr (1983) of the Purari River was the first comprehensive limnological investigation of a Papua New Guinean river and its catchment. This study is noteworthy not only for the information collected but also for the enormous logistical difficulties overcome in mounting scientific expeditions to this remote part of the country. Significant studies have since been carried out on other rivers, notably the Fly River, through work funded by Ok Tedi Mining Limited (Smith and Hortle 1991, Smith and Morris 1992). and the Sepik River through work on *Salvinia* control (Room and Thomas 1985, 1986a, b) and a study of fisheries enhancement through introductions of exotic fishes (Coates 1986). The University of Papua New Guinea has funded a number of studies of eutrophic Waigani Lake (Osborne and Leach 1983, Osborne and Polunin 1986, Polunin et al. 1988) and oligomictic Lake Kutubu (Osborne and Totome 1991, 1992a). This chapter summarizes the significant findings of these and other studies on the lakes and rivers of Papua New Guinea.

WATER RESOURCES

As a result of the high rainfall and rugged topography most rivers in Papua New Guinea have large flow volumes and high sediment loads and are generally fast-flowing and turbulent (Table 1). The Fly Platform (Figure 1) is the largest tract of low-lying land in Papua New Guinea and is drained by the Fly and Strickland Rivers (Figure 3). The Fly River, although only 1200 km long is, on discharge, so large (6000-7500 m^3 s^{-1}) that it ranks with the world's great rivers (Holeman 1968, Welcomme 1985). The gradient in its lower course is extremely gentle as the river port of Kiunga, 800 km from the sea, is only 20 m above sea level (Table 1). The river is tidal for 250 km upstream. Rainfall in the upper catchment regularly exceeds 10 m per annum and in floods the river level may rise rapidly by up to 10 m. In the south, the area is gently undulating and flat areas are poorly drained and swampy. The middle Fly floodplain, 15-20 km wide, is a mosaic of lakes, alluvial forest, swamp grassland and swamp savanna. The river meanders extensively in this region, and in addition to tributary lakes, there are numerous backswamps and oxbows of variable depth depending on age.

The Purari River (Figure 3) drains the central highlands and discharges into the Gulf of Papua through an extensive delta (Petr 1983a). The rainfall on the catchment is high, particularly on the foothills where it reaches 8000 mm per year. This high precipitation, coupled with the high run-off, give this river system an enormous potential for hydroelectric power generation and a dam planned for Wabo in the foothills was projected to have an installed capacity of 2160 megawatts. Possible environmental impacts of this proposed dam were assessed in some detail (Petr 1983a) but the scheme has not been developed further. Other rivers draining to the south and east of the Purari include the Vailala, Lakekamu, Angabanga, Vanapa, Laloki and Kemp Welch.

Table 1. Catchment areas, lengths, discharges and average gradients of the major rivers in Papua New Guinea

River	Catchment area, km²	Length km	Discharge m³ s⁻¹	Average gradient Lowlands	Uplands
Lakekamu	5300	-	195	1:2000	1:20
Markham	12600	170	385	1:330	1:30
Kikori	16900	-	1200	1:1700	1:120
Ramu	18500	720	990	1:4000	1:50
Fly	76000	1200	7000	1:4000	1:70
Sepik	77700	1100	7000	1:2000	1:50
Purari	33670	600	2600	-	-

The Markham and Ramu Rivers (Figure 3) flow through the eastern part of an intermontane trough which is a narrow graben zone occupied by a series of alluvial fans. These fans are formed of coarse debris derived from the tectonically active Finisterre and Saruwaged ranges which rise steeply along the north-eastern margin of the trough (Figures 1 and 2). The Markham River is shallow, flows through a wide braided channel and has' no estuary. The river channel is 3 km wide at the Ramu divide and reaches its maximum width at its confluence with the Leron River. The Ramu River has a relatively small catchment area and, in its lower reaches, the floodplain terrain is very flat and swampy and the fall is imperceptible for a distance of 250 km from its mouth. Westwards, the narrow Markham-Ramu trough opens into the much more extensive Sepik depression.

The Sepik River (Figure 3), with a catchment of 77,700 km², is the largest river system in Papua New Guinea. Its discharge is reported to range between 4500 m³ s⁻¹ and 11,000 m³ s⁻¹ (Mitchell et al. 1980), although the river is poorly gauged. Flow was recorded in June 1988 by the Royal Australian Navy Hydrographic Service to be 6500 m³ s⁻¹ (see Fox 1990). The Sepik is navigable for about 500 km, the main river channel being deep (over 35 m at Angoram) and consequently so are the more recently formed ox-bow lakes in the lower floodplain. The river discharges directly into the sea through a single outlet and this contrasts with rivers in the south which invariably have extensive deltas and large estuaries. There are numerous (around 1500) ox-bow and other lakes associated with the Sepik floodplain, the largest of these is Chambri Lake (Figure 3) which is shallow (maximum 4 m) and has a highly variable area up to 250 km² in the flood season. There are no large rivers on the islands off the north coast but the short, fast-flowing mountain streams often have high discharges.

LAKES AND THEIR FORMATION

Chambers (1987) surveyed the topographic maps of Papua New Guinea and counted 5383 freshwater lakes. The lakes are mostly small, with only 22 having a surface area greater than 1000 ha (Table 2). Lake Murray is by far the largest (64,700 ha), some three times greater in area than the next largest (Lake Chambri) (Figure 3). However, these lakes are both shallow: Lake Murray, maximum depth c. 9 m, mean depth c. 5 m; Chambri Lake: maximum depth c. 4 m and contrast markedly with the deep caldera lakes: Wisdom (360 m) and Dakataua (120 m) (Figure 3). Over 80% of the lakes lie below 40 m altitude reflecting their association with the floodplains of large rivers (Table 3).

Table 2. The size distribution of lakes in Papua New Guinea (after Chambers 1987)

Area of lake	Number of lakes	% of total
<1	2143	39.8
1-2	869	16.0
3-6	794	14.7
7-10	494	9.2
11-20	740	8.7
21-50	267	5.0
51-100	161	3.0
101-200	75	1.4
201-500	74	1.4
500-1000	23	0.4
>1000	22	0.4
Total	5383	

Table 3. The altitudinal zonation of lakes in Papua New Guinea (after Chambers 1987)

Altitude of lake (m)	Number of lakes	% of total
1-40	4753	88.3
41-120	153	2.8
121-1000	149	2.8
1000-2000	106	2.0
2001-3000	133	2.5
3001-400	88	1.6
>4000	1	-

Hutchinson (1957) lists 76 geomorphic mechanisms of lake formation and in Papua New Guinea 20 of these types have been identified (Chambers 1987). In Papua New Guinea, tectonic movements and volcanic activity are important in the creation of basins which are subsequently filled with water to form lakes (Table 4). Two large

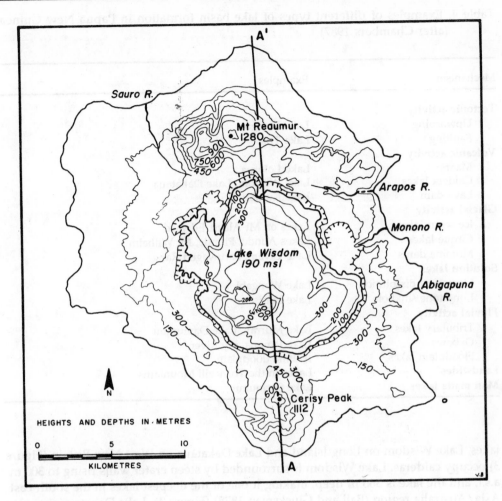

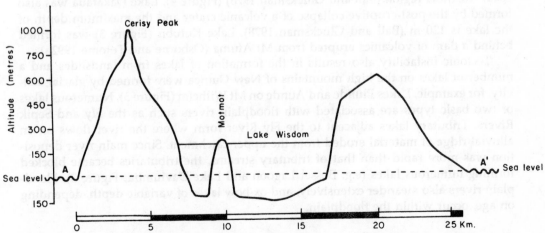

Figure 4. Map of Long Island and caldera Lake Wisdom, Papua New Guinea with altitudinal cross-section as indicated (adapted from Specht et al. 1982, Ball and Glucksman 1978).

Table 4. Examples of different types of lake basin formation in Papua New Guinea (after Chambers 1987)

Mechanism	Examples
Tectonic activity	
Upwarping	Lake Parago
Faulting	Lake Trist
Volcanic activity	
Maars	Lake Lolorua
Caldera lakes	Lake Wisdom, Lake Dakataua
Lava dam	Lake Kutubu
Glacial activity	
Ice scour lakes	Lakes on Mt Albert Edward
Cirque lakes	Lakes Aunde, Piunde, Mt Wilhelm
Moraine dams	Lake Givam, Saruwaged Range
Solution lakes	
Limestone dissolution	Lake Wongabi
Limestone sinkhole	Lake Louise
Fluvial activity	
Tributary lakes	Lake Murray, Lake Daviumbu
Oxbows	Lake Pangua, Fly River
Floodplain lakes	Aramia floodplain
Landslides	Lakes in the Torricelli Mountains
Man made lakes	Lake Surinumu

lakes, Lake Wisdom on Long Island and Lake Dakataua on West New Britain (Figure 3) occupy calderas. Lake Wisdom is surrounded by steep crater walls rising to 300 m a.s.l. and the lake is 360 m deep, making it one of the deepest lakes in the south-east Asia/Australia region (Ball and Glucksman 1978) (Figure 4). Lake Dakataua was also formed by the post-eruptive collapse of a volcanic crater and the maximum depth of the lake is 120 m (Ball and Glucksman 1978). Lake Kutubu (Figure 3) was formed behind a dam of volcanics erupted from Mt Afuma (Osborne and Totome 1992a).

Tectonic instability also results in the formation of lakes from landslides and a number of lakes on the high mountains of New Guinea were formed by glacial activity, for example, Lakes Piunde and Aunde on Mt Wilhelm (Figure 3). Numerous lakes of two basic types are associated with floodplain rivers such as the Fly and Sepik Rivers. Tributary lakes adjacent to the Fly River form where the river flows on an alluvial ridge of material eroded from the upper catchment. Since main river deposition was more rapid than that of tributary streams, the tributaries became blocked forming numerous lakes (e.g. Bosset Lagoon and Lake Daviumbu, Figure 3). Floodplain rivers also meander extensively, and ox-bow lakes of variable depth, depending on age, occur within the floodplain.

PHYSICO-CHEMICAL LIMNOLOGY

Water Quality and Sediment Loads in Rivers

Rivers in New Guinea are characterised by high discharges with heavy sediment loads. The main processes which add sediment to rivers are slopewash, landsliding and reworking of river bed material. The sedimentary discharge from the combined rivers of the Papua New Guinean mainland has been calculated to be 240 x 10^6 tons year^{-1} (Fox 1990) and this is greater than either that of the Orinoco or Mississippi rivers (Milliman and Meade 1983). It was predicted that the proposed reservoir at Wabo on the Purari River would receive 57 x 10^6 tons year^{-1} of sediments (Pickup 1983). In the impact assessment for the reservoir considerable attention was paid to water and sediment quality in the catchment rivers (Petr 1983 a, b, c). From flow and suspended sediment measurements made in June 1988, Fox (1990) calculated a sediment discharge for the Sepik River of 90 x 10^6 tons year^{-1}.

Slopewash occurs under rainforest in Papua New Guinea (Ruxton 1971, Turvey 1974). Turvey (1974) recorded a maximum suspended sediment load in Ei Creek, Sogeri, near Port Moresby of 1945.7 ppm at a peak flow of 51 m^3 s^{-1}. As a result of this flood a very large bedload was moved, the bed was scoured and the stream carried large amounts of organic debris including trees. He concluded that while some of this material was derived from gardens close to the stream, most was probably derived from minor landslips which occurred throughout the catchment.

Landslides in the upper catchment of the Fly River are usually small but occasionally massive slides from the limestone escarpment add millions of tonnes to the river system. Such a slide occurred in January 1977 when between three and a half and five million tonnes of rock slipped from the Hindenburg Wall and entered the Ok Tedi within a few days. The river as far down as Ningerum ran white with suspended limestone particles for several weeks, the bed of the river was raised by more than two metres and fish kills occurred downstream. Within a month, however, the river had returned to its previous load (Jackson undated). Sediment concentrations in the Fly River decrease downstream as water from the sediment source is diluted by cleaner runoff from the lower catchment and there tends to be a poor correlation between discharge and sediment transport in this system (Pickup et al. 1981). In contrast, Pickup (1983) found, in the Purari River, a direct correlation between discharge and transport of suspended solids.

A very large copper mine is located in the upper catchment of the Ok Tedi, a tributary of the Fly River. Waste rock and tailings are currently dumped into the Ok Tedi and Pickup et al. (1981) identified two potential, detrimental effects on the middle Fly River. First, increased sediment loads in the Fly River could lead to increased siltation in the river system, and second, increased heavy metal concentrations in the water and sediments may result from mining activities. Mowbray (1988a, 1988b) predicted that under conditions of low river flow, the effects of tailings from the Ok Tedi mine would be confined to the upper reaches of the Ok Tedi but chronic effects could extend down the Fly River. Even the mining company projected and subsequently demonstrated that the impact on the Ok Tedi and Fly River would be reduced numbers of fish species and lower populations (Smith and Hortle 1991, Smith and Morris 1992; see section on Water Pollution). Osborne et al. (1988) showed that sediments transported by the Fly River are deposited in Lake Daviumbu, a tributary lake near the junction of the Strickland and Fly Rivers. This contrasts with the environmental impact assessment which predicted that little river-borne sediment was expected to reach these lakes and wetlands (Maunsell and Partners 1982). Recent work has detected elevated levels of trace metals (particularly copper) in surface sediments of lakes adjacent to the Fly River (Ok Tedi Mining Limited 1993).

Table 5. Altitudinal gradients of temperature, conductivity and dissolved silica content in the streams of the Purari River Basin (Petr 1983)

Altitude (m)	Temperature (°C)	Conductivity (μS cm^{-1})	SiO$_2$ (mg L^{-1})
4000-3500	9.1-14.4	13-43	7-13
3000-2500	12.3-15.6	12-44	8-20
2500-2000	14.7-19.8	15-62	9-29
2000-1500	17.7-22.8	49-135	16-33
1500-1000	20.8-24.9	69-170	21-26
1000-100	21.0-24.6	86-195	12-19
100-20	23.8-26.5	108-180	9-24
10	24.2-26.5	120-150	12-16

Petr (1983b, 1983c) has shown that temperature, conductivity and the concentration of dissolved silica vary with altitude (Table 5). Concentrations of dissolved silica increased downstream to a mean of 23.5 mg L^{-1} between 1000 and 1500 m. Below this altitude range, concentrations decreased and this is probably due to absorption of silica onto clay particles. There is no possibility that this reduction can be attributed to algal uptake of silica because the Purari River is too turbid and turbulent for primary production by silica-fixing diatoms. Similarly, orthophosphate had relatively higher concentrations in the highlands than downstream, again suggesting its absorption onto clay (Viner 1979). Inorganic combined nitrogen (NH_4-N + NO_2-N + NO_3-N), like most other components, increased progressively downstream. These longitudinal gradients are, however, susceptible to abrupt changes, particularly through alterations in the flow regime. Over a three day period, the Purari River discharge at Wabo increased from 773 m^3 s^{-1} to 4015 m^3 s^{-1}. This resulted in decreases in conductivity from 147 μS cm^{-1} to 115 μS cm^{-1} and silica concentration from 17 mg L^{-1} to 9 mg L^{-1}, pre and post-flood.

Thermal Stratification and Water and Sediment Chemistry in Lakes

Climate and lake morphometry are the overriding determinants of thermal regime in lakes. According to the Hutchinson and Löffler (1956) schematic arrangement of thermal lake types, based on altitude and latitude, all lakes in Papua New Guinea should be oligomictic, polymictic or warm monomictic. However, the thermal regime of lakes can not, given these basic geographical data, be predicted with certainty and few lakes in Papua New Guinea have been studied in sufficient detail to categorise them on thermal behaviour. It is likely that most lowland (below 120 m) lakes in Papua New Guinea are warm polymictic, stratifying temporarily, often on a diurnal basis, with surface cooling at night causing partial or complete breakdown of stratification. Chambers (1987) presents a factual review of physical and chemical features of water bodies in Papua New Guinea. Additional information is presented here.

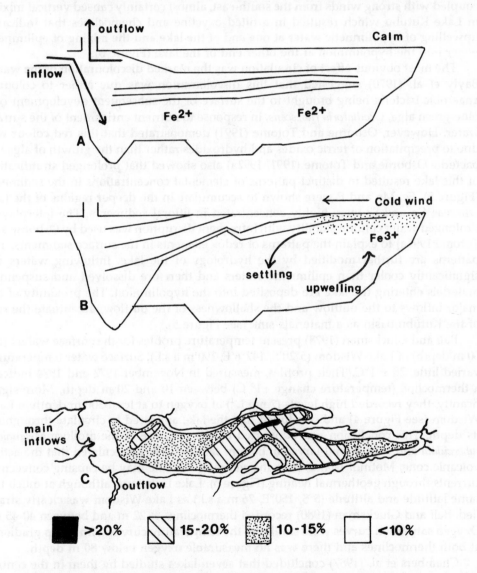

Figure 5. Isopleths of oxygen (mg L^{-1}) measured in Lake Kutubu, Papua New Guinea on 7 April 1989 (A) and on 24 and 25 September 1990 (B). The distribution of iron (as Fe$_2$O$_3$) in surface sediment samples collected from 55 sites is shown in (C) (adapted from Osborne and Totome 1991, 1992).

Lake Kutubu (altitude 808 m a.s.l.) has been shown to be oligomictic (Osborne and Totome 1991, 1992a). When the lake is stratified, distinct chemoclines in soluble reactive phosphorus, ammonium-nitrogen, nitrite-nitrogen and nitrate-nitrogen were recorded (Osborne and Totome 1992a). The epilimnion was well-oxygenated but oxygen concentrations below 25 m were low to undetectable. Stratification breakdown was observed at the lake in September 1960 (Rule personal communication) and September 1990 (Osborne and Totome 1991, 1992a). Unusually cold weather was recorded in the Papua New Guinean highlands in August and September 1990. This cold weather, coupled with strong winds from the south-east, almost certainly caused vertical mixing in Lake Kutubu which resulted in a tilted oxycline and chemoclines that indicated upwelling of hypolimnetic water at one end of the lake and the mixing of epilimnetic water into the hypolimnion at the other end of the lake (Figure 5).

The most obvious effect of circulation was the marked discolouration of the water. Bayly et al. (1970) suggested that this discolouration was due either to coloured anaerobic bacteria being brought to the surface or the subsequent development of a blue-green alga, *Oscillatoria rubescens*, in response to nutrient enrichment of the surface water. However, Osborne and Totome (1991) demonstrated that this red colour was due to precipitation of ferric oxides and hydroxides rather than the growth of algae or bacteria. Osborne and Totome (1991, 1992a) also showed that prolonged stratification of this lake resulted in distinct patterns of elemental concentrations in the sediments (Figure 5). Fe, Mn and P were shown to accumulate in the deeper regions of the lake whereas Ca and Sr were highly concentrated in littoral sediments. The interplay of prolonged water column stability with infrequent disruption was used by Osborne and Totome 1992a) to explain the patterns of redox elements in the surface sediments. The patterns are further modified by the hydrology of the lake. Inflowing waters are significantly cooler than epilimnetic waters and therefore dissolved and suspended materials entering the lake are deposited into the hypolimnion. The proximity of the major inflows to the outflow and the shallowness of the outflow, accentuate the role of the Kutubu basin as a materials sink (see Figure 5).

Ball and Glucksman (1978) present temperature profiles for the surface waters (50-60 m depth) of Lake Wisdom (5°20'S, 147°6'E, 190 m a.s.l.). Surface water temperatures varied little: 28 ± 1°C. Their profiles, measured in November 1972 and 1974 indicate a thermocline (temperature change ±1° C) between 10 and 20 m depth. More significantly, they recorded high levels (7 mg L^{-1}) of oxygen to at least 300 m depth in Lake Wisdom (see Figure 4) and concluded that the lake appeared to circulate throughout its depth. This conclusion was supported by the presence of the mollusc *Melanoides tuberculata* and chironomid larvae in bottom samples. They speculated that the active volcanic cone, Motmot Island, near the centre of the lake may be causing convection currents through geothermal heating (Figure 6). Lake Dakataua, although at much the same latitude and altitude (5°S, 150°E, 76 m a.s.l.) as Lake Wisdom was clearly stratified. Ball and Glucksman (1980) recorded thermoclines at 22 m and between 40-45 m. Oxygen saturation curves were similar to the temperature curves with sharp gradients at both thermoclines and there was no measurable oxygen below 80 m depth.

Chambers et al. (1987) concluded that seven lakes studied by them in the central highlands of Papua New Guinea were probably not deep enough to exhibit permanent stratification, and suggested that they were warm polymictic. These lakes may stratify temporarily, often on a diurnal basis, with surface cooling at night causing partial or complete mixing. Chambers et al. (1987) observed a significant inverse relationship between altitude and bottom water temperature in these highland lakes (Figure 7). These lakes had a low nutrient status, although two in limestone catchments had high alkalinities.

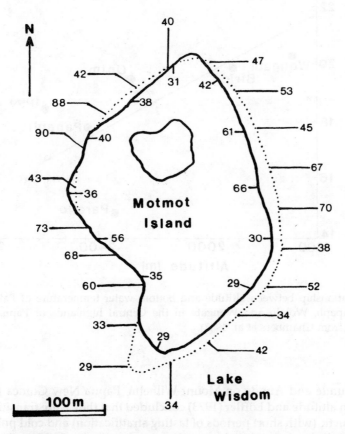

Figure 6. Water temperatures at the margins of Motmot Island, Lake Wisdom, Papua New Guinea (see Fig 4) measured in 1969, one year after the island formed by volcanic eruption (redrawn from Ball and Glucksman 1975).

These lakes and other small lakes between 3530 and 3920 m altitude on Mt Wilhelm are of glacial origin. They receive runoff from small, rocky catchments of gabbro and associated ultrabasic rocks where the soils are shallow and predominantly acidic. The lakes are characterised by low turbidity with Secchi disc depths ranging up to 10 m (Löffler 1973). Except for pH, a rainwater sample collected near Lake Aunde had a conductivity and water chemistry very similar to that of Brass' Tarn, indicating that runoff water receives little in the form of ions from rocks and soils at these high altitudes. Nutrient concentrations in these lakes were consequently very low. Löffler (1973) found 0.3 μg L^{-1} of total phosphorus in the surface water of Aunde and nitrate was undetectable.

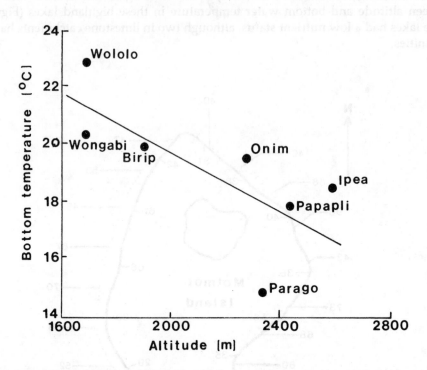

Figure 7. Relationship between altitude and bottom water temperature of Lakes Birip, Ipea, Onim, Papapli, Wololo and Wongabi in the Central highlands of Papua New Guinea (redrawn from Chambers et al. 1987).

Lakes Piunde and Aunde on Mount Wilhelm, Papua New Guinea (Figure 3) are above 3500 m altitude and Löffler (1973) concluded that they were transitional between warm polymictic (with short periods of lasting stratification) and cold polymictic (with almost daily full circulations). Lake Aunde was isothermal at 09:00 on 29 and 31 March but exhibited significant temperature gradients in the evenings of 28 March and 1 April (Figure 8). Marked stratification was recorded at 14:30 on 30 March in Lake Piunde. Löffler (1973) indicated that it was very likely that during the rainy season, both these lakes circulate frequently, a condition which is further promoted by increased inflow, whereas, during the drier season, a shift towards warm polymixis occurs.

Detailed surveys of the elemental concentrations in the surficial sediments of four lakes have been carried out (Table 6). Lake Kutubu is oligomictic and Osborne and Totome (1991, 1992a) relate the distribution patterns and high concentration of iron, manganese, phosphorus and other elements to the interruption of the prolonged thermal stability of the water column by rare, short-lived vertical mixing events (Figure 5). The high concentration of calcium in the littoral sediments of this lake reflect the occurrence of limestone pinnacles in its catchment area and sequestration of this element by littoral-dwelling molluscs and aquatic plants. The dichotomy in the elemental composition between deep and littoral sediments in this lake is manifested

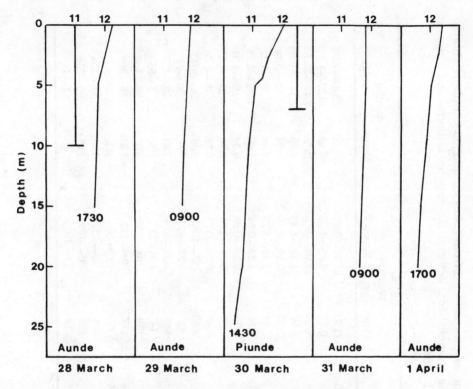

Figure 8. Thermal profiles of Lakes Aunde and Piunde on Mount Wilhelm, Papua New Guinea. Vertical lines indicate Secchi disc depth (redrawn from Löffler 1973).

in the wide concentration ranges recorded (Table 6). Lake Kopiago is a small, shallow lake situated in a catchment also dominated by limestone at an altitude of 2200 m. The major inflow to the lake is through an herbaceous wetland and some subsistence gardening is carried out in the otherwise pristine, small catchment. Elemental concentrations in this lake were less variable than those recorded in Lake Kutubu and this is probably due to the absence of oligomixis in Lake Kopiago. In Lake Kopiago mean Si concentrations were higher and mean Ca concentrations lower than those recorded in Lake Kutubu.

Elevated concentrations of silica in Lakes Waigani and Daviumbu can be related to their low altitude (20 m) and high diatom production, particularly in sewage-enriched Waigani Lake (Table 6). An analysis of the elemental content of core sections from Waigani Lake indicated a marked increase in the concentrations of phosphorus, manganese, iron, sulfur, magnesium, sodium, calcium, zinc, lead, strontium and barium in the recent sediments; increases which correlate with the progressive urbanization of the catchment area (Polunin et al. 1988). The accelerated accumulation of these elements in the sediments may help to explain the decline in the emergent vegetation (see section on aquatic plants) and it is possible that the different vegetation stages may have influenced patterns of sediment geochemistry. Elemental concentrations in the sediments of Lake Daviumbu were measured in 1984 and therefore provide a pre-mining baseline of contamination by trace metals.

Table 6. Mean and ranges of elemental concentrations in sediment samples collected from Lakes Kutubu (55 samples, Osborne and Totome 1991, 1992), Kopiago (30 samples, Osborne unpublished), Waigani (26 samples Osborne and Totome unpublished) and Daviumbu (32 samples, Osborne et al. 1988)

Element	Kutubu		Kopiago		Waigani		Daviumbu	
	Mean	Range	Mean	Range	Mean	Range	Mean	Range
SiO_2 (%)	42.79	3.36—75.08	57.98	49.88—66.30	71.21	65.97—75.24	74.05	63.49—86.8
TiO_2 (%)	0.92	0.090—1.96	0.97	0.90—1.04	0.71	0.65—1.02	0.62	0.23—1.11
Al_2O_3 (%)	19.47	1.58—36.34	23.20	18.68—25.74	16.29	14.90—20.03	16.39	7.47—23.55
Fe_2O_3 (%)	11.37	0.76—19.8	10.23	6.63—13.95	5.69	4.47—6.49	4.66	2.44—10.85
MnO (%)	0.27	0.01—1.56	0.05	0.03—0.08	0.10	0.40—0.19	0.04	0.02—0.14
MgO (%)	1.10	0.50—1.91	1.43	1.13—1.72	1.59	1.38—1.73	0.66	0.20—1.35
CaO (%)	16.75	1.67—80.31	1.89	0.61—5.80	2.14	1.45—3.54	1.00	0.52—2.75
Na_2O (%)	0.33	0.08—1.29	0.63	0.51—0.97	0.36	0.20—0.88	0.39	0.06—1.01
K_2O (%)	0.63	0.02—1.39	2.03	1.63—2.24	0.61	0.39—1.06	0.90	0.21—2.25
P_2O_5 (%)	0.77	0.11—1.74	0.35	0.22—0.51	0.40	0.14—0.71	0.18	0.40—0.38
SO_3 ($\mu g\,g^{-1}$)	7571	556—33500	3856	422—11763	3650	987—10872	509	71—5043
Cr ($\mu g\,g^{-1}$)	129	12—275	124	108—143	82	73—97	69	30—94
Ba ($\mu g\,g^{-1}$)	264	80—403	300	233—362	443	339—606	283	98—427
Co ($\mu g\,g^{-1}$)	22	11—32	19	14—24	14	8—21	19	3—55
Cu ($\mu g\,g^{-1}$)	106	38—194	60	35—95	130	104—155	64	28—167
Zn ($\mu g\,g^{-1}$)	102	6—173	150	123—180	117	94—132	180	36—309
Ni ($\mu g\,g^{-1}$)	37	8—69	52	33—86	73	59—96	41	20—66
Zr ($\mu g\,g^{-1}$)	139	27—261	178	157—281	101	89—152	125	51—234
Sr ($\mu g\,g^{-1}$)	210	110—460	389	244—278	123	85—189	115	60—236
Pb ($\mu g\,g^{-1}$)	15	5—28	34	16—249	119	13—1979	1	1—11

Aquatic Plants, Phytoplankton and Primary Production

The freshwater flora of Papua New Guinea comprises eight species of Characeae, twenty-one species of ferns and fern-allies and 130 flowering plants. Leach and Osborne (1985) provides a taxonomic treatment with keys to families, genera and species, species descriptions and notes on taxonomy, habitat and distribution. Freshwater algae in Papua New Guinea have been poorly studied and most work has been taxonomic (Thomasson 1967, Watanabe et al. 1979a, 1979b, Yamagishi 1975, Yamagishi and Watanabe 1979, Vyverman 1989, 1990, 1991, in press). Vyverman 1991 studied desmids in 145 freshwater habitats in Papua New Guinea. He identified five main assemblages: one from tropical lowlands, one extending from lowlands to mid-altitudes, one from mid-altitudes and two from medium to high altitude waters. The dominant taxa in all assemblages were cosmopolitan but some with restricted geographical distribution were recorded. The number of desmid taxa with an Indo-Malaysian-North-Australian, pantropical and palaeotropical distribution decreased with increasing altitude while Arctic-Alpine taxa were only found in highland waters.

Phytoplankton production has not been measured in any of the high altitude lakes but their very poor nutrient status, high water clarity and low phytoplankton density, suggest that it would be very low indeed. The phytoplankton in the Mt Wilhelm lakes was dominated by desmids (Thomasson 1967) indicative that the lakes are nutrient poor. Phytoplankton production of the small lakes at lower altitudes within the highlands has not been studied but Chambers et al. (1987) described a limnological study of seven lakes between 1700 and 2500 m altitude.

Lake Tebera, situated at an altitude of 586 m, is approximately 7 km long and up to 1.5 km wide. Conn (1979a) described the islands of floating vegetation found on this lake as being predominantly composed of *Leersia hexandra*, sedges, other hydrophytic grasses, *Ludwigia adscendens*, *Limnophila indica* and *Polygonum*. Lake Tebera is known to dry out occasionally. The floating islands then settle down, apparently overgrowing the whole lake area. The aquatic flora of the lake was similar in species composition and zonation to that of Lake Kutubu (Conn 1979b, 1983, Osborne et al. 1990). The very steep rocky shores of Lake Kutubu were devoid of plants but diverse assemblages occur at either end of the lake. Submerged aquatic plant beds were dominated by *Ceratophyllum demersum*, *Hydrilla verticillata*, *Ottelia alismoides* and *Vallisneria natans*. Nearer shore, *Nymphoides indica*, *Polygonum attenuatum*, *Limnophila indica* and *Pistia stratiotes* occurred. Phytoplankton production has not been measured in either of these lakes but Osborne et al. (1990) indicated that phytoplankton production in Lake Kutubu is likely to be very low as algal biomass is low and nutrient cycling is impeded through oligomixis (Osborne and Totome 1991, 1992a). Primary production has been studied in two lowland lakes (Waigani Lake and Lake Murray) and the results of these are described below.

The Waigani wetland (Figure 3) comprises a number of small, shallow lakes near Port Moresby which drain into the extensive swamp/river system dominated by the Brown and Laloki Rivers. Waigani Lake is shallow (1-2 m deep) with an open water area of 120 ha and *Phragmites karka*, *Typha domingensis* and *Hanguana malayana* dominated the emergent littoral vegetation. *Oreochromis mossambica* and *Cyprinus carpio* were introduced to the lake in the 1950s and dominated the catches of a small but productive fishery. Sewage disposal into the lake began in 1965 and the settling ponds were subsequently enlarged to cater for the rapidly expanding population of Port Moresby (now approximately 200,000). The climate of the Port Moresby area is monsoonal with a dry season from April-November and a wet season from December to March. Surface water temperatures varied little throughout the year, with a minimum of 26°C and a maximum of 32°C (Osborne 1991). Periods of weak and temporary thermal stratification may occur in this shallow lake (1-2 m deep) but stronger oxy- and chemoclines have been observed (Totome, personal communication).

Phytoplankton productivity in Waigani Lake was high throughout the year but production was markedly lower during the wet season (Figure 9). Prior to the wet season (December) algal populations were high (chlorophyll a levels around 300 mg m^{-3}) and most production occurred at the surface, relatively little at depth. During the wet season, algal populations declined, (chlorophyll a levels fluctuating between 100-200 mg m^{-3}), water clarity increased and phytoplankton production was lower with more uniform depth profiles (January, February, March). Phytoplankton production increased in April and remained very high in May and early June. High surface productivity was recorded from August to December. However on 22 June 1981 and 10 July 1981, the weather was overcast and this explains the lower production recorded on these days (Figure 9). This indicates that light penetration through the very turbid waters of this lake controls primary production. As a result of this high production, algal biomass increased during the dry season reaching very high levels (over 400 mg m^{-3}) in July and August. Levels declined in September owing to higher flushing rates resulting from early heavy rain in August but increased again in early October (Osborne 1991).

Major changes in the distribution and abundance of aquatic plants in the Waigani wetland have occurred over the last forty years. The main lake is now devoid of submerged and floating-leaved plants but in the late 1960s and early 1970s nymphaeids (*Nymphoides indica, Nymphaea pubescens* and *Nymphaea dictyophlebia*) dominated the area which is now open water. Aerial photographs taken in 1942 and 1956 both show the central area of Waigani Lake covered by emergent vegetation (Osborne and Leach 1983). The increase in sewage effluent disposal correlates with the decline in floating-leaved plants and by 1974 only a few small stands remained. By 1978 no floating-leaved plants could be found in the main lake and their decline in Waigani Lake was accompanied by a regression of the surrounding reedswamp. This decline in the area of the emergent reedswamp has continued subsequent to the work by Osborne and Leach (1983) (Osborne and Totome 1992b). *Salvinia molesta* infested lakes in this wetland in 1980 but biological control measures were successful. In 1990, *Eichhornia crassipes* invaded the wetland and by 1992 half of the main lake was covered with a dense mat (Osborne and Totome 1992b).

Osborne and Polunin (1986) collected short sediment cores from the lake and were able to reconstruct the ecological history of the lake. The lowermost sections of their sediment cores had low nitrogen and phosphorus concentrations and undetectable levels of plant pigments and high densities of epiphytic diatom frustules. These characteristics are indicative of an herbaceous swamp and correlate with the aerial photographs taken in 1943 and 1956 as described by Osborne and Leach (1983). Following this phase, nitrogen and phosphorus concentrations in the sediments increased and indicate the onset of sewage disposal into the lake. Further nutrient enrichment with the expansion of the sewage system in the 1970s resulted in higher nutrient deposition

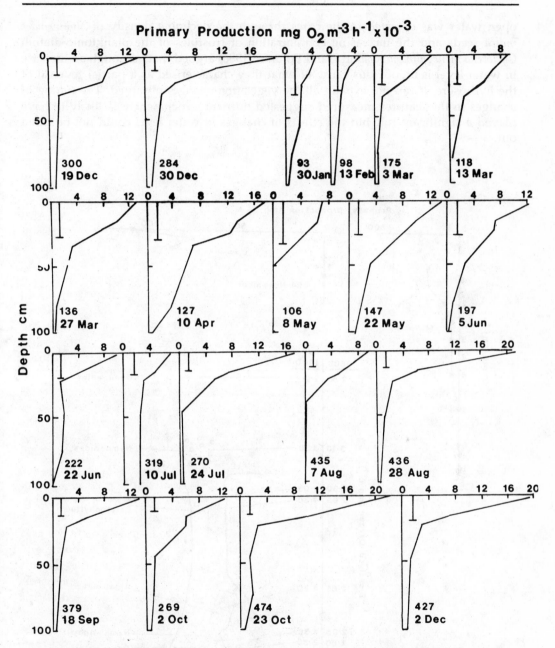

Figure 9. Depth distribution of phytoplankton production in Waigani Lake, Papua New Guinea from 19 December 1980 to 2 December 1981. Numbers above the date are surface concentrations of chlorophyll a in mg m^{-3} and vertical lines with a terminal bar indicate Secchi disc depth (redrawn from Osborne 1991).

in the sediments and at around this time the switch from emergent vegetation to one dominated by floating-leaved plants occurred. The subsequent increase in the area of open water was detected in the cores through the declining density of *Nymphoides indica* seeds and the increasing concentration of frustules of the planktonic diatom *Cyclotella meneghiniana*. Osborne and Polunin (1986) argued that, although an increase in water-level is an obvious cause of what they characterised as a partial reversal of the hydrosere, it can not explain all the vegetation changes observed. The timing of changes in the features measured suggested nutrient enrichment was likely to have played a significant role but the effects of changes in water level could not be ruled out.

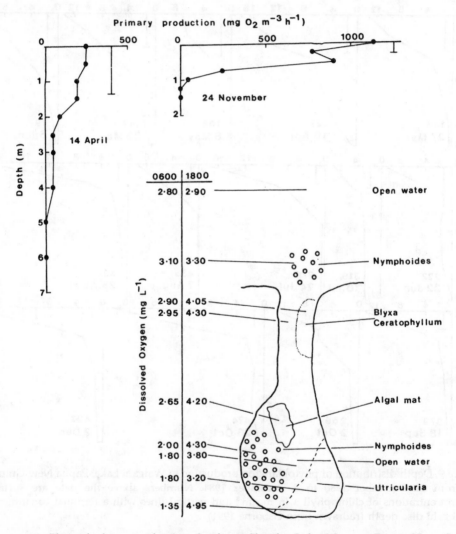

Figure 10. Phytoplankton production depth profiles for Lake Murray, Papua New Guinea, sampled in April and November 1982 (vertical lines indicate Secchi disc depths) and oxygen concentrations measured at various sites in a canoe channel near Lake Murray Patrol Post at 1800 h and 0600 h on 14 and 15 April 1982, respectively (redrawn from Osborne 1987).

Lake Murray, a tributary lake with a surface area of 647 km^2 and a high-water convoluted shoreline 2038 km long is the largest lake (by area) in the tropical Pacific. It is situated in a low-lying tract of swamp-forest between the Fly and Strickland Rivers occupying a shallow depression and its outflow, the Herbert River, joins the Strickland. Osborne et al. (1987) recorded marked seasonal fluctuations in water level and described the consequent effects on water chemistry, phytoplankton production and aquatic plants. In November 1982, at the end of a very dry year, the lake water level had fallen 4 m from its April 1982 level. The lake was surrounded by a wide expanse of barren mud, and pH had risen from 5.3 to 9.6, conductivity from 12 to 100 μS cm^{-1}, total hardness from 80 to 400 mM and suspended solids from 11 to 45 mg L^{-1}. In November 1982, maximum production of phytoplanktonic oxygen was 1120 mg O$_2$ m^{-3} h^{-1} at the surface but declined sharply with depth because of light attenuation by suspended solids, this maximum production was much higher than that recorded in April 1982: 250 mg O$_2$ m^{-3} h^{-1} (Figure 10).

The long shoreline and the shallowness (maximum depth 10 m) of Lake Murray result in an extensive littoral zone. During periods of high water level, the aquatic vegetation could be divided into two broad zones: an outer zone dominated by *Nymphoides indica* with some *Nymphaea nouchali*, *Ceratophyllum demersum* and *Blyxa novoguineensis* and an inner zone of hydrophytic grasses with *Ipomoea aquatica*, *Azolla pinnata* and *Utricularia* sp. *Limnophila indica* occurred on newly exposed mud and in shallow water. The large differences in diurnal dissolved oxygen levels in the aquatic plant beds contrasted with the values from the open water site where little diurnal variation was noticed (Figure 10). This high littoral production is lost during periods of low water level. In November 1982 the large areas of exposed mud were not colonized by any plants and the high-water-level littoral zone was marked by a band of decaying plant matter. Consequently, during periods of high water level, the low, open water production is compensated by high littoral zone production (Osborne et al. 1987).

Aquatic Weeds

Salvinia molesta was first recorded in Papua New Guinea in 1977 at Wau but probably infested the Sepik River in the early 1970s (Mitchell 1978/1979). By 1979 *Salvinia* covered 80 km^2 of the ox-bow lakes and lagoons along the Sepik floodplain. The weed disrupted the lives of Sepik villagers by interfering with fishing, crocodile hunting, sago gathering and the use of water transport (Mitchell et al. 1980, Coates 1982, 1987a). Physical, chemical and biological control methods were tested (Thomas 1979, 1985) and biological control using the South American weevil *Cyrtobagous salviniae* was spectacularly successful (Thomas 1985, Thomas and Room 1986). The initial development of the weevil population introduced to the Sepik in 1982 was nitrogen limited (Room and Thomas 1985, 1986a, 1986b) but once-established on plants enriched with fertilizer, populations became self-sustaining. By June 1985, the weevil had destroyed an estimated 2 million tonnes of weed which had covered 250 km^2 and the local people have now resumed their former lifestyles (Thomas and Room 1986).

Eichhornia crassipes was first found in Papua New Guinea in 1962 growing in abandoned gold mining dredge ponds near Bulolo. It has, despite warnings (Mitchell

1978/1979, Osborne and Leach 1984), became widespread through lowland areas of Morobe, Madang, East Sepik and Central Provinces (Osborne and Totome 1992b). Attempts at biological control using the weevil *Neochetina eichhorniae* have produced some promising results. So far, neither *Salvinia molesta* nor *Eichhornia crassipes* has been recorded from the Fly River system.

Invertebrates

The freshwater invertebrate fauna of Papua New Guinea has been poorly studied. Lakes in Papua New Guinea feature low zooplankton diversities, with a notable paucity of cladoceran and copepod species. Twelve zooplankton species have been recorded from the lakes on Mount Wilhelm (Bayly and Morton 1980, Löffler 1973, McKenzie 1971). Low species diversity was attributed to the youthfulness of these lakes (estimated to be 23,000 years old) and this contrasts with the greater diversity of older high-altitude lakes elsewhere in the tropics (Löffler 1973). Chambers et al. (1987) recorded a total of 27 species (2 calanoids, 6 cyclopoids, 8 cladocerans and 11 rotifers) from seven lakes in the highlands. The communities had generally low diversities ranging from two (Lake Onim) to twelve (Lake Parago). They concluded that the paucity of species in these lakes was probably due to a combination of factors: high altitude with warm temperate conditions, low nutrient status, geographical isolation and the recent introduction of carp. Ball and Glucksman (1978) found only two plankton cladocerans in Lake Wisdom and ten species (one rotifer, one ostracod, one copepod and seven cladocerans) in Lake Dakataua (Ball and Glucksman 1980). Both these lakes are young and isolated. Bayly and Morton (1980) recorded only five zooplankton species from Lake Surinumu, a lowland reservoir near Port Moresby.

Chambers 1988 recorded 51 species of zooplankton in three lakes adjacent to the middle Fly River. He sampled the lakes on two occasions in 1984, once during the wet season (June-July) and once in the dry season (December). Only three species occurred in each lake on both sampling occasions: *Bosminopsis dietersi*, *Chydorus eurynotus* and *Calamoecia ultima*. Of the remaining 48 species, five were collected from Lake Daviumbu and 20 were confined solely to Lake Pangua which lies two kilometres to the north of Lake Daviumbu. Of these 20 species, 16 were rotifers recorded only in the dry season samples. In Lakes Daviumbu and Pangua the diversity and density of zooplankton were inversely related with higher dry season densities occurring at the times of lowest diversity. Numbers were always low with the maximum density recorded being only 84 L^{-1}. Higher wet season diversity in these lakes was attributed at least in part to littoral species being flushed into the open water.

Dudgeon (1990) studied benthic macroinvertebrates in two upland streams of the Sepik-Ramu River system. He concluded that despite generalizations concerning the poverty of freshwater fauna in Papua New Guinea (Gressitt 1982), both Koje and Maram Creeks yielded diverse collections of benthic macroinvertebrates, dominated by insects. In terms of morphospecies richness, they did not differ greatly from stream communities in the Oriental tropics. The composition of the fauna was, however, rather different from that of Oriental streams. This difference could not be attributed to the inclusion of Australian elements but reflected a lack of certain Oriental groups and a radiation of others. For example, Heptageniidae, Ephemerellidae and Ephemeridae among the mayflies, Psephenidae among the aquatic beetles, and Plecoptera were absent from the Papua New Guinean collections although these animals are abundant in similar streams on the Asian mainland. Naucorid bugs, by contrast, were well-represented and may have occupied the vacant stonefly-predator niche. Dudgeon (1990) also found differences in species composition between the two streams he studied. Four of the most numerous Koje Creek taxa (Orthocladiinae: Diptera, Caenidae: Ephemeroptera, Naucoridae: Heteroptera and Nymphulinae: Lepidoptera) were relatively scarce in Maram Creek while Hydroptilidae, Philopotamidae (Trichoptera) and Simuliidae (Diptera) were significantly more abundant in Maram than Koje Creek. Dudgeon (1990) suggested that the differences may have arisen through the influence of riparian vegetation on allochthonous and autochthonous food sources in both habitats. Koje Creek was unshaded, draining secondary forest and gardens whereas Maram Creek drained rain forest and was 95-100% shaded.

Taxonomic works on freshwater invertebrates include: Holthius (1974, 1982) (Decapoda); Richardson (1977) (leeches); Robertson (1983) (*Macrobrachium*); Benthem-Jutting (1963) (Mollusca); McKenzie (1956) (mussels); McMichael and Hiscock (1958) (mussels).

Freshwater Fishes, Crocodiles and Food Webs

The island of New Guinea lies east of "Wallace's Line" and thus forms part of the Australian zoogeographic region. The ichthyofauna can be clearly divided into two zoogeographic regions. Freshwater bodies to the south of the central cordillera have an ichthyofauna closely allied with that of northern Australia as the two land masses were formerly joined. Several species with diadromous habits can be found in both southern and northern rivers but almost invariably freshwater species in northern water bodies are different from those in water bodies to the south of the central cordillera. Of those fish families common to both northern and southern rivers, species diversity is lower in the north (Coates 1987b). Several fish families are also absent from the north whilst all those present there, are also present in southern rivers. The freshwater fish fauna was first comprehensively described by Munro (1967). Since then, however, a number of new species have been recorded (e.g. Allen and Cross 1980, 1982, Allen and Boeseman 1982, Allen and Hoese 1986, Allen 1991). The most up to date treatment of the freshwater fishes and their distribution is that of Allen (1991) which covers mainland Papua New Guinea and Irian Jaya. Allen (1991) described 329 species. Of these, 13 species are introduced forms, and about 102 species are fishes that are believed to have a marine larval stage and are relatively widespread outside New Guinea. Two closely related families are unique to Australasia: Melanotaeniidae (Rainbowfishes) and Pseudomugilidae (Blue-eyes) and this fauna further differs from that of other continental tropical regions which are dominated by cichlids and primary division Ostariophysan fishes (carps, barbs, loaches, characins and catfishes). The Ostariophysan assemblage is represented in New Guinea - Australia only by plotosid and ariid catfishes. All the freshwater fishes except the lungfish (*Neoceratodus*), bony tongues (*Osteoglossus*) and possibly galaxiids are considered to be derived from marine ancestors.

The southern rivers of Papua New Guinea have abundant fish and compared with the Sepik and highland rivers are richer in species. The Fly River ichthyofauna comprises over 100 species in 33 families and has 33 species in common with that of northern Australia (Allen 1991). The ichthyofauna of the Sepik River appears to be less diverse than that of the Fly River and many of the species recorded are endemic to rivers of northern New Guinea and some are only known from the Sepik (Coates 1985, 1987b). Of twenty-nine native species recorded by Coates (1983) only *Anguilla bicolor pacifica* and *Lutjanus argentimaculatus* are of any importance to the subsistence fishery. Almost all the other native species are small. Two exotic species: *Oreochromis mossambica* and *Cyprinus carpio* are more productive and.it has been recommended that further exotic species be introduced (Petr 1984, Coates 1983, 1984a, 1984b, 1986, 1987b).

Indigenous fish species in the upper Purari belong to the families Anguillidae, Ariidae, Plotosidae, Melanotaeniidae, Theraponidae and Gobiidae but a complete list is not available. The freshwater fish fauna of the lower Purari has forty-nine species from twenty-four families. Berra et al. (1975) recorded forty-three native species belonging to nineteen families and six exotic species from the Laloki, Brown and Goldie Rivers draining the western half of Central Province. The Laloki fauna is closely related to that of Northern Australia but about half the species are endemic to New Guinea. The seven small highland lakes studies by Chambers et al. (1987) contained only introduced carp.

Lake Kutubu in the Southern Highlands (Figure 3) has the richest lacustrine fauna in New Guinea, apart from floodplain lakes. A total of 13 species have been recorded there, including 11 which are endemic. Allen (1991) indicates that, although the lake remains in a pristine state, its future is threatened through the development of oil reserves within the lake's environs.

Moore (1982), Moore and Reynolds (1982) and Reynolds and Moore (1982) described in some detail the growth, reproduction and catadromous migration of *Lates calcarifer* (Barramundi). Barramundi from the Lake Murray (Figure 3) region have been shown to accumulate mercury and the average mercury concentration recorded is close to the limit set by the Austrialian Government (Lamb 1977, Sorentino 1979, Petr 1979, Kyle and Ghani 1982, 1984). Barramundi from other freshwaters in Papua New Guinea have low levels of mercury and it would appear that the source of the mercury is the catchment area of the Strickland River (Natural Systems Research 1988).

At least twenty-two species of freshwater fish representing nineteen genera, eleven families and all six continents have been introduced into Papua New Guinea for various reasons (West and Glucksman 1976, Glucksman et al. 1976, Allen 1991). Most introductions have been unsuccessful or were never released into the wild. Of the successful introductions, most have had a negligible impact as either food fishes or in the control of mosquitoes (Allen 1991). *Oreochromis mossambica* is an exception as it now provides the major subsistence source of protein to villagers living along the Sepik River and it is the basis of a thriving commercial fishery on Waigani Lake near Port Moresby. The common carp (*Cyprinus carpio*) is well-established and abundant in highland lakes and also constitutes a significant component of catches from the Sepik River system and the wetlands in the Port Morseby area. Rainbow trout *(Oncorhynchus mykiss)* was introduced to the highlands of Papua New Guinea in 1952. There are a few self-sustaining populations in some highland streams and in the upper reaches of the Strickland River. The impact of trout on native fish species is likely to be minimal as there are few, often no, native fishes above 2000 m elevation (Allen 1991). However, the impact of trout on the aquatic invertebrates inhabiting these streams is unknown. *Tilapia rendalli* has recently been introduced to the Sepik and Ramu Rivers but it is still too early to say whether it has been successful (D. Coates, personal communication). Approval has also been given for the introduction of the Java carp (*Puntius gonionotus*) to the highlands streams in the Sepik catchment (D. Coates, personal communication). Gourami (*Trichogaster trichopterus*) are found in the streams of the Port Moresby area and form an important food fish for people living along the mid-reaches of the Lakekamu River (Menzies, personal communication).

Allen (1991) regards most of the earlier introductions as having had a negative impact through competition for space and limited food resources, or by feeding on the native species. Even the popular *Oreochromis mossambica* has adversely affected the environment, creating turbid conditions in formerly clean lakes and over-crowding the indigenous fauna due to its prolific breeding. On the positive side, the number of established introductions is relatively few and Allen (1991) states that the Fly River appears to be free of introductions. Coates (*in litt.*), however, indicates that common carp (*Cyprinus carpio*) occur in the Fly River and furthermore, that he recorded the climbing perch (*Anabas testudineus*) from the Fly River in 1985. Allen (1991) indicates that the latter species has only been recorded from Morehead River but points out that this hardy fish is capable of migrating long distances overland. The fish fauna of New Guinea sets it apart from that of the Indonesian Archipelago lying west of "Weber's Line" and Allen (1991) regards it as "particularly sad to witness the introduction of fishes from the Indonesian side of the Line". Lakes Dakataua and Wisdom still lack a fish fauna. Robertson and Baidam (1983) found only one species (*Oxyeleotris fimbriata*) in Lake Wangbin, a remote lake in the Star Mountains of Western Province.

Two species of crocodile are found in Papua New Guinea. These are the New Guinea or Freshwater Crocodile (*Crocodylus novaeguineae*) and the Saltwater Crocodile (*Crocodylus porosus*). Both species are still found in relatively large numbers and are 1xavily exploited for hides and meat. The endemic New Guinea crocodile prefers a freshwater environment but is occasionally found in brackish waters such as the Fly delta. It is more often found in sluggish, shallow water rather than swifter-flowing or deeper areas and hides, by day, in thick grass or under fallen trees (see Burgin 1980, Niell 1946, Pernetta and Burgin 1983).

Characteristically, the saltwater crocodile occurs in brackish areas such as estuaries and mangroves. Although once thought to be restricted to the coastal tidal areas, the species is now known to occur in fast-flowing rocky streams up to 1000 km inland (Burgin 1981). This species is now rare in the large mangrove areas of Gulf and Western Provinces and also in East and West Sepik Provinces where it was once apparently common.

Numbers of both species declined during the late 1950s and 1960s through indiscriminate hunting. In 1969 the Crocodile Trade (Protection) Act (Chapter 213) was implemented which, to protect breeders, placed a ban on trade in skins greater than 51 cm belly width. This halted further decline in crocodile numbers, indicated by a steady level of export during the 1970s. Both species are listed on Appendix 2 of CITES which means they are regarded as vulnerable but trading is allowed to continue. Papua New Guinea for many years has been the only country allowed by CITES to trade in *C. porosus*.

Figures 11 and 12 present outline food webs for Lake Murray (Natural Systems Research 1988) and for the Purari River (Haines 1983). These figures indicate the absence of plankton as a source of food for fishes and demonstrate the importance of allochthonous food sources such as terrestrial insects and terrestrial plant materials which enter the system. Aquatic plants form a small but significant food source for omnivorous fishes in Lake Murray but apart from some algal production in the deltaic areas of the Purari, aquatic plants are absent from this food web. No quantitative data

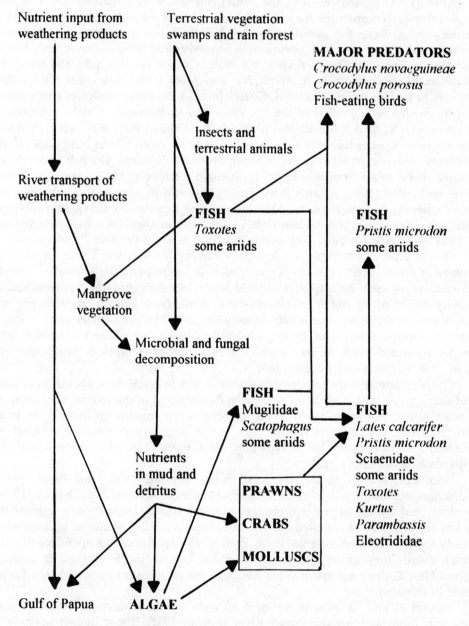

Figure 11. A simplified food web for Lake Murray, Papua New Guinea
(adapted from Natural Systems Research 1988).

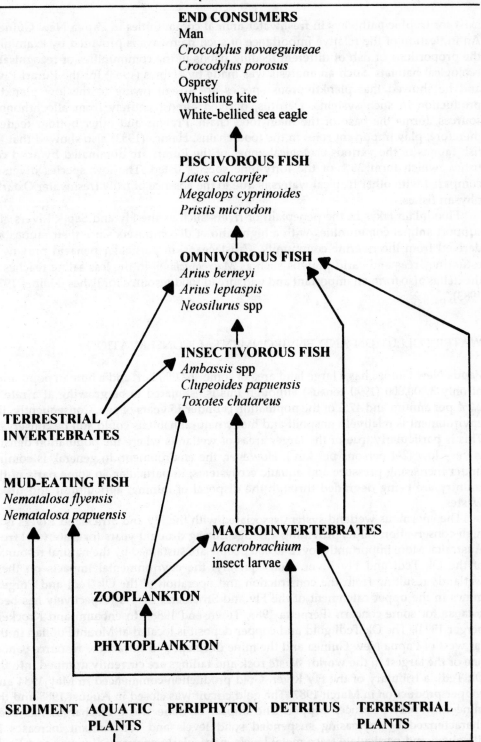

END CONSUMERS
Man
Crocodylus novaeguineae
Crocodylus porosus
Osprey
Whistling kite
White-bellied sea eagle

PISCIVOROUS FISH
Lates calcarifer
Megalops cyprinoides
Pristis microdon

OMNIVOROUS FISH
Arius berneyi
Arius leptaspis
Neosilurus spp

INSECTIVOROUS FISH
Ambassis spp
Clupeoides papuensis
Toxotes chatareus

**TERRESTRIAL
INVERTEBRATES**

MUD-EATING FISH
Nematalosa flyensis
Nematalosa papuensis

MACROINVERTEBRATES
Macrobrachium
insect larvae

ZOOPLANKTON

PHYTOPLANKTON

**SEDIMENT   AQUATIC   PERIPHYTON   DETRITUS   TERRESTRIAL
PLANTS   PLANTS**

Figure 12. Food chain and nutrient flow in the Purari River, Papua New Guinea
(adapted from Haines 1983).

exist for trophic pathways in freshwater animal communities in Papua New Guinea. An indication of the relative importance of such pathways is provided by examining the proportions of fish of different feeding habits in the communities of recognisable ecological habitats. Such an analysis was made by Haines (1983) for the Purari River and he showed that planktivorous species are absent owing to the low plankton production in such systems. Detritus, derived almost entirely from allochthonous sources, forms the base of the main food chain. Prawns and other bottom feeders, therefore, play important roles in the food chains. Haines (1983) also showed that the fish faunas of the various ecological zones of the Purari are dominated by ariid catfishes, which form 25% of the forty-nine species listed. The low species diversity compared with other tropical waters is due to the absence of truly freshwater Ostariophysan fishes.

Floodplain lakes in the peneplain of rivers such as the Fly and Sepik Rivers also support animal communities with a high ratio of decomposers since their faunas are derived from the riverine community. Crustaceans, in particular penaeid prawns in estuarine areas and carid prawns such as *Macrobrachium* in the less saline reaches of the deltas also form an important and widspread food resource for fishes (Haines 1979, 1983).

WATER POLLUTION AND ENVIRONMENTAL CONSERVATION

Papua New Guinea has a large land area of some 462,000 km^2 and a human population of only 3,900,000 (1990 census) although this is estimated to be growing at a rate of 2.7% per annum and 47% of the population is under 15 years of age. Consequently, the environment is relatively unspoilt and many natural habitats could still be conserved. This is particularly true of the larger areas of wetlands where the population density is very low (2-4 persons per km^2). However, the environment, in general, is coming under increasing pressure and aquatic ecosystems, in particular, in some parts of the country are being degraded through the disposal of mining, agricultural and urban wastes.

The enormous wetland system associated with the Fly and Strickland Rivers is of high conservation value, providing a refuge during drought years for waterfowl from Australia. More importantly, over 40,000 people are sustained by the natural resources of the Ok Tedi and Fly River. Consequently, the environmental impacts on these wetlands resulting from the construction and operation of the Ok Tedi and Porgera mines in the upper catchment of the Fly and Strickland Rivers respectively has been a cause for some concern (Pernetta 1988, Townsend 1988, Rosenbaum and Krockenberger 1993). The Ok Tedi gold and copper deposit is located at Mount Fublian in the far west of Papua New Guinea and the mine developed to extract the resource is now one of the largest in the world. Waste rock and tailings are currently dumped into the Ok Tedi, a tributary of the Fly River. Gold production commenced in May 1984 and copper production in March 1987. The gold circuit was closed in August 1988 and the mine now only produces copper. The impact of mine waste discharges has been characterized by increasing suspended solid levels and concomitant increases in dissolved and particulate trace metal levels, particularly copper (Salomons and Eagle 1990).

Biologists working for the mining company monitored fish populations at two sites in the Ok Tedi and one site in the Fly River (Smith and Hortle 1991, Smith and Morris 1992). They found that at the upstream site, catches were reduced to low levels shortly after mine operations commenced. In the lower Ok Tedi, there were distinct changes in the fish assemblage during the different phases of mine operation (Figure 13). At Kuambit, below the Ok Tedi-Fly River junction, mine contaminants were considerably diluted by the waters of the Fly River. The fish stocks at this site were also greater and

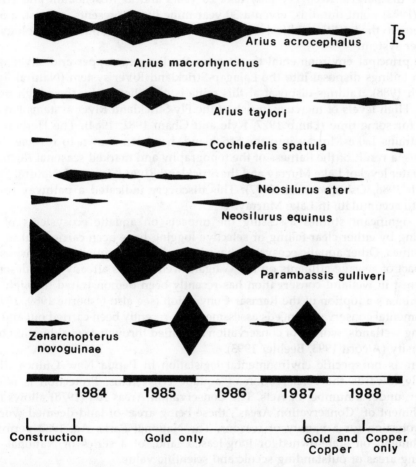

Figure 13. Kite diagrams of the numbers of the dominant fish species caught in the Ok Tedi at Ningerum, Papua New Guinea from 1983 to 1989. As shown in the time line, this sampling period overlapped with the construction and operation of the Ok Tedi mine in the upper catchment of the Ok Tedi. The scale bar indicates five fish. The following species were recorded before but not after the end of 1985: *Clupeoides papuensis*, *Cynoglossus heterolepis*, *Glossamia aprion*, *Glossamia trifasciata*, *Lutjanus goldei*, *Nedystoma dayi* and *Thryssa scratchleyi*. One individual each of *Megalops cyprinoides* and *Melanotaenia splendida* (on two occasions) were collected post 1986.

more diverse than those of the lower Ok Tedi. Consequently, changes in the fish assemblages have been more gradual with the exception of a dramatic reduction in herring (*Nematalosa* spp.) abundance. Smith and Morris (1992) attributed the reduction in herrings to very high levels of cyanide recorded on 13-14 October 1986 and a subsequent inability of the population to recover. Smith and Hortle (1991) predicted that the greatest impact of the mine will be felt between 1989 and 1993 following which catches should be close to 1988 levels for the remainder of the mine life. Recovery of the fishery following the cessation of mining will depend on the rate of erosion of accumulated mine wastes in the bed of the Ok Tedi and at the mine site and on the availability of recruits from fish stocks in water bodies less seriously affected by mine discharges. Recovery may take 20 years and as Rosenbaum and Krockenberger (1993) point out, this, given a 30 year mine life, represents, at least, a 50 year disruption to the traditional lifestyles of the local inhabitants and to the ecology of the Fly River system.

The principal environmental threat from the Porgera copper and silver mine is through tailings disposal into the Laiagap-Strickland River system (Natural Systems Research 1988). Tailings disposal at this mine is complicated by their high mercury content. High levels of mercury in fish of the Fly-Strickland River systems have been known for some time (Lamb 1977, Kyle and Ghani 1982, 1984). The Herbert River, which drains Lake Murray into the Strickland, has been shown to reverse flow on occasions, a result of the flatness of the topography and marked seasonal fluctuations in the water level of Lake Murray and the Strickland River (Figure 14, Natural Systems Research 1988, Osborne et al. 1987). This discovery indicated a pathway for mine wastes to accumulate in Lake Murray.

No significant studies assessing the impacts on aquatic ecosystems of forest harvesting by either clear-felling or selective logging have been carried out in Papua New Guinea. Other aquatic ecosystem have been affected through waste disposal and the impact of sewage effluents on the Waigani wetland has already been described.

Interest in wetland conservation has recently been demonstrated through Papua New Guinea's adoption of the Ramsar Convention (see also Osborne 1989, 1993). An environmental conservation needs assessment has recently been carried out and areas, including wetlands, worthy of conservation identified through a consideration of their biodiversity (Alcorn 1993, Beehler 1993).

There is no specific environmental legislation in Papua New Guinea directed primarily towards the conservation of aquatic ecosystems. Protection is afforded, however, under a number of Acts. The Conservation Areas Act (1978) allows for the establishment of "Conservation Areas", these being areas of land deemed worthy of legal protection for a variety of reasons. The National Parks Act 1982 permits the establishment, on state-owned or long-leased land, of a series of National Parks, protecting areas of outstanding scenic and scientific value.

The purpose of the Fauna (Protection and Control) Act 1974-1982 is to allow the systematic management, use and conservation of the fauna of Papua New Guinea. The International Trade in Endangered Species of Fauna and Flora Act (1979) controls the export and import of certain wildlife species among countries which are signatories to the international agreement.

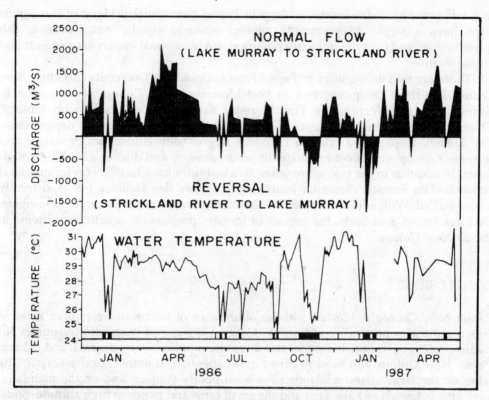

Figure 14. Figure showing flow reversal of the Herbert River which drains Lake Murray into the Strickland River. Periods of reversed flow (from the Stickland River to Lake Murray) were also detected through the lower temperatures of the Strickland River water (adapted from Natural Systems Research 1988).

Two Acts control the disposal of a wide range of pollutants which could be detrimental to the environment (Dumping of Wastes at Sea Act 1981 and Environmental Contaminants Act 1978). The Environmental Planning Act 1978 controls the exploitation of environmental resources, particularly with regard to the preparation of environmental impact assessments for projects which may have massive and long-term effects upon the quality of the environment.

The Water Resources Act can regulate land drainage, river/system channels (diversion and damming) and the disposal of wastes to land, swamps and water courses and bodies. It encompasses both fresh and saline waters to the territorial boundaries of Papua New Guinea. It is specifically designed for public water supply protection but could be used to include environmental conservation.

LIMNOLOGICAL RESEARCH AND EDUCATION

Limnological research (and, indeed, research and development in general) in Papua New Guinea has been severely hampered by the rugged topography, inadequate basic infrastructure and a lack of trained manpower. Osborne (1988) lists 174 publications in a bibliography of freshwater ecology in Papua New Guinea. Many of the papers cited have a strong bias towards applied ecology: aquatic weed control, fish introductions and fisheries, mercury pollution, environmental impact assessments and eutrophication.

There are two universities in Papua New Guinea. The University of Papua New Guinea has three campuses; two in Port Moresby and a College of Education in Goroka. The main campus in Port Moresby has a Science Faculty with Biology, Chemistry, Environmental Science, Geology, Mathematics and Physics departments. The Biology Department offers a four-year degree with courses in limnology and fisheries management. Post-graduate diplomas, masters and doctorates can be undertaken. In addition to the two universities, two institutes have facilities for limnological research. The Forestry Research Institute in Lae has fine facilities but is currently under-staffed. With additional staff, this Institute would be well-placed to investigate, on a catchment area basis, the impact of forestry projects on aquatic ecosystems in Papua New Guinea.

CONCLUSIONS

Papua New Guinea is blessed with an abundance of freshwater resources most of which remain in pristine condition. With increasing use of freshwater resources for hydro-power generation, industrial and domestic supplies, waste disposal and fishing, Papua New Guinea will need to direct more attention to limnological research. The lakes on the large offshore islands have been poorly studied, and on the mainland, very little is known of Lake Trist and the small tarns and ponds at high altitude. Some of the large rivers and wetlands, particularly those adjacent to the Gulf of Papua, are virtually unknown and our knowledge of lowland swamps forests and swamp savanna is restricted to an incomplete inventory of the plants and animals present in these areas.

There has been little coordination of limnological or, for that matter, other ecological research activity within Papua New Guinea. There are, however, notable exceptions. The comprehensive study of the Purari River Basin, coordinated by Petr (1983a), is one and the research funded by Papua New Guinea's largest resource developer (and, by some accounts, the country's biggest source of aquatic pollution), the Ok Tedi mine, has produced a significant amount of useful limnological information, both pure and applied, on the Fly River system. Similarly, research efforts into the control of *Salvinia molesta* and the assessment of the impact of further fish introductions have enhanced our knowledge of the limnology of the Sepik River and its floodplain. However, further basic and strategic research, and greater coordination of that research effort, is clearly needed. While a basic understanding of tropical aquatic ecosystems is highly desirable, research in Papua New Guinea should continue to be directed towards problem solving and environmental damage mitigation. Detailed monitoring programmes of rivers and lakes under threat from resource development projects need to be established and a thorough understanding of the impacts of mine and other wastes on tropical water bodies is required. Armed with this information, the impact of future development projects could be predicted with greater accuracy. Furthermore, waste disposal criteria which are environmentally-sound, relevant and applicable to aquatic ecosystems in tropical, high rainfall countries, such as Papua New Guinea, must be developed.

Current environmental protection legislation is adequate but funding to Government Departments charged with implementing the legislation is not. The capacity of the Government's Department of Environment and Conservation for ecological research, environmental monitoring, impact assessment and enforcement needs to be enhanced. A 'user-pays' policy is currently under consideration but assistance from developed countries is still needed and this should be in the form of trained man-power, training and financial support for both capital equipment and maintenance costs.

Visiting scientists have contributed an enormous amount to our knowledge and understanding of ecosystems in Papua New Guinea but this reliance on outside expert-ise is neither desirable nor cost-effective. This problem needs addressing in two ways. First, science education in Papua New Guinea needs to be expanded at all levels and its quality enhanced. Second, ecological research activity by Papua New Guinean ecologists must be facilitated through the provision of adequate resources. The activity of visiting scientists needs to be more carefully inter-woven with that of local scientists and with the country's goals and priorities.

Papua New Guinea is recognised as a significant area of high biodiversity (Alcorn 1993, Beehler 1993). Although biodiversity within freshwater systems in Papua New Guinea is not high, coastal and marine areas surrounding the country are among the most biodiverse ecosystems in the world. As these marine systems, particularly those near the mouths of large rivers, are significantly impacted by activity within adjacent watersheds, conservation of inland waters within Papua New Guinea assumes a grea-ter importance: not only for the provision of freshwater resources but also for the conservation of Papua New Guinea's marine resources. Papua New Guinea is in an enviable position with its wealth of natural resources, mostly pristine and diverse environments and relatively low human population. A commitment to natural resource conservation is enshrined in the national constitution and environmental awareness among Papua New Guineans is becoming increasingly apparent. Papua New Guinea is, therefore, well-placed to design and implement strategies for the conservation and sustainable development of its freshwater and other natural resources.

REFERENCES

Alcorn, J. 1993. Papua New Guinea Conservation Needs Assessment. Volume I. Department of Environment and Conservation, Waigani, Papua New Guinea. 216 pages.

Allen, G.R. 1991. Freshwater Fishes of New Guinea. Christensen Research Institute, Madang, Papua New Guinea. 268 pages.

Allen, G.R. and Boeseman, M. 1982. A collection of freshwater fishes from western New Guinea with descriptions of two new species (Gobiidae and Eleotridae). Records of the Western Australian Museum 10: 67-103.

Allen, G.R. and Cross, N.J. 1980. Descriptions of five new rainbow fishes (Melanotaeniidae) from New Guinea. Records of the Western Australian Museum 8: 377-396.

Allen, G.R. and Cross, N.J. 1982. Rainbowfishes of Australia and Papua New Guinea. T.F.H. Publications, New Jersey. 141 pages.

Allen, G.R. and Hoese, D.F. 1986. The eleotrid fishes of Lake Kutubu, Papua New Guinea with descriptions of four new species. Records of the Western Australian Museum 13: 79-100.

Ball, E. and Glucksman, J. 1975. Biological colonisation of Motmot, a recently created tropical island. Proceedings of the Royal Society of London Series B 190: 421-442.

Ball, E. and Glucksman, J. 1978. Limnological studies of Lake Wisdom, a large New Guinea caldera lake with a simple fauna. Freshwater Biology 8: 455-468.

Ball, E. and Glucksman, J. 1980. A limnological survey of Lake Dakataua, a large caldera lake on West New Britain, Papua New Guinea, with comparison to Lake Wisdom, a younger nearby caldera lake. Freshwater Biology 10: 73-84.

Bayly, I.E.A. and Morton, D.W. 1980. A note on zooplankton from four Papua New Guinea lakes (altitudinal range 538-3630 m). pp. 3-5, In: Petr, T. (Editor) Purari River (Wabo) Hydro-electric Scheme Environmental Studies, Vol. 11: Aquatic Ecology of the Purari River Catchment. Office of Environment and Conservation, Waigani, Papua New Guinea.

Bayly, I.E.A., Peterson, J. and St. John, V.P. 1970. Notes on Lake Kutubu, Southern Highlands of the Territory of Papua New Guinea. Bulletin of the Australian Limnological Society 3: 30-47.

Beehler, B. 1993. Papua New Guinea Conservation Needs Assessment. Volume II. Department of Environment and Conservation, Waigani, Papua New Guinea. 434 pages.

Benthem-Jutting, W.S.S. van. 1963. Non-marine molluscs of West New Britain, Part I, Mollusca from fresh and brackish waters. Nova Guinea, Zoology 20.

Berra, T.M., Moore, R. and Reynolds, L.F. 1975. The freshwater fishes of the Laloki River system of New Guinea. Copeia 1975: 316-326.

Burgin, S. 1980. The status of the biology and ecology of Papua New Guinea's crocodile, *Crocodylus novaeguineae* (Schmidt). Science in New Guinea 7: 163-171.

Burgin, S. 1981. The biology of *Crocodylus porosus* (Schneider). Science in New Guinea 8: 9-37.

Chambers, M.R. 1987. The freshwater lakes of Papua New Guinea: An inventory and limnological review. Journal of Tropical Ecology 3: 1-23.

Chambers, M.R. 1988. Dissolved oxygen, temperature and zooplankton studies of Lakes Bosset, Daviumbu and Pangua. pp. 19-30, In: Pernetta, J.C. (Editor), Potential Impacts of Mining on the Fly River. UNEP Regional Seas Reports and Studies No. 99; South Pacific Regional Environment Programme Topic Review 33.

Chambers, M.R., Kyle, J.H., Leach, G.J., Osborne, P.L. and Leach, D. 1987. A limnological study of seven highlands lakes in Papua New Guinea. Science in New Guinea 13: 51-81.

Coates, D. 1982. On the biological problems caused by the introduced water-weed *Salvinia molesta* Mitchell in the Sepik River. Regional Workshop on Limnology and Water Resource Management in Developing Countries of Asia and the Pacific, Kuala Lumpur.

Coates, D. 1983. Notes on the miscellaneous fish species from the Sepik River, roundwaters and floodplain. Report No. 83-20. Department of Primary Industry, Fisheries Research and Surveys Branch, Port Moresby, Papua New Guinea.

Coates, D. 1984a. The occurrence, spread and potential effects of common carp, *Cyprinus carpio* L., in the Sepik River. Report No. 84-13. Department of Primary Industry, Fisheries Research and Surveys Branch, Port Moresby, Papua New Guinea.

Coates, D. 1984b. The fisheries and fish fauna of the Sepik River System: Recommendations for species introductions. Report No. 84-10. Department of Primary Industry, Fisheries Research and Surveys Branch, Port Moresby, Papua New Guinea.

Coates, D. 1985. Fish yield estimates for the Sepik River, Papua New Guinea, a large floodplain system east of "Wallace's Line". Journal of Fish Biology 27: 431-443.

Coates, D. 1986. Fisheries development of the Sepik River, Papua New Guinea: Proposed fish introductions. pp. 367-370. In: Maclean, J.L., Dizon, L.B. and Hosillos, L.V. (Editors), The First Asian Fisheries Forum, Asian Fisheries Society, Manila, Philippines.

Coates. D. 1987a. On the biological problems caused by the introduced water weed *Salvinia molesta* Mitchell in the Sepik River, Papua New Guinea. Archiv für Hydrobiologie 28: 205-208.

Coates, D. 1987b. Consideration of fish introductions into the Sepik River, Papua New Guinea.

Aquaculture and Fisheries Management 18: 231-241.

Conn, B.J. 1979a. *Phragmites karka* and the floating islands at Lake Tebera (Gulf Province) with notes on the distribution of *Salvinia molesta* and *Eichhornia crassipes* in Papua New Guinea. pp. 31-36, In: Petr, T. (Editor), Purari River (Wabo) Hydroelectric Scheme Environmental Studies, Vol. 10: Ecology of the Purari River Catchment. Office of Environment and Conservation, Waigani, Papua New Guinea.

Conn, B.J. 1979b. Notes on the aquatic and semi-aquatic flora of Lake Kutubu (Southern Highlands Province), Papua New Guinea. pp. 63-90, In: Petr, T. (Editor), Purari River (Wabo) Hydroelectric Scheme Environmental Studies, Vol. 10: Ecology of the Purari River Catchment. Office of Environment and Conservation, Waigani, Papua New Guinea.

Conn, B.J. 1983. Aquatic and semi-aquatic flora of the Purari River System. pp. 283-293, In: Petr, T. (Editor), The Purari - Tropical Environment of a High Rainfall River Basin. Dr. W. Junk bv. Publishers, The Hague.

Dudgeon, D. 1990. Benthic community structure and the effects of rotenone piscicide on invertebrate drift and standing stocks in two Papua New Guinea streams. Archiv für Hydrobiologie 119: 35-53.

Fox, L. 1990. Geochemistry of dissolved phosphate in the Sepik River and Estuary, Papua New Guinea. Geochimica et Cosmochimica Acta 54: 1019-1024.

Glucksman, J., West, G. and Berra, T.M. 1976. The introduced fishes of Papua New Guinea with special reference to *Tilapia mossambica*. Biological Conservation 9: 37-44.

Gressitt, J.L. 1982. Biogeography and Ecology of New Guinea. Dr. W. Junk bv. Publishers, The Hague. 983 pages.

Haines, A.K. 1979. The subsistence fishery of the Purari Delta. Science in New Guinea 6: 80-95.

Haines, A.K. 1983. Fish fauna and ecology. pp. 367-384. In: Petr, T. (Editor), The Purari - Tropical Environment of a High Rainfall River Basin. Dr. W. Junk bv. Publishers, The Hague.

Holeman, J.N. 1968. The sediment yield of major rivers of the world. Water Resources Research 4: 737-747,

Holthuis, L.B. 1974. Notes on the localities, habitats, biology, colour and vernacular names of New Guinea freshwater crabs (Crustacea, Decapoda, Sundathelpusidae). Zoologische Verhandlungen 13: 3-47.

Holthuis, L.B. 1982. Freshwater Crustacea Decapoda of New Guinea. pp. 603-619. In: Gressitt, J.L. (Editor), Biogeography and Ecology of New Guinea. Dr. W. Junk bv. Publishers, The Hague.

Hutchinson, G.E. 1957. A Treatise on Limnology., Volume 1. Geography, Physics and Chemistry. Wiley and Sons, New York. 1015 pages.

Hutchinson, G.E. and Löffler, H. 1956. The thermal classification of lakes. Proceedings of the National Academy of Sciences, Washington 42: 84-86.

Jackson, R. (undated). Ok Tedi: The Pot of Gold. The University of Papua New Guinea Press, Port Moresby. 199 pages.

Kyle, J.H. and Ghani, N. 1982. Methylmercury in ten species of fish from Lake Murray. Science in New Guinea 9: 48-59.

Kyle, J.H. and Ghani, N. 1984. Mercury in barramundi (*Lates calcarifer*) from the Gulf of Papua. Science in New Guinea 11: 105-113.

Lamb, K.P. 1977. Mercury levels in nine species of fish from the Ok Tedi and upper Fly River. Science in New Guinea 5: 7-11.

Leach, G.J. and Osborne, P.L. 1985. Freshwater Plants of Papua New Guinea. University of Papua New Guinea Press, Port Moresby. 254 pages.

Löffler, E. 1977. Geomorphology of Papua New Guinea. Australian National University Press, Canberra. 195 pages.

Löffler, H. 1973. Tropical high mountain lakes of New Guinea and their zoogeographical relationship compared with other tropical high mountain lakes. Arctic and Alpine Research 5: 193-198.

McAlpine J,R., Keig, G. and Falls, R. 1983. Climate of Papua New Guinea. CSIRO and Australian National University Press, Canberra. 200 pages.

McKenzie, K.G. 1956. Notes on the freshwater mussels of New Guinea. Nautilis 70: 38-48.

McKenzie, K.G. 1971. Ostracoda from Lake Piunde, near Mt Wilhelm, New Guinea. Zoologische Anzeiger 186: 391-403.

McMichael, D.F. and Hiscock, I.D. 1958. Monograph of the freshwater mussels (Mollusca: Pelecypoda) of the Australian Region. Australian Journal of Marine and Freshwater Research 9: 372-508.

Maunsell and Partners. 1982. Ok Tedi Environmental Study. Vols.1-6. Ok Tedi-Fly River Aquatic Survey. Ok Tedi Mining Limited, Port Moresby, Papua New Guinea.

Milliman, J.D. and Meade, R.H. 1983. World-wide delivery of river sediments to the oceans. Journal of Geology 91: 1-21.

Mitchell, D.S. 1978/1979. Aquatic weeds in Papua New Guinea. Science in New Guinea 6: 154-160.

Mitchell, D.S., Petr, T. and Viner, A.B. 1980. The water fern *Salvinia molesta* in the Sepik River, Papua New Guinea. Environmental Conservation 7: 115-122.

Moore, R. 1982. Spawning and early life history of barramundi, *Lates calcarifer* (Bloch) in Papua New Guinea. Australian Journal of Marine and Freshwater Research 33: 647-661.

Moore, R. and Reynolds, L.F. 1982. Migration pattern of barramundi, *Lates calcarifer* (Bloch) in Papua New Guinea. Australian Journal of Marine and Freshwater Research 33: 671-682.

Mowbray, D.L. 1988a. Assessment of the biological impact of Ok Tedi mine tailings, cyanide and heavy metals through toxicity testing. pp. 45-74, In: Pernetta, J.C. (Editor), Potential Impacts of Mining on the Fly River. UNEP Regional Seas Reports and Studies 99 and South Pacific Regional Environment Programme Topic Review 33, UNEP, Nairobi.

Mowbray, D.L. 1988b. Evaluation of the Ok Tedi mine environmental monitoring programme, and the impact of tailings derived heavy metal residues in the Ok Tedi and Fly River system, 1981-1985. pp. 75-98, In: Pernetta, J.C. (Editor), Potential Impacts of Mining on the Fly River. UNEP Regional Seas Reports and Studies 99 and South Pacific Regional Environment Programme Topic Review 33, UNEP, Nairobi.

Munro, I.S.R. 1967. The Fishes of New Guinea. Department of Agriculture, Stock and Fisheries, Port Moresby, Papua New Guinea. 650 pages.

Natural Systems Research. 1988. Porgera Gold Project Environmental Plan, Volumes A, B and C. Porgera Joint Venture, Report CR 257/13.

Niell, W.T. 1946. Notes on *Crocodylus novae-guineae*. Copeia 1: 17-20.

Ok Tedi Mining Limited. 1993. Fly River flood-plain copper monitor (Addendum to the APL Compliance and Additional Monitoring Programme: 1993 Annual Report). Ok Tedi Mining Limited Report No. ENV 93-06, Tabubil, Papua New Guinea.

Osborne, P.L. 1988. Bibliography of Freshwater Ecology in Papua New Guinea. Biology Department Occasional Paper 9, University of Papua New Guinea. 65 pages.

Osborne, P.L. 1989. Papua New Guinea. Introduction. pp. 1111-1119. In: Scott, D.A. (Editor), A Directory of Asian Wetlands. IUCN, Gland, Switzerland and Cambridge.

Osborne, P.L. 1991. Sesonality in nutrients and phytoplankton production in two shallow lakes: Waigani Lake, Papua New Guinea and Barton Broad, Norfolk, England. Internationale Revue der gesamten Hydrobiologie 76: 105-120.

Osborne, P.L. 1993. Wetlands of Papua New Guinea. pp. 305-344, In: Whigham, D.F., Hejny, S., and Dykyjova, D. (Editors), Wetlands of the World I: Inventory, Ecology and Management. Handbook of Vegetation Sciences 15. Dr. W. Junk bv. Publishers, The Hague.

Osborne, P.L., Kyle, J.H. and Abramski, M. 1987. Effects of seasonal water level changes on the chemical and biological limnology of Lake Murray, Papua New Guinea. Australian Journal of Marine and Freshwater Research 38: 397-408.

Osborne, P.L. and Leach, G. 1983. Changes in the distribution of aquatic plants in a tropical swamp. Environmental Conservation 10: 323-329.

Osborne, P.L. and Leach, G. 1984. The spread of water hyacinth in Papua New Guinea - a second warning or is it too late? Harvest 10: 51-53.

Osborne, P.L. and Polunin, N.V.C. 1986. From swamp to lake: Recent changes in a lowland tropical swamp. Journal of Ecology 74: 197-210.

Osborne, P.L. and Polunin, N.V.C. 1988. Progress in elucidating the sediment record of two shallow lakes in Papua New Guinea. pp. 31-37, In: Pernetta, J.C. (Editor), Potential Impacts of Mining on the Fly River. UNEP Regional Seas Reports and Studies 99 and South Pacific Regional Environment Programme Topic Review 33, UNEP, Nairobi.

Osborne, P.L., Polunin, N.V.C. and Nicholson, K. 1988. Geochemical traces of riverine influence on a tropical lateral lake. Verhandlungen der internationale Vereinigung der theoretische und angewandte Limnologie 23: 207-211.

Osborne, P.L. and Totome, R.G. 1991. Sediment deposition in Lake Kutubu. Verhandlungen der internationale Vereinigung der theoretische und angewandte Limnologie 24: 3018-3021.

Osborne, P.L. and Totome, R.G. 1992a. Influences of oligomixis on the water and sediment chemistry of Lake Kutubu, Papua New Guinea. Archiv für Hydrobiologie 124: 427-449.

Osborne, P.L. and Totome, R.G. 1992b. Long-term impacts of sewage effluent disposal on a tropical wetland. Proceedings AWWA-IAWQ Conference on Wetland Systems and Water Pollution Control, pp. 29.1-29.8.

Osborne, P.L., Totome, R.G., Gwyther, D. and NSR Environmental Consultants. 1990. Lake Kutubu investigation. Kutubu Petroleum Development Project Environmental Plan, Technical Support Document, Report 2. NSR Environmental Consultants, Pty Ltd., Melbourne, Australia.

Pernetta, J.C. 1988. The Ok Tedi mine: environment, development and pollution. pp. 1-8. In: Pernetta, J.C. (Editor), Potential Impacts of Mining on the Fly River, UNEP Regional Seas Reports and Studies 99 and South Pacific Regional Environment Programme Topic Review 33, UNEP, Nairobi.

Pernetta, J.C. and Burgin, S. 1983. The status of crocodiles in the Purari. pp. 409-414. Petr, T. (Editor), The Purari - Tropical Environment of a High Rainfall River Basin. Dr. W. Junk bv. Publishers, The Hague.

Petr, T. 1979. Mercury in the Papua New Guinea environment. Science in New Guinea 6: 161-176.

Petr, T. 1983a. The Purari - Tropical Environment of a High Rainfall River Basin. Dr. W. Junk bv. Publishers, The Hague. 624 pages.

Petr, T. 1983b. Limnology of the Purari basin. Part 1. The catchment above the delta. pp. 141-177, In: Petr, T. (Editor) The Purari - Tropical Environment of a High Rainfall River Basin. Dr. W. Junk bv. Publishers, The Hague.

Petr, T. 1983c. Limnology of the Purari basin. Part 2. The delta. pp. 179-203, In: T. Petr (Editor), The Purari - Tropical Environment of a High Rainfall River Basin. Dr. W. Junk bv. Publishers, The Hague.

Petr, T. 1984. Technical report on the possibilities of Sepik River fish stock enhancement. FAO Fisheries Travel Report 2505, FAO, Rome.

Pickup, G. 1983. Sedimentation processes in the Purari River upstream of the delta. pp. 205-225, In: Petr, T. (Editor), The Purari - Tropical Environment of a High Rainfall River Basin. Dr. W. Junk bv. Publishers, The Hague.

Pickup, G., Higgins, R.J. and Warner, R.J. 1981. Erosion and sediment yield in Fly River drainage basins, Papua New Guinea. pp. 438-456. In: Davies, T.R. and Pearce, A.J. (Editors), Erosion and Sediment Transport in Pacific Rim Steeplands. International Association of Hydrological Sciences Publication 132, Canberra.

Polunin, N.V.C., Osborne, P.L. and Totome, R.G. 1988. Environmental archive: Tropical urban development reflected in the sediment geochemistry of a flood-plain lake. Archiv für Hydrobiologie 114: 199-211.

Reynolds, L.F. and Moore, R. 1982. Growth rates of barramundi, *Lates calcarifer* (Bloch) in Papua

New Guinea. Australian Journal of Marine and Freshwater Research 33: 663-670.

Richardson, L.R. 1977. The zoological importance of the freshwater leeches of the Papuan subregion. Science in New Guinea 5: 115-120.

Robertson, C.H. 1983. Aspects of the biology of various *Macrobrachium* species found in the Sepik River. Report 83-05. Fisheries Research and Surveys Branch, Department of Primary Industry, Port Moresby.

Robertson, C.H. and Baidam, G. 1983. Fishes of the Ok Tedi area with notes on five common species. Science in New Guinea 10: 16-27.

Room, P.M. and Thomas, P.A. 1985. Nitrogen and establishment of a beetle for biological control of the floating weed *Salvinia* in Papua New Guinea. Journal of Applied Ecology 22: 139-156.

Room, P.M. and Thomas, P.A. 1986a. Nitrogen, phosphorus and potassium in *Salvinia molesta* in the field: effects of weather, insect damage, fertilizer and age. Aquatic Botany 24: 213-232.

Room, P.M. and Thomas, P.A. 1986b. Population growth of a floating weed *Salvinia molesta*. Field observations and a global model based on temperature and nitrogen. Journal of Applied Ecology 23: 1013-1028.

Rosenbaum, H. and Krockenberger, M. 1993. Report on the Impacts of the Ok Tedi Mine in Papua New Guinea. Australian Conservation Foundation, Fitzroy, Australia. 48 pages.

Ruxton, B.P. 1971. Slopewash under mature primary rainforest in northern Papua. pp. 85-94, In: Jennings, J.N. and Mabbutt, J.A. (Editors), Landform studies from Australia and New Guinea. Australian National University Press, Canberra.

Salomons, W. and Eagle, A.M. 1990. Hydrology sedimentology and the fate and distribution of copper in mine-related discharges in the Fly River system, Papua New Guinea. Science of the Total Environment 97/98: 315-334.

Smith, R.E.W. and Hortle, K.G. 1991. Assessment and predictions of the impacts of the Ok Tedi copper mine on fish catches in the Fly River system, Papua New Guinea. Environmental Monitoring and Assessment 18: 41-68.

Smith, R.E.W. and Morris, T.F. 1992. The impacts of changing geochemistry on the fish assemblages of the Lower Ok Tedi and Middle Fly River, Papua New Guinea. The Science of the Total Environment 125: 321-344.

Sorentino, C. 1979. Mercury in marine and freshwater fish of Papua New Guinea. Australian Journal of Marine and Freshwater Research 30: 617-623.

Specht, J., Ball, E.E., Blong, R.J., Egloff, I.M., Hughes, H., McKee, C.O. and Pain, C.F. 1982. Long Island, Papua New Guinea: Introduction. Records of the Australian Museum 34: 407-417.

Thomas, P.A. 1979. Proposals for the Management of *Salvinia molesta* in Papua New Guinea. Port Moresby: FAO Report to the Department of Primary Industry. 56 pages.

Thomas, P.A. 1985. The management of *Salvinia molesta* in Papua New Guinea. FAO Plant Protection Bulletin 32: 50-56.

Thomas, P.A. and Room, P.M. 1986. Successful control of the floating weed *Salvinia molesta* in Papua New Guinea: A useful biological invasion neutralises a disastrous one. Environmental Conservation 13: 242-248.

Thomasson, K. 1967. Phytoplankton from some lakes on Mt Wilhelm, East New Guinea. Blumea 15: 285-296.

Townsend, B. 1988. Giving away the river: environmental issues in the construction of the Ok Tedi mine, 1981-84. pp. 101-119. In: Pernetta, J.C. (Editor), Potential Impacts of Mining on the Fly River. UNEP Regional Seas Reports and Studies 99 and South Pacific Regional Environment Programme Topic Review 33, UNEP, Nairobi.

Turvey, N.D. 1974. Water quality in a tropical rain forested catchment. Journal of Hydrology 27: 111-125.

Viner, A.B. 1979. The status and transport of nutrients through the Purari River (Papua New Guinea). In: Viner, A.B. (Editor), Purari River (Wabo) Hydroelectric Scheme Environmental Studies, Vol. 9. Office of the Environment and Conservation, Waigani, Papua New Guinea. 52 pages.

Vyvermann, W. 1989. Desmids (Zygnemaphyceae, Desmidales) from Mount Giluwe (Southern Highlands Province, Papua New Guinea). Nova Hedwigia 48: 317-339.

Vyvermann, W. 1990. Desmids and diatoms from Papua New Guinea. Systematics, ecology and biogeography. Ph.D. Thesis, University of Gent. 425 pages.

Vyvermann, W. 1991. Desmids from Papua New Guinea. Bibliotheca Phycologia 87. 200 pages.

Vyvermann, W. (in press). Freshwater algae from the Sepik floodplain (Papua New Guinea). Bulletin of the Belgian Royal Society of Botany.

Watanabe, M., Prescott, G.W. and Yamagishi, T. 1979a. Freshwater algae of Papua New Guinea (2). Desmids from Woitape, Central District. pp. 49-66, In: Kurokawa, S. (Editor) Studies on Cryptogams of Papua New Guinea. Academia Scientific Book Inc., Tokyo.

Watanabe, M., Prescott, G.W. and Yamagishi, T. 1979b. Freshwater algae of Papua New Guinea (3). Blue-green algae from Mt Wilhelm. pp. 67-85, In: Kurokawa, S. (Editor) Studies on Cryptogams of Papua New Guinea. Academia Scientific Book Inc., Tokyo.

Welcomme, R.L. 1985. River Fisheries. FAO Fisheries Technical Report 262, 330 pages. F.A.O., Rome.

West, G.J. and Glucksman, J. 1976. Introduction and distribution of exotic fish in Papua New Guinea. Papua New Guinea Agricultural Journal 27: 19-48.

Yamagishi, T. 1975. The plankton algae from Papua New Guinea. pp. 43-74. In: Otani, Y. (Editor), Reports on the Cryptogams in Papua New Guinea. National Science Museum, Tokyo.

Yamagishi, T. and Watanabe, M. 1979. Freshwater algae of Papua New Guinea (1). On some filamentous green-algae. pp. 19-48, In: Kurokawa, S. (Editor) Studies on Cryptogams of Papua New Guinea. Academia Scientific Book Inc., Tokyo.

Gopal, B. and Wetzel, R.G. (Editors) **Limnology in Developing Countries**: 163-189
© 1995, International Association for Limnology

Status of Limnological Research and Training in Malaysia

Sino-Chye Ho

School of Biological Sciences, Universiti Sains Malaysia, 11800 Penang, Malaysia

ABSTRACT

Limnological research and training Malaysia have progressed steadily in the last 15 (post IBP/PF) years from the efforts of an increasing number of trained limnologists and scientists of related fields in the local universities, government departments (e.g. Department of Environment, Government Chemistry Department, Drainage and Irrigation Department, State Water Authorities), research centres (e.g. Freshwater Fish Research Centre). Non-governmental organizations (e.g. Malayan Nature Society Asian Wetland Bureau) and the private sector (e.g. hydro-engineering firms) do play an active supporting role also in this respect.

The main driving force has been the pace of implementation of Malaysia's own long-term socio-economic and urban development plans which require a thorough inventorying and optimal utilization of its limited freshwater resources. Malaysian limnololgists have been jointly involved in the search for solutions related to water resource protection and formulation of environmental conservation strategies and methods. The latter is prodded by Malaysia's Environmental Quality Act (1974) with its inherent Environmental Impact Assessment Regulation (1985).

The current trend is towards organized, multi-disciplinary, applied studies at the watershed or ecosystem level. This is made possible by the enhancement of research and training infrastructure at the universities and research institutions which still serve as the main repositories and sources of trained man-power, aquatic biologists in general and limnologists in particular. There has been regular review and introduction of new courses to the teaching curricula to reflect the awareness of man-power needs and changing perspective of the importance of the country's finite aquatic resources and fragile environment.

Funding opportunities coming both from the government and private sector have been encouraging in recent years. Local initiatives have made possible the extra financial, technological and human resources inputs from collaborating countries like Japan (JSPS, JICA), Canada (IDRC), Europe (ASEAN-EEC), Australia (ASEAN-AUSTRALIA), United Kingdom (Royal Society of United Kingdom), WHO and UNESCO.

There is as yet no national body for coordinating limnological research and training. A national journal of limnology likewise does not exist.

Regional institutional linkages through post-graduate studies, exchange of research or academic staff, library exchange services and fellowship offers amongst developing countries are deemed beneficial, timely and as such should be promoted and sustained.

INTRODUCTION

In the first SIL workshop for the promotion of limnology in developing countries held in August 1980 at Kyoto, Japan, Furtado (1980), Ho (1980a) and Lim (1980a) presented a composite picture of the status of limnological research and training with reference to natural and man-made aquatic ecosystems as observed then in Malaysia.

This paper appraises the state of limnological development in Malaysia with particular emphasis on the last 15 post-IBP/PF years. The report is compiled based on a survey of available literature, information feedback from colleagues in the various Malaysian institutions involved with limnological or at least freshwater biological research and/or training, and also on my personal experience and observations.

GEOCLIMATIC FEATURES OF MALAYSIA

Geographic Location

Malaysia lies just above the equator, between latitudes 0° 60' and 6° 40' North, longitudes 99° 45' to 119° 25' East. The country is a federation of thirteen States, eleven of which are located on southeast Asia's southernmost peninsula, south of the Kra Isthmus, occupying a land area of 131,235 km². The remaining two States of Sabah (76,115 km²) and Sarawak (124,499 km²) are located on the north and north-western parts of the Borneo island mass. The 11 States of the so-called West or Peninsular Malaysia are separated geographically from the 2 States of East Malaysia by about 500 km of the South China Sea.

Climate and Rainfall

Proximity to the equator has given Malaysia a climate of high humidity (mean: 80%), high temperature (annual mean: 26.7°C) and abundant rainfall (2000-5000 mm). There is very little variation in day length which averages to that atleast 8 hours of intense sunshine per day. The diurnal temperature range is 8.9°C. For every 100-m increase in altitude, the air temperature drops by roughly 0.6°C. Freezing point is reached only rarely, and this too only at the highest spot in Malaysia, namely on the peak of Mount Kinabalu (4,102 m) in Sabah.

The equatorial climate is modified by the region's insularity and exposure to a monsoonal wind system that originates in the Indian Ocean and the South China sea. Precipitation cycles are linked to the monsoon seasons (Figure 1). The northeast and southwest monsoons divide the year into two periods. The northeast monsoon begins in October/November and ends by February/March. The southwest monsoon blows from mid-April/May to September/mid-October. In between these are the two inter-monsoonal periods, each lasting generally about eight weeks. There are no prevailing winds during the inter-monsoonal periods but daily convectional rain is abundant. The country experiences between 150-200 rain-days per year. Rainfall of the heaviest intensities occurs during the inter-monsoon periods.

The northeast monsoon period brings the greatest amount of rain as a whole. The average rainfall in peninsular Malaysia is about 2500 mm a year. Its east coast receives an average of 4000 mm per year. Maxwell Hills near Taiping receives 5000 mm while the Jelebu district which is sheltered from both monsoons, receives 1650 mm per year. A large area of Sarawak gets about 3000-5000 mm of rain per year while Sabah receives about 1600-4500 mm of rain per year. In spite of the high average rainfall, the total water resources of Malaysia are only moderate due to the high potential evaporation. In fact, drought does occur in certain areas of the country owing to wide spatial and temporal variations in rainfall. Malaysia lies outside the belt of tropical cyclones (e.g. typhoons) and tornadoes.

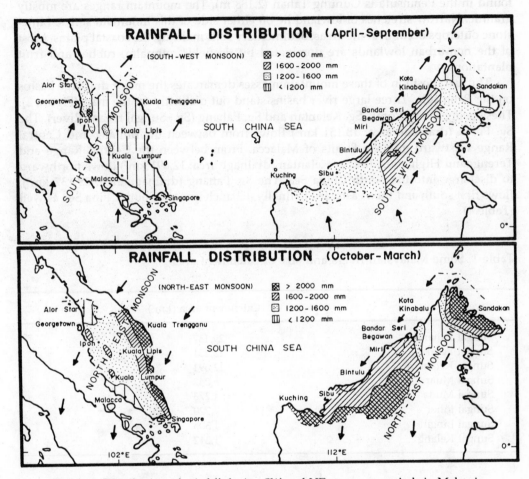

Figure 1. Distribution of rainfall during SW and NE monsoon periods in Malaysia

Relief and Drainage

About 18.5 million hectares (56.3%) of Malaysia's 32.9 million hectares of land area are covered with forests.

Peninsular Malaysia

The topography of Peninsular Malaysia is dominated by two mountain ranges, namely the Main Range and the Bintang Range. The Main Range is aligned just out of line with the longitudinal axis of the peninsula. It extends from near the Thai border in the mid north to as far south as Tampin in Negri Sembilan. North-west of the Main Range is the Bintang Range which extends from the Thai border to the Taiping area. East of the Main Range are the highland areas of Kelantan and Terengganu. The highest peak found in the Peninsula is Gunung Tahan (2,188 m). The mountain ranges are mostly granitic. Narrow stretches of lowland lie on either side of this mountain series. Limestone outcrops occur in some areas. Sedimentary soils make up the coastal plains. Most of the non-urban lowlands are dominated by ricefields, oil-palm, rubber and fruit plantations.

The juxtaposition of these mountain masses demarcates the major drainage basins on the Peninsula. Three large river basins stand out distinctly on the map (Figure 2). These being the Sg.Porak, Sg. Kelantan and Sg. Pahang (Sg.=Sungai means River). The Sg. Perak (drainage area: 15,151 km²) flows from between the Bintang and Central Range westward into the Straits of Malacca. From between the Central Range and Terengganu Highlands, the Sg. Kelantan (drainage area: 12,691 km²) flows northward to discharge into the South China Sea. The Sg. Pahang (drainage area: 29,137 km²), flows first south and then eastward to finally debauch into the South China Sea as well (Table 1).

Table 1. Some Malaysian rivers and size of catchment area

River	Catchment area (km²)
Sungai Pahang	29,137
Sungai Perak	15,151
Sungai Kelantan	12,691
Sungai Muar	6,062
Sungai Muda	4,273
Sungai Johor	2,720
Sungai Lingii	1,306
Sungai Kelang	1,212

High rainfall contributes greatly to the unceasing flow of fresh water in the fluvial system within most watersheds. The rivers are generally narrow and swift in their upper courses. In the lower reaches, their descent to the coastal plain is gradual. On the west coast the lower courses of the rivers sometimes flow through swampy land. On the east coast, their entry into the sea is sometimes impeded by coastal sand bars. An account of the limnology of lowland streams in West Malaysia has been given by Ho and Furtado (1982).

Most rivers and streams flood more or less regularly during the northeast monsoon season especially on the east coast. Sg. Pahand floods annually. The tendency for floods is aggravated by human activities such as logging and mining which disrupt the equilibrium of the hill forest ecosystem as well as the natural hydrological regimes of rivers.

Sabah and Sarawak

East Malaysia is traversed by relatively dissected high-lands, with peaks generally less than 1,800 m in height. An exception is Mount Kinabalu in Sabah, which towers over all others with a height of 4,102 m thus making it Malaysia's highest peak. The Crocker Range in Sabah which culminates in Mount Kinabalu is the only fairly continuous mountain range. Mount Murud (2,438 m) is the highest mountain in Sarawak. Much of the interior of Sarawak is forested and relatively undeveloped. Interspersed among the mountain ranges are the lowlands.

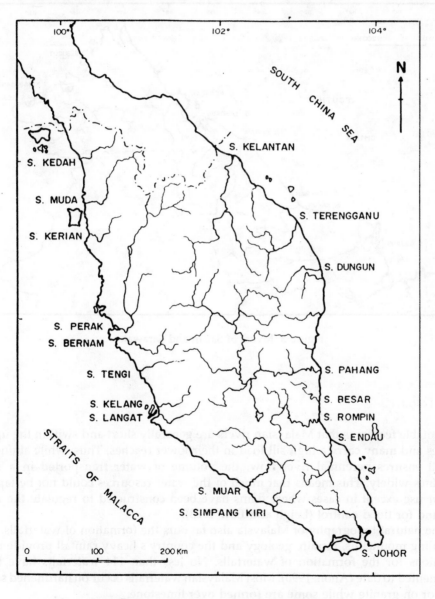

Figure 2. Rivers of Peninsular Malaysia

An alluvial plain runs northeast-southwest all along the coasts of Sarawak and western Sabah. This low lying coastal land varies in width from less than one to tens of kilometers. It is interrupted in a few areas by encroaching cliffs of low mountains. Coastal swamps are less extensive in Sabah than in Sarawak. The Sabah coastline is transected by about 37 rivers and several large estuaries many of which are swift flowing and laden with silt. Sarawak is drained by about 20 rivers of various sizes. The generally flow north-east into the South China Sea (Figure 3).

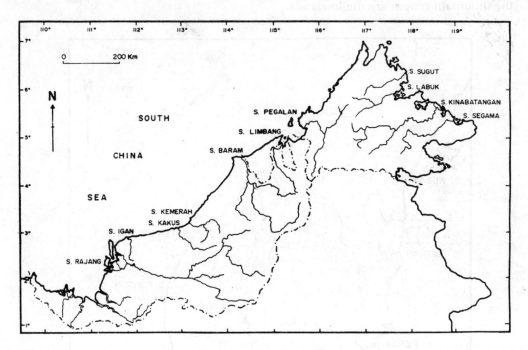

Figure 3. Rivers of Sabah and Sarawak

Other Features

One notable feature is that Malaysian rivers are generally short and swift in the upper reaches and many carry a high silt load in their lower reaches. Thus, while abundant rainfall ensures perennial river flow, the volume of water transported in a river fluctuates widely. This means that much of the water resources could not be tapped for our use except in cases where dams have been constructed to regulate the river flow and for flood control (Leigh and Low 1973).

The natural topography of Malaysia also favours the formation of waterfalls. The prevailing mountains, terrain, geology and the country's heavy rainfall provide ideal conditions for the formation of waterfalls. No less than 114 waterfalls have been documented to date (Anon. 1990). Most Malaysian waterfalls occur on hardnened sand-stone or on granite while some are formed over limestone.

Malaysia has very few natural lakes. The two better known freshwater swamp lakes, namely Tasek Bera and Tasek Cini are located in Pahang and have drainage linkage with the Pahang River. Tasek Bera was the subject of extensive limnological study under IBP/PF Programme (Furtado and Mori 1982). Another example is the Ulu Lepar river-lake wetland ecosystem also in Pahang (see Nather Khan 1990a).

As far as impoundments are concerned, there are 51 man-made dams in Malaysia, of which 46 are located in Peninsular Malaysia, 3 in Sabah and 2 in Sarawak (Figure 4). These range in water surface areas from 10 ha (Mahang Dam, Pahang) to 37,000 ha (Kenyir Dam, Terengganu) (Table 2). The oldest being the Bukit Merah Reservoir (3,500 ha) in Perak which was built in 1906. A few more new dams will be built in the next few years to meet projected water demand of the country. Among the roles intended of these dams are hydro-electric power generation, irrigation, drinking water supply, river flow regulation, flood mitigation, inland water fisheries development and of late the added roles of recreational and tourist promotion. The total reservoir area in Peninsular Malaysia has been estimated to be about 80,000 ha. It is estimated that by the year 2000, this figure could escalate to· 206,000 ha owing to the demand for irrigation and hydropower dams.

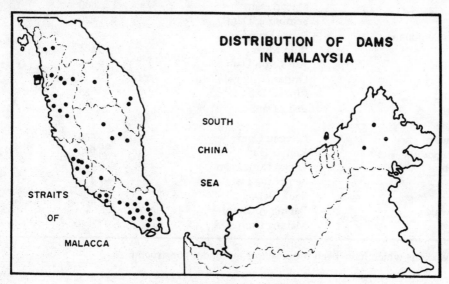

Figure 4. Distribution of dams in Malaysia

Natural Vegetaion

The natural vegetation of Malaysia is tropical rainforest. Lowland dipterocarp forest occupy areas below 300 m, hill dipterocarp forest dominate between 300 m and 1300 m, and montane forest above this. Many of the hill forests are located in water catchment areas. Peat swamp and freshwater swamp forests occupy lowlying areas. Mangrove forests are found fringing estuaries and coastal mudflats.

Forests play an important role in the hydrological cycle and in maintaining the water balance of watersheds. In Malyasia, forested land has 38% water retainibility, whereas rubber estate has 27% and oil palm estate 16 percent.

Table 2. Partial list of dams in Malaysia

State	Dam	Water Surface Area (ha)
Perlis	* Timah Tasun Dam	1,330
Penang	Air Itam Dam	
Perak	Bukit Merah Dam	3,500
	Cenderoh Dam	2,500
	Jor Dam	20
	Kenering Dam	-
	Mahang Dam	10
	* Taiping Dam	70
	Temenggor Dam	15,200
Federal Territory	Klang Gates Dam	
Selangor	Semeyih Dam	350
	Subang Dam	10,455
Johore	* Linggiu Dam	5,600
	Macap Dam	800
	Sembrong Dam	820
Negri Sembilan	Pedas Dam	-
	*Ulu Muar	7605
Malacca	Air Keroh Dam	-
	Durian Tunggal Dam	-
Pahang	Ringlet Dam	55
Kedah	Pedu Dam	6,400
Muda	-	
Kelantan	*Pergau Dam	430
Terengganu	Kenyir Dam	37,000
Sabah	Lahad Datu Dam	-
	Semporna Dam	-
	Sook Dam	-
Sarawak	Batang Ai Dam	-
	Matang Dam	-

* New dams which have been proposed or are under construction.

FRESHWATER RESOURCES

Freshwater Supply and Demand

The average annual rainfall for the country is 990×10^9 mega-litres (ML). Out of this, 360×10^9 ML return to the atmosphere as evapotranspiration, 64×10^3 ML to recharge ground water and the remaining 566×10^3 ML appear as surface runoff. Rivers and other forms of surface water supply about 97% of the country's total water needs while ground water accounts for the remaining 3 percent. However, in some States like Perlis and Kelantan, ground water contributes significantly (30-70%) to the State's water budget. A study conducted in 1989 found that 43% of the treated water is wasted through leakage caused by factors like water pipe deterioration, inferior materials and workmanship, earth movement, excessive pressure, irresponsible public usage and water theft.

The present annual domestic, industrial and irrigation water demand is about 11.6 x 10^9 ML and is projected to increase to 15.2 x 10^9 ML by the year 2000. The toal water demand in the country is about 4,979 megalitres per day (ML d^{-1}) while the total production capacity is 6,513 ML d^{-1} (Table 3). Although these figures show that there is an excess capacity, yet the fact remains that there are still areas experiencing water

Table 3. Water supply situation in Malaysia

Water Resource	Peninsular Malaysia	Sabah	Sarawak
Storage capacity (ML d^{-1})			
1990	5,758	367	388
1995	9,417	-	709
Water Demand (ML d^{-1})			
1990	4,334	363	282
1995	7,254	-	433

shortage owing to geographical barriers and factors related hydrologic cycle disruption in the affected watersheds. The current water shortage crisis in Malacca and the Muda area are two cases in point. In the case of the former, the situation has reached such a critical stage that the Government is resorting to multi-million dollar cloud seeding venture involving foreign expertise to try to overcome the acute water shortage problem. Attempts are now being made to promote inter-basin and inter-state water transfer. This approach may become the prominent form of water resource development in the future with the Malaysian government itself playing an increasing role. The country's water works engineers have called for the setting up of a central body with statutory duties and powers to develop and manage water in the country. At present, water supply comes under the jurisdiction of the States in accordance with provisions stipulated in the Federal Constitution.

The National Water Resources Study carried out in 1982 by a team of consultants from Japan International Cooperation Agency (JICA) produced a master plan for up to year 2000. The Malaysian Government updates this plan from time to time to meet the anticipated demand on water resources beyond year 2000.

Water Use and Misuse

Water use in Malaysia can be categorised as domestic water supply, industrial water supply, agricultural irrigation, supply to livestock and wildlife, recreation and aesthetics, hydropower generation, navigation (transportation), waste disposal, flood mitigation, and prevention of seawater intrusion.

In Malaysia today, development on all fronts is occurring at a rapid pace in order to achieve the targeted socio-economic objectives. This has inevitably resulted in adverse changes in the natural environment. Foremost among these are the impacts on the hydrology and ecology of Malaysian river ecosystems. The Department of Environment (DOE) has ascertained that a total of 42 rivers in the country is biologically dead. Some of these rivers are listed in Table 4. The main pollutants are domestic garbage, animal farm wastes, raw sewage, limestone quarry sludge, untreated or poorly treated chemical and/or organic wastes from palm-oil, rubber and wood-based industries.

Table 4. Partial list of seriously polluted rivers

Sg. Cuping, Perlis	Sg. Pinang, Penang
Sg. Juru, Penang	Sg. Raja Hitam, Perak
Sg. Sepetang, Perak	Sg. Perak, Perak
Sg. Kinta, Perak	Sg. Semagagah, Perak
Sg. Tumboh, Perak	Sg. Klang, Muala Lumpur
Sg. Sepang, Selangor	Sg. Batang Benar, N. Sembilan
Sg. Malacca, Malacca	Sg. Seriong, Johor
Sg. Sarawak, Sarawak	

River otters, swimming ducks, fishes, prawns, crabs and other riverine wildlife are now a thing of the past in these rivers. About 65,000 kg of garbage is estimated to be dumped daily into the Sungai Kelang (Selangor). About 45 pollutants are known to enter the Sungai Pinang (Penang). According to the Ministry of Agriculture, Malaysia has 52 freshwater fish species which are of commercial importance. It has been reported that the Sungai Gombak (Selangor) has over the last 20 years lost about 60% of its indigenous fish species which once totalled up to 27 species. The reasons cited were excessive land clearing activities in the watershed area resulting in river bank erosion and severe silt pollution. The Sg. Perak has lost 6 out of the 9 commercially important riverine fish species over the last 15 years (Khoo et al. 1987). According to the farmers and breeders of the giant-prawn (*Macrobrachium rosenbergii*) in the Tanjung Tualang area, the pollution of the Sungai Kinta (Perak) and its tributaries by suspended solids (> 300 mg L^{-1}) has reduced by 50% the cultured prawn harvest in the last 10 years in this area.

The level of many riverbeds in the country has been raised over the years by siltation brought about by improper watershed development for various large-scale projects including urban housing schemes. The consequences include poor water quality, reduced drainage and flash floods. The JICA proposed flood mitigation plan for Penang Island is estimated to be M$260 million. It involves extensive improvement and diversion work on the existing St. Penang drainage system and the construction of dual purpose retention ponds and water pumping stations. The frequent occurrence of flash floods have also promoted the Federal and Perak State Governments to allocate M$5 million to alleviate flood problems in the Taiping (Perak) district.

In the case of reservoirs, sediment pollution is a major cause for concern in Malaysia. It causes silting of dams. This problem occurs at the 50 ha Ringlet Reservoir in Camceron Highlands (Pahang) and has promoted National Electricity Board (Tenaga National) to construct a "desander" across the Sungai Telom at a cost of M$3 million. This same reservoir was also plagued by water hyacinth (*Eichhornia crassipes*) infestation in mid-1989. Clearing this menace incurred a cost of M$200,000.

The ricefield ecosystem too has its share of pollution problems. The excessive use of pesticides such as gramaxone, thiodan, malathion, gramma-BHC and sevin has resulted in declining fish yield in ricefields. The problem is also compounded by the double cropping practice which shortens the rice growing season and in going so, limits the production of the rice-fish culture system.

Sound planning and proper management of water resources on the basis of an entire river basin are therefore necessary in order to overcome such pollution problems so as to ensure continuing economic development and social advancement. Malaysian limnologists can and do in fact play an important role here.

DEVELOPMENT OF LIMNOLOGY IN MALAYSIA

Historical Development

An account of the historical development of freshwater ecology (limnology) as a scientific discipline in Malaysia up to the late 1970s has been given by Furtado (1980). The focus and overall trend in Malaysia during the said period has been elaborated by Lim (1980a) and Ho (1980a) respectively. Briefly, limnology in Malaysia had its beginning in the early 1980s. Several key scientists played important roles during the formative years. They included known personalities like M.W.F. Tweedie, D.S. Johnson, G.A. Prowse, M.K. Soong, C.H. Fernando and J.I. Furtado. The period 1965-70 witnessed the gradual establishment of a pool of researchers, lecturers and graduate students trained in aquatic ecology at the University Malaya, Kuala Lumpur which subsequently enabled Malaysia to host and participate actively in the joint Malaysian/ Japanese IBP/PF Tasik Bara Project in the early 1970s (Furtado and Mori, 1982). Well known Japanese limnologists like S. Mori, I. Ikusima, T. Mizuno, S. Kumano and several others contributed to the Tasek Bera project.

In the ensuing years, more specialists in aquatic biology were recruited in the other local universities like Universiti Kebangsaan Sains Malaysia (UKM) in the country. Undergraduate and postgraduate programmes in aquatic biology were introduced and these invariably included a limnology component.

Present Trend

Today, the trend towards interdisciplinary research and training in Malaysia continues in areas related to water resources development and management as well as water pollution studies. This is due partly to the rapid pace of socio-economic development in the country which often necessitated, among other things, a thorough inventory and optimal utilization of its limited aquatic resources. Tasks like these require a holistic approach involving multidisciplinary inputs. With advances in analytical techniques, computer technology and availability of other high-tech tools like remote-sensing technique, these tasks have been made less daunting and time consuming. Several

Image Processing Systems (IPS) cum software (e.g. DGARON, MERIDIAN, ERDAS) and at least ten different Geographical Information Service (GIS) software packages, (e.g. ARC/INFO, RAISON, SPANS, TERRASOFT, etc.) are currently in use for various planning and management purposes (see MARCES 1991). These include river basin planning and management as well as environmental protection studies.

Another noteworthy change is that the number of Malaysian scientists, whether locally or foreign-trained has increased over the year. This is made possible through long-term human resource development planning and improved training and research facilities now available in the country. Malaysian limnologists are often jointly involved in the search for solutions related to water resource development and the formulation of environmental conservation strategies and methodology. Some are involved in Environmental Impact Assessment (EIA) studies while others lend their expertise towards the evaluation of EIA Reports upon the request of the Department of Environment (DOE). For a proposed development project of a certain scale, an EIA is mandatory inaccordance with the requirements of the Environmental Quality (Amendment) Act (1985) and the Environmental Quality (Prescribed Activities) (Environmental Impact Assessment) Order (1987). It is a prerequisite for final project approval.

Research funding, especially when limited, seems to favour applied research. While studies on plant and animal systematics seem to have been overshadowed by the popularity of applied biological studies, the academic community remains fully aware of the fundamental importance of a sound knowledge on systematics in freshwater ecology research. Such taxonomy-based courses still form core courses in university curricula. Fortunately, basic research in these areas is still very much alive owing to the efforts of researchers who are attracted to the rich diversity of Malaysia's aquatic flora and fauna, coupled with the recognition that gaps still exist in our knowledge of the aquatic biota in the country.

Today, biologists in general and limnologists in particular at the local level universities and government research institutions (e.g. fisheries, medical and health departments) as well as the Department of Environment continue to play their respective roles in this field.

MAJOR FIELDS OF LIMNOLOGICAL RESEARCH

Both the basic and applied type studies have been carried out on the streams/rivers, reservoirs, rice-fields and irrigation canal ecosystems in the country. The main areas and scope of limnological work carried out so far are briefly reported below.

Rivers and Streams

Much of the earlier limnological work on rivers and streams could be attributed to pioneers like Alfred (1964), Johnson (1957, 1967), Cheng (1965, 1966), Cheng and Fernando (1969) and Furtado (1969).

The first conprehensive study of the limnology of a lowland river, the Sg. Gombak in Malaysia was carried out by Bishop (1973). This was followed by the work of Ho (1973, 1975, 1976a, b) who studied the impacts of water pollution on the ecology of Sg. Renggam at Shah Alam industrial estate, Selangor. An account of the general ecology of lowland rivers/streams in West Malaysia has been given by Ho and Furtado (1982). Study on the ecological impacts of changes in river quality as a result of watershed development drew much interests from Malaysian limnologists. Peh (1981) studied the sediment loads of small forested drainage basins in Peninsular Malaysia. Lai and Samsuddin (1985) compared the suspended and sissolved sediment loads in two disturbed lowland watersheds in the Air Itam Forest Reserve, Selangor. An environmental study on the Sg. Klang which examined especially the impacts on its fauna was carried out by Mohsin and Law (1980). The fish fauna of rivers in Taman Negara and Ulu Endau has been studied by Zakaria-Ismail (1984, 1987). The riverine fisheries potential in Malaysia has been discussed by Tan (1980) and Khoo et al. (1987). Chiang and Leong (1979) surveyed the fish parasites in two rivers in Penang. Lim (1989) examined the water quality and faunal composition in streams and rivers of the Ulu Endua area (Johor). More recently, Nather Khan (1990b, c) conducted seperate studies on the pollution status of the Sg. Sedili Kecil and Sg. Linggi. Of late, even tourism seems to have exerted some influence on limnological study. Lai and Lim (1988) did a quantitative assessment of the riverscape (cf. landscape) of the Sg. Endau, based on its physico-chemical, biological and human use characteristics, to project its recreational potential.

In the applied study area, the focus has mainly been on river water quality monitoring and management. It is here that the Department of Environment (DOE) plays a key coordinating role. The approach adopted is one of integrated multi-disciplinary study at the river basin level (Ho 1976c). Scientists from various fields including limnologists participate in one way or another. In 1978, DOE initiated a national water quality monitoring programme (NWQMP). The programme started by setting up study sites on 33 rivers in 13 river basins. These numbers have grown since then. The monitoring programmes called for the collection of data on rivers which are known to be polluted by various forms of wastewater discharges, in particular those from palm-oil and rubber factories. The data so collected were used to indicate the trend and status of water quality in the country's river systems. Phase I of the programme, which involved an extensive water quality standards study, was carried out by the Universiti Malaya (1986). Phase II dealt with the development of criteria and standards for water quality for Malaysia. A study team comprising a private consultancy firm in association with the Universiti Pertinian Malaysia (UPM), the Universiti Teknologi Malaysia (UTM) and the Universiti Malaya (UM) was commissioned by DOE to do the Phase II study (see DOE-SHB 1989). Six rivers basins were studied in detail. These being Sg. Muda, Sg. Perak, Sg. Kelang, Sg. Linggi, Sg. Muar and Sg. Pahang. A computerised integrated river basin information system (IRBIS) was subsequently developed for DOE. The user-friendly IRBIS system provides a rationalised database of river basin data (e.g. catchment data, pollution sources and river water quality). Its data can be used for GIS application. Phase III of the programme was concerned with river basin classification based on beneficial use. Data on river flow, water chemistry, pollution sources, landuse, population statistics, catchment data, beneficial use were collected and analysed. The resultant criteria (based on human wealth, aquatic life protection, livestock drinking, irrigation and recreation) and a water quality index system for water quality management (see Norhayati 1981). Under Phase IV which was completed in 1994, extended similar studies to another ten river basins for classifying them into water usage for conservation of natural environment, domestic water supplies, fisheries and aquaculture, recreational use, irrigation, etc. Five local universities (UM, UKM, UPM, USM, UTM) were involved in the collection and analysis of data of Sg. Selangor, Sg. Bernam, Sg. Kelantan, Sg. Sugut, Sg. Perlis, Sg. Juru, Sg. Prai, Sg. Terengganu, Sg. Sarawak, Sg. Melaka and Sg. Rompin (DOE 1994a, b). Phase IV developed a new River Basin Management Information System (RB-MIS) which comprises of six data modules: Water Quality Database Module, Pollution Sources Module, Aquatic Ecology Module, Flow and Catchment Data Module, Landuse Data Module, and Socio-economic Module.

Lakes and Freshwater Swamps

Owing to the scarcity of natural lakes in Malaysia, there has been limited limnological work sone on such ecosystems. One exception is the Tasik Bera swamp lake ecosystem which was studied intensively under IPB/PF Program (Furtado and Mori 1982, Furtado et al. 1980). Fatimah et al. (1986) studied the zooplankton fauna in another freshwater swamp. With the support of the Asian Wetland Bureau, Nather Khan (1990a) made a preliminary assessment of the water quality and pollution threat at the Ulu Lepar wetland system in Pahang. This shallow wetland system (ca. 18,000 ha), comprimising Tasik Beringin, Tasik Bungor and 12 other permanent or semi-permanent lakes, was one of the major wetlands identified and included in the Malaysian Wetlands Directory (DWNP 1987).

In the case of small man-made lakes, reference is made to the work of Fatimah et al. (1984) and Fatimah and Sharr (1982, 1987). In recent years, some interests have been directed towards the development of the aquaculture potential of ox-bow lakes. An economic feasibility study has been carried on one such lake, isolated from Sg. Perak at Telak Intun has been carried out by Yap et al. (1989).

Reservoirs and Disused Mining Pools

Although there are at least 50 reservoirs of various sizes in Malaysia (Figure 4), yet the amount of published work on the limnology of these reservoirs is scarce. Scarcer still is the work on disused tin-mining pools (Jothy 1968). The work of Ho (1967a) on the Ampang Reservoir, Lai and Chua (1976) on the Pedu and Muda reservoirs and that of Arumugan and Furtado (1980a, b) on the Subang Reservoir are three examples of earlier attempts. Of course, data on the water quality aspects of these water bodies are collected routinely by the relevant state water authorities, but these are seldom published. An attempt at establishing water-quality criteria for the protection of aquatic life in tropical Asian reservoirs has been made by Yap (1988a).

The fisheries and aquaculture potential of reservoirs in Malaysia has not been fully exploited to date. Studies carried out on the fish species composition in reservoirs like the Muda and Pedu Reservoirs (Lai and Chua 1976), Temengor Reservoir (Khoo et al. 1982), Bukit Merah Reservoir (Yap 1988b) and Cenderuh Reservoir (Lee 1989, Lee and Ahyaudin 1989) indicate that these water bodies can with proper planning and management be developed to increase fish production in the country. Such findings have been reaffirmed by feasibility studies carried out by the Freshwater Fish Research Centre (FFRC) at Batu Berendam, Malacca. During the period 1984-87, feasibility studies involving determination of the physico-chemical characteristics and plankton composition were conducted by FFRC on six reservoirs in Peninsular Malaysia. These are the Bukit Merah Reservoir (Taiping, Perak), Ringlet Reservoir, Jor Reservoir, Mahang Reservoir, (all three are in Cameron Highlands, Pahang), Sembrong Reservoir, (Batu Pahat, Johor) and Macap Reservoir (Kluang, Johor) (FFRC Report 1987). The results were encouraging. The FFRC then proposed that both the open-water stocking as well as cate-culture techniques be tried using both indigenous lacustrine and riverine fish species. Other studies on the feeding ecology (Yap and Furtado 1981) and food resource utilization partitioning of selected species of fish in reservoirs (Yap 1987, 1988b) have also been done. Leong et al. (1987) reported the parasite fauna of the fishes at Temengor Dam.

Ricefields and Irrigation Canals

Limnological interest on the ricefield ecosystem has focussed mainly on aspects like water quality, phyto- and zoo-plankton composition and fish culture potential. Fernando et al. (1980) discussed the ecological importance aquatic fauna in ricefields. Niryati (1981) studied the diversity of algal communities in the ricefields of Balik Pulau, Penang. Ali and Ahmad (1988) studied the water quality in ricefields and sump ponds and its relationship to phytoplankton growth in ricefield fish culture system. Yunus and Lim (1971) and Lim et al. (1984) studied the problem of insecticide usage in ricefields in West Malaysia. The freshwater molluscs have been studied by Berry (1963, 1974a, 1974b) with reference to their parasitological significance. Lim (1980b) studied the changes in aquatic invertebrate populations while Mohamad (1982) surveyed the freshwater protozoa in ricefields. Studies on ricefield fish populations (Ali 1988, 1990a) and microcrustaceans and rotifers (Ali 1990b) have also been reported. Zaman and Leong (1987, 1988) studied the seasonal occurrences of cestode and nematode parasites on the common catfishes *Clarias batrachus* and *C. macrocephalus* in the Krian rice growing district. Mashhor et al. (1989) studied the problem of aquatic weed infestation in the same district. The aquaculture potential of ricefields and sump-ponds for integrated rice-fish farming has long been recognised (Tab 1973). Today, the Malaysian government has renewed its efforts to develop this potential using modern technology.

On irrigation canals, Ho (1980b) studied the chemistry and algal growth potential of the surface water in the Muda Rice Irrigation System. Leong (1986) studied the seasonal occurrence of metazoan parasites of *Puntius binotatus* in the irrigation canal system of Sungai Pinang West in Penang.

Systematic Studies

The literature reveals that only a few groups of freshwater organisms have been studied from a taxonomic angle. Prowse (1957, 1958, 1962) studied the desmids, flagellates and diatom flora in Malaysian fresh waters. A few genera of freshwater red algae such as *Batrachospermum* and *Ballia* have been described (Kumano 1978, Kumano and Phang 1987, 1990, Ratnasabapathy and Kumano 1982, Kumano and Ratnasabapathy 1984). Our knowledge ofd the taxonomy and biology of freshwater crabs and prawns are due mainly to the efforts of Ng (1988, 1990), Ng and Choy (1989) and Ng and Steubing (1989). The cyclopoid Copepoda and Cladocera have been studied by Fernando and Pony (1981), Idris and Fernando (1981) and Lim and Fernando (1985).

The rotifers have also been described by Fernando and Zankai (1981) and also Karuna-karan and Johnson (1978). As for fishes, Tweedie (1952, 1953a, b), Soong (1948, 1949, 1950), Alfred (1964, 1969, 1971), Mohsin (1980), Mohsin and Ambak (1982a, b), Chin (1989), Zakaria-Ismail (1989) and Lim et al. (1989) contributed significantly to our knowledge on the taxonomy of fish species inhabiting the rivers, stream and fresh-water swamps of Peninsular Malaysia. Jones and Leong (1986) described the parasitic trematodes (amphistomes) found in freshwater fishes.

TRAINING IN LIMNOLOGY

Role of Local Universities

Educational Role

Malaysian universities form the main repository of a pool of trained limnologists and other aquatic biologists. They also have training facilities not available elsewhere. The teaching curricula too have evolved and expanded in scope to meet the demands of a rapidly developing nation. Of the seven established universities in Malaysia, four have both basic and applied biology programmes at the undergraduate as well as post-graduate levels. The four are Universiti Malaya (UM), Universiti Kebangsaan Malayasi (UKM), Universiti Pertanian Malaysia (UPM), and Universiti Sains Malaysia (USM).

Taking Universiti Sains Malaysia (USM) as an example, since its establishment in 1969, there has always been a strong aquatic biology component in the teaching program of the School of Biological Sciences. The School established an undergraduate thrust area in Aquatic Biology in the early 1970s. Third and final-year courses offered in this thrust include Physico-chemical Limnology and Oceanography, Plankton and Productivity, Tropical Aquatic Ecosystems, Malaysian Fisheries, Fisheries Management, Aquaculture, and Water Pollution and Conservation. Postgraduate degree programmes by research in the field of limnology are also offered programmes by research in the field of limnology are also offered by the school. Short courses such as Geographical Information Systems application to environmental studies and inland fisheries management are also conducted. USM also conducts a diploma level programme aimed at producing qualified field and laboratory technologists. In this regard, USM is perhaps not very different from other universities like UM, UKM and UPM. In the case of UM, courses related to freshwater biology are offered by the departments of Zoology, Ecology and Botany. The Institute for Advanced Studies, UM also conducts short-term courses for its graduate students. At UPM, the Faculty of Fisheries and Marine Sciences and the Faculty of Science and Enviromental Studies offer under-graduate courses in aquatic botany, ecology, limnology and pollution biology. Similar courses are also offered by the Faculty of Life Sciences at UKM.

Research Role

Over the years, universities in Malaysia have evolved from a largely teaching insti-tution to one with increasing emphasis on research. One sees a gradual increase in the amount of limnological research within the four mentioned universities. A scan of the academic staff registers and relevant departmental annual reports indicate that each of the four names universities has at least five faculty members who are involved in limnological or freshwater-based biological research.

This pool of expertise is often used by various government and quasi-government authorities and also the private sector in various ways. The DOE and the private sector often invite university staff including limnologists to undertake studies, advise, or sit in committees to utilize the available expertise. Examples of this include invitations to sit in State Pollution Committees, Watershed Management Committee, EIA Review Panels and various adhoc committees related to resource and environmental protection.

Malaysian universities are frequent initiators and hosts to many national and international scientific seminars and symposia. Three such examples are (i) National Seminar on Water Resources Modelling and Management held on 26-27 August 1991 at the Universiti Sains Malaysia, Penang; (ii) Regional Seminar on the Ecology and Conservation of South East Asian Marine and Freshwaters held on 4-6 November 1991 at the Universiti Malaya, Kuala Lumpur; and (iii) National Biology Symposium held on 26-27 November 1991 at Universiti Kebangsaan Malaysia, Bangi.

Role of Freshwater Fish Research Centre

The Freshwater Fish Research Centre (FFRC) at Batu Berendam, Malacca was established in 1957. It is a branch of the research division of the Department of Fisheries, Ministry of Agriculture, Malaysia. The Centre is charged with the function of carrying out research in the field of aquaculture and inland fisheries.

The current research programme of the FFRC includes the experimental breeding of indigenous and exotic fish in captivity, studies on fish nutrition, fish diseases, live-feed culture, experimental culture of fish and prawn in ponds and in suspended cages, water quality in aquaculture, and reservoir limnology. Besides research activities the Centre also provides technical advice to fish farmers, carries out training programmes for field staff and farm managers, provides practical training facilities to university students, and supplies fish fry to farmers.

In 1989 the FFRC established bilateral linkage with the Department of Fish Culture and Fisheries (DFCF) of the Wageningen Agricultural University in the Netherlands, under the framework of the ASEAN-EEC Aquaculture Development and Coordination Programme (AADCP 1990). A joint project entitled the "Department of Lakes and Reservoirs for Fish Production in Malaysia" was initiated in 1990 through December 1994. The project was formulated in response to the rapid development of reservoirs in Malaysia. Such water bodies have immense potential for fishery development. The study will focus on two Malaysian reservoirs: the Kenyir Reservoir in Terengganu and the Semenyih Reservoir in Selangor. Aspects studied will include physico-chemical characteristics, plankton diversity and productivity, feeding biology and stock assessment of native fish species, and cage-culture feasibility using introduced fish species.

The workplan of the AADCP component-2 also includes an exchange programme for the staff of the FFRC and DFCF, three training courses for ASEAN participants, two workshops and two M.Sc. fellowships for FFRC staff. The proposed themes of the training courses are: Modelling and Management of Reservoir Fisheries, Fish Ecology in Asean Lakes and Reservoirs, and Dynamic Simulation Modelling in Aquatic Production.

Regional and Institutional Linkages

Various forms of technical cooperation exist amongst South East Asian countries, which involves some form of participation from institutions of higher learning. One example is the training programmes and institutions of the South-East Asian Members of Education Organization (SEAMEO). The Tropical Biological programme (SEAMEO/ BIOTROP) in Bogor, Indonesia organises aquatic biology workshops, where limnologists from Malaysian universities have participated as instructors, resource persons, or just as trainees. However, this is channelled through the Ministry of Education rather than through direct institutional linakages between BIOTROP and the universities.

Another area where limnologists have played a part is in the coastal study programmes implemented in ASEAN countries under the framework and guidance of the ASEAN Committee on Science and Technology (COST) and involving three ASEAN dialogue partners, namely, Australia, Canada and USA. An example is the direct technical study (Task 200-M) of the ASEAN/US Coastal Resources Management project (CRMP) which developed a water quality management scheme for South Johor, Malaysia. Both the coastal waters and inland waters (rivers) were included in this Johor study as they are inextricably linked. These programmes provide opportunities for aquatic biologists from ASEAN countries to meet to exchange information and research findings. However, such programmes are again coordinated by the Ministry of Science, Technology and Environment and the linkages between participating institutions are not formed.

Regional institutional linkages through jointly developed post-graduate limnological study programme, research and academic staff exchange, inter-library data exchange service and fellowship offers amongst developing countries themselves is currently lacking. A concerted move in this direction is indeed timely and beneficial and as such should be encouraged.

FUNDING OPPORTUNITIES AND AGENCIES

Aid from the Malaysian Government

Under the Sixth Malaysian Plan (1991-95), a total sum of 1.16 billion ringgit (MYR$, where US$1.00 = MYR$2.78) has been allocated for research and development. About 560 million ringgit will be channelled to research institutions and universities to finance research projects approved under the Intensification in Research and Priority Areas (IRPA) Programme. As far as limnological research is concerned, funding for projects related to aquaculture, fisheries and water pollution research, is available under IRPA's R & D Programmes for Aquaculture and Strategic Development.

Limnologists involved in government funded projects as in the case of the DOE's own National Water Quality Monitoring Project as mentioned in Section 5.1 are also provided with appropriate financial support.

Aid from the Private Sector

Funds from the private sector are usually channelled through short-term doner-defined problem oriented projects. Some of these projects may involve limnologists as in the case of aquaculture feasibility studies, water pollutions studies, and EIA studies on flood mitigation, reservoir/dam construction and so on.

Aid from International Agencies

The integration of limnology in Malaysia has to some extent been reinforced for financial, technical and human resource inputs through international agencies like the Japan Society for the promotion of Sciences (JSPS), Japan International Cooperation Agency (JICA), Royal Society of United Kingdom (RSUK), International Development Research Centre of Canada (IDRC), Gesellschaft für Technische Zusammenarbeit (GTZ) of Germany and the United Nations Educational Scientific and Cultural Organization (UNESCO). Furthermore, scholarships and fellowships are also offered by organizations such as the Canadian International Development Agency (CIDA), the European Community and Association of South-East Asian Nations (EC-ASEAN) and European Environmental Research Organization (ERRO).

SCIENTIFIC SOCIETIES AND THEIR PUBLICATIONS

Of the few scientific societies existing in Malaysia, there is not one that deals specifically with limnological work or even freshwater studies. The Ecological Association of Malaysia (EAM) was established in July 1990 to serve as a platform for its members to help ensure a high quality of life for present and future generations through activities which curb environmental degradation. Besides organising seminars, workshops and conferences from time to time, the EAM produces its own *Journal of Ecological Science* and the *Malayaian Ecology Bulletin*.

Another more established scientific society is the Malayan Nature Society (MNS) which produces a quarterly scientific journal called the *Malayan Nature Journal* (MNJ) and also a quarterly magazine called the *Malayan Naturalist*. The MNJ publishes referred original scientific articles on the natural history, biology and conservation of Malaysia and the surrounding region. The *Malayan Naturalist* publishes articles, directed at the layman, on natural history, environmental and conservation issues. Periodically, MNS also organises national workshops, seminars and international conferences and publishes the Proceedings of such meetings.

Limnological research in Malaysia has increased somewhat over the years. Certain areas have received well merited attention while others have not, as reflected in the literature. The published works are scattered in a variety of journals. A journal of limnology does not as yet exist in the country. Meanwhile, many of the limnological papers written are submitted for publication either in the local or international journals. Malaysian limnologists frequently submit their less technical research papers for government and local universities, e.g. *Malaysian Agricultural Journal, Journal of Bioscience* (USM), *Journal of Science* (UM), *Pertanika* (UPM), *Journal of Ecological Science* (UPM), and *Science Malaysiana* (UKM). The more technical research papers are sent to such international journals as the *Hydrobiologia, Archiv für Hydrobiologie, Limnology and Oceanography, Freshwater Biology, Tropical Ecology, Journal of Phycology* and so on for publication.

ROLE OF NGOS IN PROMOTING LIMNOLOGY

Non-governmental organizations (NGOs) are today contributing significantly toward raising public awareness on environmental issues and problems. They play an active role in raising environmental issues at state, national and international levels. These NGOs include the World Wide Fund for Nature (WWF), Asian Wetland Bureau (AWB), the Sahabat Alam Malaysia (SAM), the Environmental Protection Society of Malaysia (EPSM) and the Consumer's Association of Penang (CAP) with their associated networks such as the Tropical Rainforest Network and the Asian and Pacific Environmental network (APPEN). The International Organization of Consumer Unions (IOCU) has a base in Malaysia but their involvement in environmental issues is focussed at the regional and international level rather than at national level. The long established (51 years) Malayan Nature Society (MNS) is also an active NGO.

Issues taken up by some of these organizations are very broad in scope. From its office at the Institute for Advanced Studies, Universiti Malaya, AWB sponsors and coordinates projects in the fields of biodiversity and water resources, helps in the strengthening of local institutions and in wetland studies and management. AWB also undertakes certain activities in collaboration with other international NGOs such as WWF and IUCN. National NGOs like SAM, EPSM and MNS, though not directly involved in any form of limnological work, have been pivotal in raising the issues on the impacts of water pollution on Malaysian rivers (e.g. Juru Estuary) and the impacts of deforestation in the ecologically sensitive water catchment areas. The MNS too has played important roles in the controversy on the logging of the proposed Endau-Rompin National Park, the proposed construction of a hydropower dam in Taman Negara and, in conjunction with CAP and SAM, on the proposed mega development of Penang Hill. The MNS Malaysian Heritage and Scientific Expedition to Rompin-Endau in 1985-1986 has resulted in 36 scientific papers in a special issue of the *Malayan Nature Journal* (Davison 1989). A few of these papers relate to limnological work done on the Sg. Kinchin in Pahang. In some cases, the NGOs have been able to mobilize considerable public support which have led to the reconsideration of certain development projects.

CONCLUDING REMARKS

It is clear that as the pace of socio-economic development accelerates in Malaysia, greater demands on its limited water resources will be imposed. Hence wise use and careful management of all such resources are imperative to prevent their scarcity from limiting the nation's socio-economic growth in the future. In this respect, Malaysian limnologists must continue to play active roles not only in conducting basic and applied studies, but also help in the formulation of the country's water resource management policies and future development plans.

There are presently still gaps in our knowledge of the limnology of inland water bodies in Malaysia. An in-depth knowledge of the nutrient budget and trophic relationships amongst food-web organisms in almost all reservoirs in the country is still lacking. The aquaculture potential of these water bodies cannot be fully realised without such basic quantitative data. There is a dirth of basic limnological information on the inland water systems, especially the rivers in Sabah and Sarawak. Large tropical river ecosystems like those of the Sg. Kinabatangan (Sabah) and Sg. Rajang (Sarawak) warrant closer studies which should go beyond physico-chemical and water quality considerations. The aquarium or tropical hobby fisheries potential of Malaysia's abundant streams and soft-acid swamps has yet to be tapped. The solution lies in long-term integrated multidisciplinary study programmes. Given sufficient financial support, Malaysian limnologists together with other local scientists are capable of formulating as well as implementing such programmes, as has proven in other major research or study programmes.

On a regional basis, ASEAN member countries should explore and make concerted efforts in formulating limnological research and training programmes for their mutual benefits. This could be done either amongst themselves or with potential international dialogue partners like Australia, Canada, EEC countries, Japan and USA. In the case of Malaysia, it is unfortunate that following the successful completion of the Malaysian/Japanese IBP/PF Tasik Bera Project in the late 1970s, no limnological study of a similar scale and nature has been organised to look at other inland water bodies in the country. Besides the large rivers of East Malaysia, some of the large rivers of East Malaysia, some of the large man-made reservoirs in Peninsular Malaysia, for example the Kenyir Reservoir (37,000 ha) in Terengganu, make good candidates for a multinational limnological research venture.

ACKNOWLEDGEMENTS

I thank the Vice Chancellor and the Dean of the School of Biological Sciences, University Sains Malaysia (USM) for their support. This reciew was first presented at the International Conference on Conservation and Management of Tropiocal inland Waters (Hong Kong, 1991). The financial support provided by USM, the Conference Organising Committee and UNESCO is gratefully acknowledged.

REFERENCES

AADCP. 1990. Research Programme for the Development of Lakes and Reservoirs for Fish Production in Malaysia. Organised jointly by Freshwater Fish Research Centre (FFRC), Batu Berendam, Malaysia and Department of Fish Culture and Fisheries (DFCF), Wageningen, The Netherlands.

Alfred, E.R. 1964. Notes on a collection of freshwater fishes from Penang. Bulletin of Singapore Natural Museum 32: 143-154.

Alfred, E.R. 1969. The Malayan cyprinid fishes of the subfamily Rasborinae. Federal Museum Journal 16: 99-122.

Alfred, E.R. 1971. The Malayan crpyinid fishes of the subfamily Garrinae. Federal Museum Journal 16: 97-103.

Ali, A.B. 1988. Some ecological aspects of snakeskin goramy, *Trichogaster pectoralis* (Regan) populations harvested from ricefields-fish culture system. Indo-Malayan Zoology 5: 101-110.

Ali, A.B. 1990a. Some ecological aspects of fish populations in tropical ricefields. Hydrobiologia 190: 215-222.

Ali, A.B. 1990b. Seasonal dynamics of microcrustacean and rotifer communities in Malaysian ricefields used for rice-fish farming. Hydrobiologia 206: 139-148.

Ali, A.B. and Ahmad, M. 1988. Water quality in ricefields and sump ponds and its relationship to phytoplankton growth in ricefields fish culture system. Tropical Ecology 29: 63-70.

Anon. 1990. Waterfalls of Malaysia. Published by Design Dimension Sdn. Bhd., Petaling Jaya, in collaboration with Department of Irrigation and Drainage, Ministry of Agriculture and Tourist Development Cooperation, Malaysia. 181 pages.

Arumugam, P.T. and Furtado, J.I. 1980a. Physico-chemistry, destratification and nutrient budget of a lowland eutrophicated Malaysian reservoir and its limnological implications. Hydrobiologia 70: 11-24.

Arumugan, P.T. and Furtado, J.I. 1980b. Eutrophication of a Malaysian reservoir: Effects of agroindustrial effluents. Tropical Ecology 22: 272-275.

ASEAN-USAID. 1989. Final Report on Task 220-M: Water Quality Management Scheme, South Johore, Malaysia. Coastal Resources Management Project. ASEAN/US Cooperative Programme on Marine Sciences.

Berry, A.J. 1963. An introduction to the non-marine molluscs of Malaya. Malayan Nature Journal 17: 1-18.

Berry, A.J. 1974a. Freshwater bivalves of Peninsular Malaysia with speicla referemce to sex and breeding. Malayan Nature Journal 27 (3 and 4): 99-110.

Berry, A.J. 1974b. The anatomy of West Malaysian snails of parasitological significance. Malayan Nature Journal 27 (3 and 4): 131-165.

Bishop, J.E. 1973. Limnology of a small Malayan river: Sungai Gombak. Monographiae Biologicae. Dr W. Junk Publishers, The Hague, Netherlands, 285 pages.

Chee Phaik Ean. 1975. Some dissolved nutrient salts and their availability from submerged leaf litter in a tropical hill-country stream. B.Sc. (Hon.) dissertation, Universiti Sains Malaysia, Penang, Malaysia.

Cheng, L. 1965. The Malayan pond skaters. Malayan Nature Journal 19: 115-123.

Cheng, L. 1966. Three new species of *Esakia* Lundblad (Heteroptera: Gerridae) from Malaya. Proceedings of the Royal Environmental Society, London (B) 35: 16-22.

Cheng, L. and Fernando, C.H. 1969. Taxonomy of Malayan Gerridae (Hemiptera: Heteroptera), with notes on biology and distribution. Oriental Insects 3: 97-160.

Chiang, G.L. and Leong, T.S. 1979. Parasites of fishes from Sungai Pinang and Sungai Bahang, Pulau Pinang, Malaysia. Malayan Nature Journal 32 (3 and 4): 247-251.

Chin, P.K. 1989. A new Bornean species of loach, *Elixis sabanus* (Cobitidae) from Mendolong, Sabah. Malayan Nature Journal 43: 72-76.

Davison, G.W.H. 1990. The Malayan Nature Society Rompin-Endau Expedition: 1989. Malayan Nature Journal 43: 212-219.

DOE-SHB. 1989. Development of criteria and standards for air quality and water quality (Phase II). Draft Final Report. Department of Environment, Malaysia, and Syed Muhammad, Hooi and Binnie Sdn. Bhd, Kuala Lumpur.

DOE. 1994a. Classification of Malaysian Rivers. Final Report ofon Development of Water Quality Criteria and Standards for Malaysia (Phase IV. River Classification). Volume 1. Executive Summary. UM/UKM/USM/UPM/UTM Joint Water Quality Consultancy Group. Department of Environment, Malaysia, Kuala Lumpur.

DOE. 1994b. Classification of Malaysian Rivers. Final Report ofon Development of Water Quality Criteria and Standards for Malaysia (Phase IV. River Classification). Volume 2. Methodology and Classification of Ten Rivers. UM/UKM/USM/UPM/UTM Joint Water Quality Consultancy Group. Department of Environment, Malaysia, Kuala Lumpur.

DWNP. 1987. Malaysian Wetland Directory. Department of Wildlife and National Parks (DWNP), Kuala Lumpur, Malaysia.

Fatimah, M.Y. and Sharr, H.A. 1982. Silication in Zoo Negera Lake. Pertanika 5 (2): 240-245.

Fatimah, M.Y. and Sharr, H.A. 1987. Physico-chemical limnology of Zoo Negera lake, Malaysia. Archiv für Hydrobiologie Beihefte, Ergebnisse der Limnologie 28: 435-446.

Fatimah, M.Y., Mohsin, A.K.M. and Mustafa Kamal, A.S. 1984. Phytoplankton composition and productivity of a shallow lake. Pertanika 7 (3): 101-113.

Fatimah, M.Y., Mohsin, A.K.M. and Mustafa Kamal, A.S. 1986. Zooplankton in a tropical freshwater swamp in Malaysia. Malaysian Applied Biology 15 (1): 1-6.

Fernando, C.H. and Ponyi, J.E. 1981. The free living freshwater cyclopoid Copepoda (Crustacea) of Malaysia and Singapore. Hydrobiologia 78: 113-123.

Fernando, C.H. and Zankai. 1981. The Rotifera of Malaysia and Singapore, with remarks on some species. Hydrobiologia 78: 205-219.

Fernando, C.H., Furtado, J.I. and Lim, R.P. 1980. The ecology of ricefields with special reference to the squatic fauna; pp. 943-951. In: Furtado, J.I. (Editor), Tropical Ecology and Development. Proceedings of the 5th International Symposium on Tropical Ecology 16-21 April 1979, Kuala Lumpur, Malaysia. 1383 pages.

FFRC Report. 1987. Report on the limnological study of reservoirs in Malaysia for inland fisheries development. Freshwater Fish Research Centre, Batu Berendam, Melaka Malaysia, 75 pages.

Furtado, J.I. 1969. Ecology of Malaysian odonates: Biotope and association of species. Verhandlungen der internationale Vereinigung für theoretische und angewandte Limnologie 17: 863-887.

Furtado, J.I. 1980a. Limnological research and training in developing countries with reference to Malaysia. pp. 53-56. In: Mori, S. and Ikusima, I. (Editors), Proceedings of the First Workshop on the Promotion of Limnology in Developing Countries, 29-30 August 1980, Kyoto, Japan.

Furtado, J.I. 1980b. Freshwater swamp and lake resources: A synthesis. pp. 797-798. In: Furtado, J.I. (Editor), Tropical Ecology and Development. Proceedings of the 5th International Symposium on Tropical Ecology 16-21 April 1979, Kuala Lumpur, Malaysia. 1383 pages.

Furtado, J.I. and Mori, S. 1982. The ecology of a tropical freshwater swamp, the Tasek Bera. Monographiae Biologicae. Dr W. Junk Publishers, The Hague, Netherlands. 484 pages.

Furtado, J.I., Verghese, S., Liew, K.S. amd Lee, T.H. 1980. Litter production in a freshwater swamp forest, Tasek Bera, Malaysia. pp. 815-822. In: Furtado, J.I. (Editor), Tropical Ecology and Development. Proceedings of the 5th International Symposium on Tropical Ecology 16-21 April 1979, Kuala Lumpur, Malaysia, 1383 pages.

Ho, S.C. 1973. The ecology of a lowland stream: Sungai Renggam, with special reference to water pollution. M.Sc. thesis, Universiti Sains Malaysia, Kuala Lumpur.

Ho, S.C. 1975. Some aspects of the bacteriological conditions of Sungai Renggam, Shah Alam, Selangor. Malayan Nature Journal 29 (2): 70-82.

Ho, S.C. 1976a. Periphyton production in a tropical lowland stream polluted by inorganic sediments and organic wastes. Archiv für Hydrobiologie 77 (4): 485-494.

Ho, S.C. 1976b. The physicochemical limnology of the Ampang Impounding Reservoir, Kuala Lumpur. Malaysian Agricultural Journal 50 (4): 527-544.

Ho, S.C. 1976c. The watershed spproach to water pollution studies in peninsular Malaysia. pp. 27-38. In: Report on the International Workshop on "Energy, Resources and the Environment", February, 1975, Penang.

Ho, S.C. 1980a. Research and training in limnology with respect to man-made system in Malaysia. pp. 67-73. In: Mori, S. and Ikusima, I. (Editors) Proceeding of the First Workshop on the Promotion of Limnology in Developing Countries, 29-30 August 1980, Kyoto, Japan.

Ho, S.C. 1980b. On the chemical and algal growth potential of the surface water of the Muda river irrigation system, West Malaysia. pp. 989-998. In: Furtado, J.I. (Editor) Tropical Ecology and Development. Proceeding 5th International Symposium Tropical Ecology. 16-21 April 1979, Kuala Lumpur, Malaysia. 1383 pages.

Ho, S.C. and Furtado, J.I. 1982. The limnology of lowland streams in West Malaysia. Tropical Ecology 23(1): 86-97.

Idris, B.A.G. and Fernando, C.H. 1981. Cladocera of Malaysia and Singapore with new records, re-descriptions and remarks on some species. Hydrobiologia 77: 223-256.

John, D.S. 1957. A survey of Malayan freshwater life. Malayan Natural Journal 12: 57-65.

Johnson, D.S. 1967. On the chemistry of freshwaters in southern Malaya and Singapore. Archiv für Hydrobiologie 63: 477-496.

Jones, A. and Leong, T.S. 1986. Amphistomes from Malaysian fishes, including *Osteochilotrema malayae* gen. nov. sp. nov. (Paramphistomidae: Osteochilotrematinae subfam. nov.). Journal of Natural History 20: 117-129.

Jothy, A.A. 1968. Preliminary observations of disused mining pools in Malaysia and their potentials for fish production. IPFC/C68/Tech. 25, 13th Session, Indo-Pacific Fisheries Congress, Brisbane. 21 pages.

Karunakaran, L. and Johnson, A. 1978. A contribution to the rotifer fauna of Singapore and Malaysia. Malayan Natural Journal 32: 173-208.

Khoo, K.H., Leong, T.S., Soon, F.L., Tan, S.P. and Wong, S.Y. 1987. Riverine fisheries in Malaysia. Archiv für Hydrobiologie, Beiheft Ergebnisse der Limnologie 28: 261-268.

Khoo, K.H., Leong, T.S., Tan, S.P., Wong, S.Y. and Soon, F.L. 1982. Study Plan for Temengor Lake Fisheries Project. Report No.USM/TF/02, University Sains Malaysia.

Kovac, D. and Yang, C.M. 1990. A preliminary checklist of the semiaquatic and aquatic hemiptera (Heteropotera: Gerromorpha and Nepomorpha) of Ulu Kinchin, Pahang, Malaysia. Malayan Natural Journal 43: 282-288.

Kumano, S. 1978. Notes on freshwater red algae from West Malaysia. Botanical Magazine, Tokyo 91: 97-107.

Kumano, S. and Phang, S.M. 1987. Studies on freshwater red algae of Malaysia VII. *Batrachospermum tapirense* sp. nov. from Sungai Tapir, Johor, Peninsular Malaysia. Japanese Journal of Phycology (Sorui) 35: 259-264.

Kumano, S. and Phang, S.M. 1990. *Ballia prieurii* Kuetzing and related species (Ceramiaceae, Rhodophyta). Japanese Journal of Phycology (Sorui) 38: 125-134.

Kumano, S. and Ratnasabapathy, M. 1984. Studies on freshwater red algae in Malaysia IV. *Batrachospermum bakarense*, sp. nov. from Sungai Bakar, Kelantan, West Malaysia. Japanese Journal of Phycology 32: 19-23.

Lai, F.S. and Lim, M.T. 1988. A quantitative assessment of the riverscape of Sg. Endau. Malayan Naturalist 42(1): 26-36.

Lai, F.S. and Samsuddin, M. 1985. Suspended and dissolved sediment concentrations of two disdturbed lowland forested watersheds in Air Hitam Forests Reserve, Selangor. Pertanika 8(1): 112-115.

Lai, H.C. and Chua, T.E. 1976. Limnological features of Muda and Pedu Reservoirs with an observation on their suitability for fish culture. Malayan Agricultural Journal 50(4): 480-501.

Lai, H.C. and Fernando, C.H. 1978. The freshwater Calanoida (Crustacea:Copepoda) of Singapore and Peninsular Malaysia. Hydrobiologia 61: 113-127.

Lai, H.C. and Fernando, C.H. 1981. Zoogeographical distribution of Southeast Asian freshwater Calanoida. Hydrobiologia 74: 53-66.

Lee, K.L. 1989. A survey of fish populations in Tasik Cenderoh, Perak. B.Sc. (Hons) dissertattion, University Sains Malaysia, Penang, Malaysia.

Lee, K.L. and Ahyaudin, A. 1989. The status of reservoir fisheries in Tasik Cenderuh, Perak: A case study. Proceedings of the 12th Annual Seminar of Malaysian Society of Marine Sciences: 231-239.

Leigh, C.H. and Low, K.S. 1973. An appraisal of the flood situation in West Malaysia. Proceedings of a Symposium on Biological Research and Development: 57-72.

Leong, T.S. 1986. Seasonal occurrence of metazoan parasites of *Puntius binotatus* in an irrigation canal, Pulai Pinang. Malaysian Journal of Fish Biology 28: 9-16.

Leong, T.S., Khoo, K.H., Soong, F.L., Tan, E.S.P. and Wong, S.Y. 1987. Parasites of fishes from Tasik Tememgor in Perak, Malaysia. Malayan Nature Journal 41: 75-82.

Lim, K.K.P., Kottelat, M. and Ng, P.K.L. 1989. Freshwater fish of Ulu Kinchin, Pahang, Malaysia. Malayan Nature Journal 43: 314-320.

Lim, R.P. 1980a. Limnological research and education with reference to natural ecosystems in Malaysia. pp. 57-65. In: Mori, S. and Ikusima, I. (Editors) Proceeding of the First Workshop on the Promotion of Limnology in Developing Countries, 29-30 August 1980, Kyoto, Japan.

Lim, R.P. 1980b. Population changes of some aquatic invertebrates in ricefields; pp. 971-980. In: Furtado, J.I. (Editor) Tropical Ecology and Development. Proceeding 5th International Symposium Tropical Ecology. 16-21 April 1979, Kuala Lumpur, Malaysia. 1383 pages.

Lim, R.P. 1989. Water quality and faunal composition in the streams and rivers of the Ulu Endau area, Johor, Peninsular Malaysia. Malayan Nature Journal 41: 337-347.

Lim, R.P., Abdullah, M.F. and Fernando, C.H. 1984. Ecological studies of cladocera in the rice fields of Tanjung Karang, Malaysia, subjected to pesticide treatment. Hydrobiologia 113: 99-103.

Lim, R.P. and Fernando, C.H. 1985. A review of Malaysian freshwater Copepoda with notes on new records and little known species. Hydrobiologia 128: 71-89.

MACRES. 1991. Malaysian Remote Sensing Inventory. Compiled by Malaysian Centre for Remote Sensing (MACRES), Ministry of Science, Technology and The Environment, Malaysia. 203 pages.

Mashhor, M., Azinuddin, M. and Samsuddin, Y. 1989. Aquatic weeds of irrigation and drainage canals in Kerian Rice Growing District, Malaysia. Proceedings of the 12th Conference of Asian-Pacific Weed Science Society: 761-770.

Mohamad, N.A.H. 1982. A survey of freshwater protozoa in a ricefield ecosystem in Penang. B.Sc. (Hon.) dissertation (in Malaya), Universiti Sains Malaysia, Penang, Malaysia.

Mohsin, A.K.M. 1980. Ecology and morhphology of freshwater fishes and Selangor. Part I. Cyprinoid fishes of the subfamilies Abraminae, Rasbarinae and Garrinae and Families Homalopteridae and Cobitidae. Malayan Nature Journal 34 (2): 73-100.

Mohsin, A.K.M. and Ambak, M.A. 1982a. Cyprinoid fishes of the subfamily Cuprininae in Selangor. Malayan Nature Journal 35: 29-35.

Mohsin, A.K.M. and Ambak, M.A. 1982b. Freshwater siluroid fishes of Selangor. Malayan Nature Journal 36: 99-112.

Mohsin, A.K.M. and Law. A.T. 1980. Environmental Studies of Kelang River 2. Effect on Fish. Malayan Nature Journal 33(3&4): 189-199.

Moulton, T.P. 1973. The effect of various insecticides (especially Thiodan and BHC) on fish in paddy fields in West Malaysia. Malaysian Agricultural Journal 49: 224-253.

Nather Khan, I.S.A. 1990a. Preliminary assessment of the water quality and pollution threat at the Ulu Lepar Wetland System. Asian Wetland Bureau Publication No. 60. 21 pages.

Nather Khan, I.S.A. 1990b. Water quality survey of the Sungai Sedilli Kecil, Malaysia. A study carried out in conjunction with ASEAN/USAID Coastal Resources Management Project. Asian Wetland Bureau Publication No. 61. 32 pages.

Nather Khan, I.S.A. 1990c. Assessment of water pollution using diatom community structure and species distribution - A case study in a tropical river basin. Internationale Revue der gesamten Hydrobiologie 75: 1-22.

Nather Khan, I.S.A. 1990d. Diatom distribution and intersite relationship in the Lingii River Basin, Peninsular Malaysia. Malayan Nature Journal 44: 85-95.

Nather Khan, I.S.A. 1991. Effect of urban and industrial wastes on species diversity of the diatom community in a tropical river, Malaysia. Hydrobiologia 224: 175-184.

Nather Khan, I.S.A. and Mohamed, Hj. M. 1985. Freshwater Malaysian Algae. 2. The Diatom. Nature Malaysiana 10: 28-31.

Nather Khan, I.S.A., Lim, R.P. and Ratnasabapathy, M. 1986. Changes in river diatom structure due to natural rubber effluent. Malayan Journal of Science 8: 85-89.

Nather Khan, I.S.A., Furtado, J.I. and Lim, R.P. 1987. The periphyton of artificial and natural substrates of a tropical river. Archiv für Hydrobiologie Beihefte, Ergebnisse der Limnologie 28: 473-484.

Ng, P.K.L. 1988. The freshwater crabs of Peninsular Malaysia and Singapore. Department of Zoology, National University of Singapore, Shing Lee Publ. Singapore, 156 pages.

Ng, P.K.L. 1990. The taxonomy and biology of Parathelphusa maculata De Man, 1879 (Crustaceae: Decapoda: Brachyura: Parathelphusidae). Malayan Nature Journal 44: 45-60.

Ng, P.K.L. and Choy, S.C. 1989. The Caridean prawns (Crustacea: Decapoda) of the Endau-Rompin Park, Malaysia. Malayan Nature Journal 43 302-312.

Ng, P.K.L. and Steubing, R. 1989. Description of a new species of montane freshwater crab of the genus Sundathelphusa Bott, 1969 (Crustacea: Decapoda: Brachyura: Gecarcinucoidea). Malayan Nature Journal 43: 13-19.

Niryati, H.M. 1981. A study of the diversity of algal communities in the ricefields of Balik Pulau, Pulau Pinang. B.Sc. (Hons) Dissertation, Universiti Sains Malaysia, Penang, Malaysia.

Norhayati, M. 1981. Indices for water quality assessment in a river. M.E. thesis, Asian Institute of Technology, Bangkok.

Osman, R. 1970. Some aspects of the feeding biology of Puntius bulu Bleeker (Cyprinidae), Channa micropeltes Cuvier (Ophicephalidae) and Wallago leerii (Siluridae). B.Sc. (Hons) Thesis, Ecology Division, Sciences Faculty, University of Malaya, Kuala Lumpur, Malaysia, 19 pages.

Peh, C.H. 1981. The suspended and dissolved sediment loads of three small forested drainage basins in Peninsular Malaysia. Malayan Forester 44(4): 438-452.

Prowse, G.S. 1962. Diatoms of Malayan freshwaters. Gardner's Bulletin, Singapore, 19: 1-104.

Prowse, G.S. 1957. An introduction to the desmids of Malaya. Malayan Nature Journal 11: 42-58.

Prowse, G.S. 1958. The Eugleninae of Malaya. Gardner's Bulletin, Singapore 16: 136-204.

Prowse, G.S. and Ratnasabapathy, M. 1970. A species list of freshwater algae from the Taiping Lake, Perak Malaysia. Gardner's Bulletin, Singapore 25: 179-187.

Ratnasabapathy, M. and Kumano, S. 1982. Studies on freshwater red algae of Malaysia I. Some taxa of the genus Batrachospermum, Ballia and Caloglossa from Pulau Tioman, West Malaysia. Japanese Journal of Phycology 30: 15-22.

Soong, M.K. 1948. Fishes of Malayan paddy fields I: Sepat Siam (Trichogaster pectoralis). Malayan Nature Journal 3: 87-89.

Soong, M.K. 1949. Fishes of Malayan paddy fields II: Aruan: Serpent head fishes. Malayan Nature Journal 4:29-31.

Soong, M.K. 1950. Fishes of Malayan paddy fields III: Keli: Catfish. Malayan Nature Journal 5: 88-91.

Tan, E.S.P. 1973. The significance of sump-ponds in harvesting paddy-fields in North Krian, Perak. Malayan Nature Journal 26: 26-31.

Tan, E.S.P. 1980. Ecological aspects of some Malaysian riverine cyprinids in relation to their aquaculture potential. pp. 757-762. In: Furtado, J.I. (Editor), Tropical Ecology and Development. Proceedings of the 5th International Symposium on Tropical Ecology 16-21 April 1979, Kuala Lumpur, Malaysia. 1383 pages.

Tweedie, M.W.F. 1952. Malayan aquarium fishes. 1: The genus Rasbora. Malayan Nature Journal 7: 121-124.

Tweedie, M.W.F. 1953a. Malayan aquarium fishes. 2: The carps and loaches. Malayan Nature Journal 7: 167-172.

Tweedie, M.W.F. 1953b. Malayan aquarium fishes. 3: The anabantoid fishes. Malayan Nature Journal 8: 47-51.

Wong, W.C. and Lim, H.F. 1990. The non-governmental issues in Malaysia. Wallaceana 59 and 60: 10-15.

Yap, S.Y. 193. A holistic ecosystem approach to investigating tropical multispecies reservoir fisheries. NAGA, ICLARM Newsletter 6(2): 10-11.

Yap, S.Y. 1987. Recent developments in reservoir fisheries research in tropical Asia. Archiv für Hydrobiologie Beihefte, Ergebnisse der Limnologie 28: 295-303.

Yap, S.Y. 1988a. Food resource utilisation partitioning of fifteen fish species at Bukit Merah Reservoir, Malaysia. Hydrobiologia 157: 143-160.

Yap, S.Y. 1988b. Water quality criteria for the protection of aquatic life and its users in tropical Asian reservoirs. pp. 74-86. In: De Silva, S. (Editor) Reservoir Fishery Management and Development in Asia. Proceedings of a Workshop at Kathmandu, Nepal, 23-28 November 1987.

Yap, S.Y. and Furtado,J.I. 1981. The feeding ecology of *Cyclocheilichthys apogon*. V. (Cyprinidae) in Subang Reservoir, Malaysia. Tropical Ecology 22: 194-203.

Yap, S.Y., Ong,H.T. and Lim, K.S. 1989. Formulation of aquaculture development at an ox-bow lake in Malaysia: economic feasibility analysis. Aquaculture and Fisheries Management 20: 427-439.

Yunus, A. and Lim, G.S. 1971. A problem in the use of insecticides in paddy fields in West Malaysia - A case study. Malaysian Agricultural Journal 48: 167-178.

Zakaria-Ismail, M. 1984. Checklist of fishes of Taman Negara, Malayan Naturalist 37(3): 21-26.

Zakaria-Ismail, M. 1987. The fish fauna of the Ulu Endau river system, Johor, Malaysia. Malayan Nature Journal 41: 403-411.

Zakaria-ismail, M. 1989. First record of the loach, *Botia Beuforti* (Corbitidae) from Peninsular Malaysia. Malayan Nature Journal 43: 78-82.

Zaman, Z. and Leong, T.S. 1987. Seasonal occurrence of *Lytocestus lativitellarium* Furtado and Tan 1973 in *Clarias macrocephalus* Günther in Kedah and Perak, Malaysia. Aquaculture 63: 319-327.

Zaman, Z. and Leong, T.S. 1988. Occurrence of *Procamallanus malaccensis* Fernando and Furtado 1963 in *Clarias batrachus* and *C. macrocephalus* from Kedah and Perak, Malaysia. Asian Fisheries Science 2: 9-16.

Note: This is a revised and updated version of the review published earlier in *Mitteilungen der internationale Vereinigung für theoretische und angewandte Limnologie* 24: 129-145, 1994.

Gopal, B. and Wetzel, R.G. (Editors) **Limnology in Developing Countries**: 191-229
© 1995, International Association for Limnology

State of Limnology in Pakistan

Saiyida Nazneen
Department of Zoology, University of Karachi, Karachi 75270, Pakistan

ABSTRACT

Pakistan has diverse freshwater resources. The Indus River drainage basin constitutes a major part of the country, whereas the Baluchistan drainage system has a number of rivers which dissipate in Karachi-Sibi plain or directly fall into the Arabian Sea. Several minor streams end into temporary salt lakes or hamuns.

There are several big lakes and reservoirs like Manchar (a natural lake), Kinjhar and Haleji lakes and Hub, Tarbella, Mangla and Warsak reservoirs etc. Besides, thousands of ponds are also spread all over the country. Most of these water bodies are polluted and infested with enormous growth of aquatic weeds.

Most of the research in the country is related to the freshwater fauna and flora, whereas not much significant work has been done on environmental factors and their relations with the organisms. Only the Department of Zoology at University of Karachi has started limnological courses since 1966. Freshwater biology is taught as a special paper in about seven other institutions. Extensive studies are required to understand the impact of environmental pollution, but funds are scarce. Establishment of a Limnological Research Institute with international collaboration is needed to encourage limnological research and management of the freshwater resources of Pakistan.

INTRODUCTION

Islamic Republic of Pakistan is situated between 61°E and 78°E longitudes and 24°N and 37°N latitudes. Its total land area is about 800,000 km^2 and it has a shore line which extends over 1,045 km. Pakistan's fisheries zone is 320 nautical km wide (Gazder 1987). Current population is estimated at 120 million.

Pakistan is characterized by most types of geomorphic features including high mountains with glaciated regions, vast plains with the world's largest irrigation system, extensive deserts of sand dune/stony waste type, and some marshlands. Nearly 60 percent of the country comprises mountains and uplands over 300 m in elevation. The rest of the area (40%) consists of alluvial plains or desert areas below 300 meters (Ahmad 1969). The highlands lie to north, northwest and west of the lowlands.

The climate of Pakistan is largely arid (Ahmad 1951) and of extreme type, the temperatures range from tens of degrees below freezing in mountainous areas to as high as 53°C in some lowland areas. More than three quarter of the country has an annual rainfall of less than 250 mm while 7% of the land area receives a precipitation below 125 mm. Some desert areas may not get any rain for three years at a stretch. The rainfall is largely in summer and to a lesser extent in winter.

Apart from coastal waters of Arabian Sea, Pakistan is fortunate in having rich resources of freshwaters, brackish waters, and saline waters due to its varied topography. Despite the great variety of aquatic environments, the science of limnology continues to remain at a very low level of development. The data presented here has been collected on the basis of personal initiative. No systematically planned work has been carried out on the big rivers, lakes, ponds, etc., except that FAO initiated a project to study the major water reservoirs created by dams, but the data remain unpublished. Naik (1985) has also prepared a feasibility study on the fisheries in the major Pakistan reservoirs.

GEOCLIMATIC FEATURES OF PAKISTAN

Physiography

According to Gazder (1987), Pakistan can be divided into eight physiographic units (Figure 1) which are briefly described below.

1. Northern Mountains/Highlands comprising Himalayas, Karakorum, and Hindukush which have many glaciers and substantial areas permanently capped by snow. Melt waters from these snow-bound regions provide a large and sustained source of water supply to major rivers.
2. Western Mountain Ranges comprise Koh-e-Safed Range, Waziristan Hills and Sulaiman Range. Major part of the water draining these mountains is derived from hydrometeoric precipitation.
3. Potwar Plateau is a tableland spread over about 18,000 km². It has an elevation of 300 m to over 600 m and is situated south of the Himalayan foothills. The plateau is bordered on the south by the Salt Range (250 km long), which runs across Indus River at Kalabagh and then turns southwest (Ahmed 1969). The Plateau is fertile and intersected by many ravines and a few salt lakes.
4. Baluchistan uplands have an area of 350,000 km² and an altitude exceeding 300 m. It is separated from the Indus plain by Sulaiman Range.
5. Indus River Basin and Indus Plain: Indus Basin is the region formed by alluviation by the River Indus and its tributaries. It begins from the foothills of Himalaya and the Salt Range in the north and continues to the Rann of Kutch and Arabian Sea to the South. Indus Basin can be divided into two parts, the Upper Indus Basin and Lower Indus Basin. The Upper Indus Basin includes the plains of Punjab province. The Lower Indus Basin includes the plains of Sindh province with Thar Desert to the east and Sindh/ Baluchistan Uplands to the west. Indus River finally forms a significant delta before discharging into the Arabian Sea.
6. The Desert consists of extensive sand dunes, some stabilized. There are some lakes producing sodium carbonate or sodium bicarbonate, but many have been over-run by moving sands and disappeared. There are no perennial streams and the scant rainfall is largely absorbed by the sand dunes.
7. Lasbela and Makran lowlands contain the Porali, Hingol and Dasht rivers and are of limited extent.
8. Coastal belt is a narrow sea front well over 700 km long.

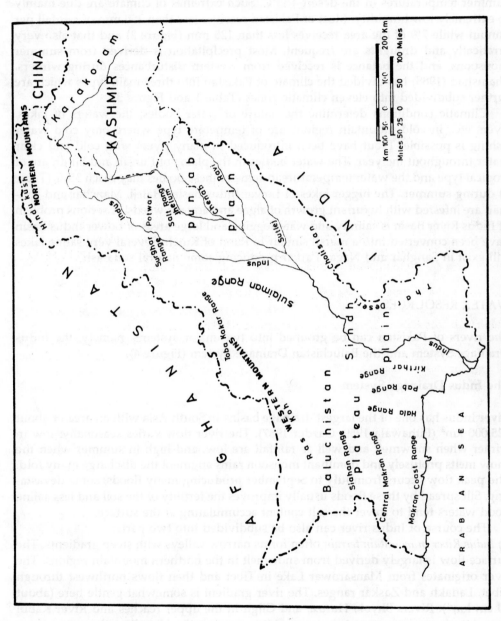

Figure 1. Physiographic regions of Pakistan

Climate

Pakistan falls in a relatively arid zone and is characterized by extremes. The range in temperature exceeds 100°C; mountain tops may have winter temperature of -50°C and summer temperatures in the desert +53°C. Such extremes of climate are due mainly to extremely low humidity. Most of Pakistan receives less than 250 mm of rainfall per annum while 7% of the area receives less than 125 mm (Figure 2) and that also very erratically and droughts are frequent. Most precipitation is derived from summer monsoons, and the balance is received from western disturbances during winters. Shamshad (1988) has divided the climate of Pakistan into three main types which are further subdivided into eleven climatic zones (Table 1 and Figure 3).

Climatic conditions determine the nature of water bodies; the waters of lakes, rivers etc., in cold mountain regions are of temperate type where only cold water fishing is possible. Trout have been introduced in many rivers with cold and clear water throughout the year. The water bodies in the plains of Punjab and Sindh are of tropical type and the water temperature in some of these bodies may reach 35°C (Table 1) during summer. The bigger lakes of Lower Indus Basin, Haleji, Manchar and Kinjhar, are infested with luxuriant growth of algae and aquatic weeds. A serious problem of Indus River Basin is salinity and waterlogging and large areas of Lower Indus Basin have been converted into a marsh similar to Rann of Kutch. Several very saline lakes still exist in Sanghar and Nagar Parkar producing some natural soda ash.

WATER RESOURCES

The rivers of Pakistan can be grouped into two major systems, namely, the Indus Drainage System and the Baluchistan Drainage System (Figure 4).

The Indus Drainage System

River Indus has one of the largest drainage basins in South Asia with an area of about 125,000 km² (Pithawala 1959, Gazder 1987). The river flow varies seasonally: low in winter when snowmelt and well as rainfall are low, and high in summer when the snow melts profusely and dominant monsoon rains augment the discharge many fold. The peak flow occurs from July to September producing many floods, some devastating. Silt spread by these floods usually improves the fertility of the soil and less saline flood waters tend to lower the salt content accumulating at the surface.

The course of Indus river can also be subdivided into two parts:
(i) *Indus River in mountain terrain* often forms narrow valleys with steep gradients. The surface flow is largely derived from snowmelt in the northern mountain regions. The river originates from Mansarowar Lake in Tibet and then flows northwest through Tibet, Ladakh and Zaskar ranges. The river gradient is somewhat gentle here (about 30 cm km⁻¹). Rivers Shyok, Hunza, and Gilgit in the upper reaches and River Kabul near Attock are important tributaries. After crossing the Himalaya through a deep gorge (5,181 m) near Bunje north of Nanga Parbat in Kashmir, it turns southwest and receives a large number of smaller rivers. It emerges out of the mountainous terrain near Kalabagh and flows southwards into the Arabian Sea, east of Karachi.

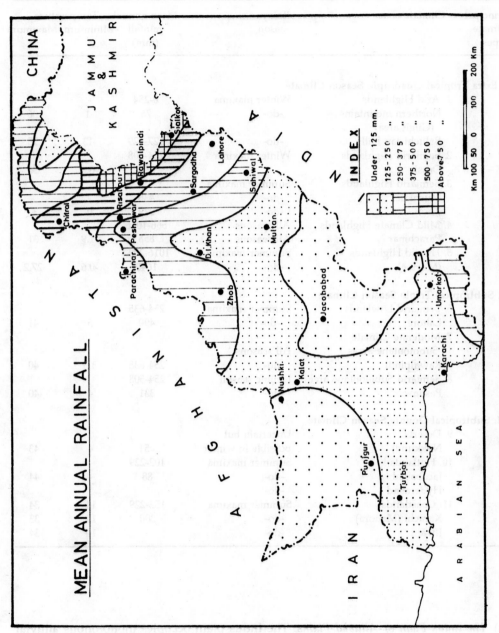

Figure 2. Mean annual rainfall in various regions of Pakistan

Table 1. Climatic features in different areas of Pakistan

Principal climate types	Climatic zones	Rainy season	Mean annual rainfall (mm)	Temperature Minimum	Maximum
I. Extra Tropical Quadruple Season Climate					
	1. Arid Highlands	Winter maxima	0-254	-	-
	Northern mountains (Gilgit area)	-do-	76	-1	36
	Baluchistan Hills	-do-	127-229	-13	25
	2. Semiarid Highlands	Winter maxima	254-508		
	Drosh		457	-0.3	36
	3. Semiarid Highlands	Summer maxima			
	Mushkhel	-do-	436	-	-
	Zhob	-do-	279	0	37
	4. Mild Climate Highlands	All seasons	566-1016		
	Parachinar	All seasons	858	-1.9	31
	5. Humid Highlands	Summer maxima	1016-2032		
	(Murree)	-do-	1640	-0.6	27.2
II. Subtropical Triple Season Climate					
	6. Semiarid Lowlands	Summer maxima	254-635		
	Lahore	-do-	490	5	41
	7. Moderate Climate Submontane areas	All seasons			
	Rawalpindi	-do-	254-635	3.3	40
	8. Semiarid Submontane area	Double season	254-508		
	Peshawar	-do-	331	4	40
III. Subtropical Double Season Climate					
	9. Deserts	Uncertain but			
	Nokkundi	possible in winter	<51	4	43
	10. Hotlands	Summer maxima	102-229		
	Jacobabad	-do-	88	-	44
	Hyderabad	-do-			
	11. Coastlands	Summer maxima	152-229	14	34
	Karachi (Manora)	-do-	200	14	33
	Jiwani	-do-	-	14	34

(ii) *The Indus Plain or Alluvial Plains*: The Indus plain occupies monotonous alluvial plain on the western flank of Indo-gangetic structural trough. On the basis of climatological and topographical features, the Indus plain can be subdivided into three parts, upper or Northern Indus plain, the lower or Southern Indus plain and Indus Delta.

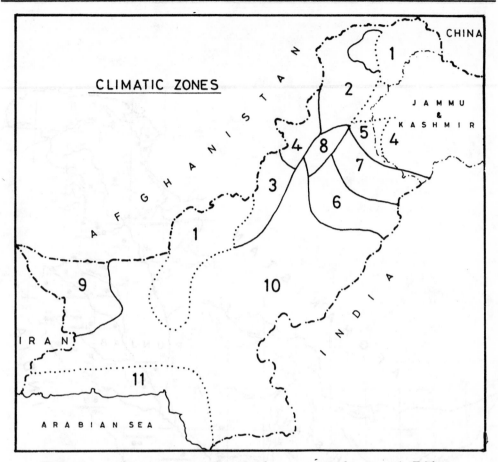

Figure 3. Climatic zones of Pakistan. Numbers correspond to zones in Table 1.

The upper or northern Indus plain is characterized by several medium or large size streams extending from Attock to Mithankot where the eastern tributaries join the Indus River, and covers about 168,000 sq. km. High velocities and turbulent flows in the upper reaches are observed during the peak flood periods. Here the gradients of rivers are moderately steep and there is little shifting of channels. The rivers carry a large amount of channels and bed loads in their upper reaches. The sediment load of Indus is high, about 450 million tons per year at Derband, upstream of Terbela Dam.

The lower or southern Indus plain extending from south of Mithankot to Thatta covers an area of 128,000 sq. km. In the lower Indus plain, the river flows alone and carries not only its water but also the water of eastern and western tributaries when it passes in the province of Sindh (Figure 4), and becomes several kilometers wide especially during the floods. The flow of Indus River is quite reduced after the upper Indus plain and the single river channel is marked by the westward shifting of the river course at some places along Jacobabad-Larkana highlands.

The river passes through an extremely arid region with low rainfall and high evapotranspiration. The river flows very slowly in this region and then merges into the Indus Delta after branching into several streams falling finally into the Arabian Sea.

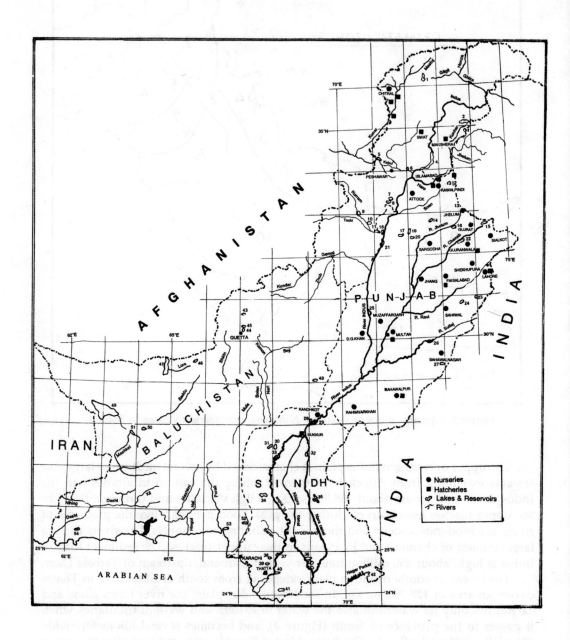

Figure 4. Freshwater resources and aquaculture centres (hatcheries and nurseries) of Pakistan. The numbers refer to lakes and reservoirs listed in Table 2.

Tributaries of Indus River

The tributaries of Indus River are grouped into: (a) Eastern Tributaries and (b) Western Tributaries.

The Eastern Tributaries

There are five main eastern tributaries, namely Jhelum, Chenab, Ravi, Sutlej and Beas, which originate in the Himalaya, pass through Kashmir before entering into Pakistan. The River Beas joins River Sutlej near Harike in East Punjab (India). The other four tributaries join together at Panjab and then confluence with the River Indus collectively at Mithankot. According to Indus Basin Treaty of 1960, Pakistan can use the water of only River Chenab, Jhelum and Indus itself.

The River Jhelum receives only a small part of its flow from snow and glaciers but depends mainly on monsoon rains. The rivers of Kunhar and Kishanganga join it 160 km downstream and then it is joined by the River Kanshi and Poonch near Mangla. After Mangla, it drops 1000 m and receives Kahan River near the town of Jhelum. It generally flows parallel to Indus in its downstream flow.

The Chenab River arising also in the middle Himalayas enters Pakistan just north of Sialkot with some minor tributaries from the northwest and southeast. The Chenab has a mean flow of 32 BCM (26 MAF). It falls less than 150 meters between Marala headworks near the Indian Border and confluences at Panjnad.

River Ravi enters Pakistan through the northwestern region of the Indo-Pak Border and passes just north of Lahore and joins Chenab River.

The Sutlej River arises in the lower Himalayan foothills and flows southwest. The other minor eastern tributaries are Haro River from East and it joins the Indus at Chariala while Soan River joins Indus at Pakhad upstream at Kalabagh.

Large seasonal and monthly fluctuations (Figure 5 and Table 2) occur in the flow of Indus River and its eastern tributaries. The level of water is minimum in winter and increases gradually with the approach of summer as the snow melts in the mountainous catchment areas. In the Indus, Chenab and Jhelum rivers the water level increases greatly after March (Johnson 1979). The higher monsoon flow of Chenab River as

Table 2. Average annual runoff and discharge rates of River Indus and its tributaries (from Johnson 1979)

River	Runoff (x 10^9 m^3)	Discharge (x 10^3 m^3 s^{-1})	
		Maximum	Minimum
Indus (including R. Kabul)	115	26	0.48
Jhelum	28	22	0.11
Chenab	32	20	0.11
Ravi	9	7	0.03
Beas	16	10	0.06
Sutlej	17	14	0.08

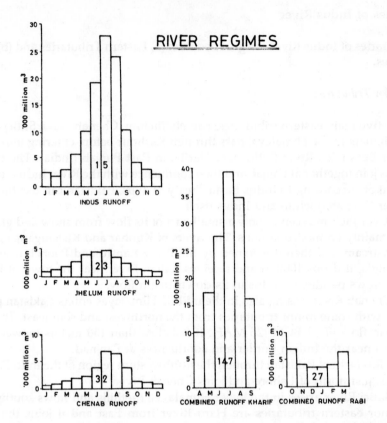

Figure 5. Monthly variations in the flow of Rivers Indus, Jhelum and Chenab

compared to that of Jhelum (Figure 5) is due to its more easterly catchment position near the monsoon airflow from the southeast. According to Johnson (1979), Rabi season (October-March) flows are much lower than the Kharif season (April-September) flows due to low winter precipitation. With the onset of the monsoon rains in late June and July the rivers approach their peak flood level of July-August. Later, the flood waves pass downstream to reach Sindh in a month or so.

The Western Tributaries

The western tributaries are River Kabul, Kunar, Swat, Panjkora, Tochi, Kurram, Gomal, Bolan and Kalapani. River Kabul is the western most tributary of the River Indus and rises at the elevation of 3350 m of the Hindukush mountain ranges of Afghanistan and passes through Khyber Pass, entering Pakistan from the Peshawar Valley where it joins the Indus River just near the Akora Khattak. The rivers of Chitral, Yarkhan flowing northsouth from Pakistan, crossover into Afghanistan and join as the Kunar River to the River Kabul 80 km west of Warsak at Pakistan-Afghanistan border and drains an area of 22,000 sq. km. The River Chitral emerges from northeast of Trich Meer and flows 320 km within Pakistan. It has two tributaries, the Luthko and the Mustuj rivers. In the downstream of Warsak, the Kabul River receives two other rivers, the Panjkora and the Swat, which originate from the northeast Himalayas. The Swat River with a drainage area of about 22,500 sq. km, contributes nearly 25% of the flow of Kabul River at Warsak where its flow is about 20 BCM, while the mean yearly flow on the Kabul River at the point where it joins River Indus at Attock is 33 BCM.

River Tochi, Kurram, Bolan and Gomal, after originating from Sulaiman Mountain Ranges passes through Tochi, Kurram and Bolan passes and join the River Indus from the western side. The River Kurram joins the Indus from the west side. At the upstream of Chasma, between Chasma and Dera Ismail Khan, the Indus is joined by the Gomal River. The last western tributary is Gaj River, joining Indus from Kirthar Ranges, downstream of Dadu.

In addition to Indus River and its tributaries, there are several small rivers and streams in different regions of Pakistan. In the North West Frontier and Punjab provinces, River Soan and streams of Kohat region, Leh and Wah streams (I to III) although small in size but are considered here because some limnological data is available on these water bodies. Soan is the principal river of Rawalpindi District where it covers 96 kilometers. It originates from the Murree hills. About 90% of its course comprises stony bed (Mirza and Kashmiri 1973). The chief tributaries of the Soan River are Korang River and Leh Stream (Ali et al. 1976a,b). Both tributaries receive the sewage and industrial wastes of Rawalpindi Region and join the River Soan near G.T. Bridge about 8 kilometers from Rawalpindi and pollute it.

The streams of Kohat and Kurram Agency are free from pollution. The streams of Kurram Agency originate from the Safed Koh Range joining the Kurram River (Ali 1968b) while some streams originate from Kohat joining to form a single stream about 14.5 kilometers on Kohat and Bannu Road which used to water the plants on the roadside (Ali and Khatoon 1979). Among the three streams of Wah, one Stream (III) flows from Taxila in the western direction and passes below the Wah Cantonment area and receives the chemical pollutants of Wah factories (Qureshi 1979). The other two streams (I and II) of Wah which have been discussed by Qureshi (1979) are biologically polluted as they pass through Wah gardens.

In the province of Sindh, there are several small rivers. Some of them confluence with the River Indus while the other as Layari, Mol, Thaddo, Sari Nadi, Khadeji, Malir etc., either confluence with the other streams or fall directly into the Arabian Sea. Among them two rivers, Layari and Malir are important for the people of Karachi. The water of these rivers was used for drinking purposes by digging wells on the banks and inside the river bed when Karachi was a small fishermen's village. After the partition of the subcontinent and the tremendous development of this city, these water resources became inadequate to fulfill the demands of this metropolis. Basically these rivers are seasonal and contain maximum water only during the rainy season. These rivers which bisect Karachi have become perennial and polluted due to the unregulated flow of sewage and industrial effluents directly into them.

Layari is a consequent stream occupying a synclinal basin, flanked on the west by Choranwari and Kaftari Hill ranges and on the northwest by Shorawand. It is 50 km long and drains an area of 350 km². It runs in a southerly direction parallel to strike of the more resistant rocks which are thick bedded to massive sandy limestones. The entire river basin has been guaged out of the rocks of Guj formation laid down 20 to 30 million years earlier. Layari basin is a part of Thar Desert with hot and dry climate. Due to the present drought conditions, upper streams is merely a string of pools containing hypersaline water (Nazneen and Begum 1988). It becomes perennial due to the continuous flow of above mentioned effluents in the downstream part. It has two tributaries, Gujar Nala and Orangi Nala and it becomes highly polluted after the confluence of these tributaries.

The Malir River is formed by the confluence of Mol and Khadeje streams, northeast of Malir bridge across the Supper Highway. It is situated in the Karachi embayment trough area which is formed by uplift, bounded on three sides by Sunbak uplift on north, Thatta-Hyderabad Highland on east, Pab Ranges on west and opens to the south, facing the Arabian Sea. Like Layari, the basin of Malir River is synclinal, eroding the upper tertiary rocks mostly belonging to Gaj and Nari formations (Muhammad 1995). It covers an area of 1520 km^2 and is mainly drained by Malir River and its tributaries, Mol, Khadeje, Sari, Thaddo, Langeje, Dhor Naro and Sukkan Nala. The valley of Malir River extends approximately 39 km from the Mol-Khadeje confluence to the sea. Among the tributaries of Malir River, Sari stream originates from Sari Jabal Range and flows in general southernly direction for about 26.5 km parallel to the strikes of the rocks. Normally, the stream is dry throughout its course and the drinking water is obtained for the population of adjacent areas by digging wells in the river bed. Near Goth Pearo, the stream changes its course in response to structural changes and flows in a southwest direction for about 20 km to its junction with Mol River. Some distance west of Goth Pearo, the Sari stream receives a major ephemeral stream, the Salinwari. After this confluence, the stream is locally called Khadeje which has perennial flow. Agriculturally, the basin of Malir is the most productive part of the Karachi Region as compared to Layari basin because it has fertile soil and is a groundwater reservoir.

The Baluchistan Drainage System

The rivers of Baluchistan are mostly ephemeral, flowing during the rainy season, sprawling out in all directions from the axis of highland formed by Quetta Knot, the Central Brahui Mountains and the Central Makran Range. The rivers of Baluchistan are of different types. Some rivers flowing northeast generally join the Indus system, which includes the River Zhob with its main tributaries, the Kundar, the Loralai and the Kalachi. The Bolan Mula Nari flowing south or southeast dissipate themselves in the Karachi-Sibi Plain. The southward flowing rivers like the Hub, the Porali and the Hingol drain into the Arabian sea. In the northwestern Baluchistan there are several streams which neither join any big river like Indus nor drain into the Arabian Sea but form temporary salt lakes or 'hamuns'; for example, the Rivers Pishin Lora, Baddo and Rakshan. The River Lora in the Quetta Pishin District, after receiving several small tributaries, takes a turn into Afghanistan and then again passes into Chagai District where it flows into Hamun-i-Lora. Similarly the river Mashkel originating from the eastern Iran enters into the western Baluchistan near the border of Kharan and Makran districts after joining the river Rakshan. It then passes northwards and drains into the Hamun-i-Makshel. The river Baddo also ends in the Hamun-i-Makshel.

In Baluchistan only the larger rivers as Zhob, Loralai, Pishin Lora, Hingol, Porali, and the Hub are perennial in their lower reaches where they contain small quantity of water throughout the year, except in rainy season when the quantity of water in the river increases.

Lentic Water Bodies of Pakistan

Pakistan is fairly rich in lentic water bodies (Figure 4). Their location, water sources and major physiographic features are given in Table 3. Most of the larger standing water bodies are reservoirs which have been built relatively recently on the rivers of the two drainage systems. All the reservoirs are state-owned and under the control of different departments of Central and Provincial Governments. Most of the water bodies in Sindh and Baluchistan Provinces are temporary and brackish or saline as some of them also receive their water from the Salt Range.

The reservoirs are used for regulating floods, domestic water supply, irrigation, hydroelectric power generation, livestock, and commercial fishing. Some are utilized for recreation. The emergent vegetation in the large littoral belt of the lakes and reservoirs is used as fodder, and for their fiber for making cots and mats by the local communities. Several of these lentic water bodies are now managed as wildlife sanctuaries as well.

HISTORICAL DEVELOPMENT OF LIMNOLOGY IN PAKISTAN

The available literature indicates that Francis Day, a surgeon in the East India Company, started studying fishes of the Indian subcontinent as a hobby. Based on his extensive collections of fishes from all sorts of water, he published the first book on fishes, "Fishes of India" (Day 1875-1878). Later, H.K. Bhatti (1895-1980) and K.A. Hussain (1907-1981) studied various aspects of freshwater fishes particularly breeding of culturable food fishes (see Javed et al. 1993). Qureshi (1965) compiled the first book on freshwater fishes of Pakistan. Since then, considerable emphasis has been laid on the systematics, biology and culturing of fishes (see p. 214-217). Some studies on the systematics of freshwater algae and invertebrate fauna were also initiated in 1960s but limnological aspects received little attention.

However, a specialization in Limnology and Freshwater Fishery Biology was started in the Department of Zoology at the University of Karachi in 1966. Since then it is the only institution where Limnology is taught as a separate subject, although freshwater biology is also taught in some other universities.

Research in limnology was initiated by the efforts of late Afzal Hussain Qadri, at the University of Karachi, when the Agricultural Research Council of Pakistan sanctioned the first research project (1968-71) on limnological studies of lakes of Sindh. Further projects were funded by Pakistan Agricultural Research Council (PARC), University Grants Commission (UGC) and the University of Karachi. So far, three Ph.D. and three M.Phil. degrees have been awarded in the field of limnology.

LIMNOLOGICAL STUDIES

Only a little knowledge is available until now on the limnological aspects of inland waters of Pakistan although both lotic and lentic habitats have been studied in recent years (Javed et al. 1993, Nazneen and Begum 1993a). Some data on various physico-chemical parameters of the rivers, springs, lakes, reservoirs, and ponds investigated so

Table 3. Physical features of important lentic waterbodies of Pakistan

Name of the waterbody	Location N.Lat	E.Long	Situation
N.W.F. Province and adjoining areas			
1. Shandar Lake	36°10'	72°37'	Gilgit Agency; atop water divide separating Gilgit and Mastuj river basins
2. Lulusar lakes	35°06'	73°55'	Hansehra District; South of Babusar pass, between Balakot and Indus river basins
3. Saiful Muluk Lake	34°50'	73°52'	Hansehra District, Naren valley
4a. Tarbela Reservoir	34°00'	72°36'	Haripur District; 48 km from Attock, 24 km from Haripur
	34°15'	72°54'	
4b. Khanpar Reservoir	33°56'	72°36'	Haripur District, 16 km from Taxila; 800 m above sealevel
5. Warsak Reservoir	34°05'	71°15'	22 km from Peshawar
6. Keshki Reservoir	34°02'	72°01'	Near Peshawar
7. Kandar Reservoir	33°36'	71°29'	Kohat District
8. Tanda Reservoir	33°35'	71°22'	8 km west of Kohat, 530 m above sea level, across a narrow gorge
9. Baran Reservoir	33°02'	70°33'	Bannu District, 10 km west of Bannu
10. Malugal Lake	32°46'	70°51'	Bannu District, 20 km northwest of Laki
11. Thanedar Wala Lagoon	32°37'	71°05'	Bannu District
Punjab Province			
12. Rawal Lake	33°45'	73°20'	14.4 km from Rawalpindi
13. Mangla Reservoir	33°12'	73°39'	32 km northwest of Jhelum, near village Mangla
14. Kalar Kahar Lake	32°46'	72°42'	25 km southwest of Chakwal
15. Marala Reservoir	32°45'	74°14'	25 km north of Sialkot
16. Rasul (Barrage) Lake	32°43'	73°33'	30 km from Jhelum
17. Nammal Lake	32°41'	71°49'	29 km from Mianwali
18. Khabbaki Lake	32°37'	71°14'	10 km northeast of Nowshera
19. Ucchali Lake	32°33'	72°01'	13 km west of Nowshera
20. Jahlar Lake	32°29'	72°07'	Khushab District
21. Chashma Reservoir	32°25'	71°22'	25 km southwest of Mianwali
22. Qadirabad Reservoir	32°19'	73°39'	53 km west of Gujranwala
23. Ghamaghar Lake	30°59'	74°00'	Kasur District
24. Kharal (Kharrar) Lake	30°53'	73°35'	20 km northeast of Okara, on the south bank of Ravi River
25. Taunsa Reservoir	30°42'	70°50'	Muzaffargarh Dist., 20 km northwest of Kot Adu
26. Ishlam Headworks	29°50'	72°34'	20 km south of Vehari
27. Patisar Lake	29°22'	71°57'	Lal Suhanra National Park

Water Source	Area (ha)	Depth (m)	Remarks
Snow and glacier melt	-	-	Drains into Gilgit River
Snow melt	-	-	A group of lakes with potable water
Snow melt	-	-	Gauged out by shouts of glaciers during last glacial period
Indus River	25000	60-137	Largest rock & earth-filled dam 148 m high, built 1974; Reservoir 48 km long, with no shallow marshy zone
Haro River	806	51	Built in 1983 for irrigation
Kabul River	-		Built in 1962 for irrigation through a canal and a tunnel
Kabul River	263	-	Receives effluents from sugar refineries and paper mills
-	251	-	Built for domestic water supply
Kohat Tai River and other streams	644	30	Behind earth-filled 34.4 m high dam, 1425 km² catchment area; used for irrigation
Kurram River through a canal	1554	25	Used for irrigation, hydropower and waterfowl hunting
Kurram River	405	1.0	Saline seasonal lake; livestock grazing is common.
Gambilla and Kurram rivers	4047	0.1-1.5	Seepage lagoon with brackish to fresh water; Deep water during March and July-Sept., Dense growth of Typha and Saccharum
Korang River	777	15	Reservoir behind 24.4 m high dam, used for irrigation and domestic supply to Rawalpindi and Islamabad
Jhelum River	26,500	51-91	Multipurpose 64.4 km long reservoir, behind 3.35 km long 116 m high earth-filled dam
Local runoff	220	-	Natural lake in the Salt Range, with brackish water
Chenab River	1620	0.2-5.0	Used for irrigation
Jhelum River	1138	2-6.5	Used for irrigation, flood control and commercial fishing; surrounded by extensive marshes and sand banks
Springs & streams rising in the hills of the Salt Range	486	4.6-5.8	Natural lake with saline to brackish water used for irrigation and fishing
Local runoff and rainfall	283	0.5	Saline to brackish; used for fishing & waterfowl
Seepage from hills of Salt Range	943	-	Hypersaline; used for fishing and recreation
Run off from hills of Salt Range	100	-	Brackish to saline
Indus River	33109	0.2-8.0	Multipurpose reservoir built in 1971 to supplement flow of Jhelum river at Trimmu Headworks; Indus Dolphin recorded from upstream stretches of the river
Chenab River	2850	-	Used for irrigation; provided with canals linking waters from Sutlej, Indus and Ravi Rivers
Local runoff and Sutlej River	80	0.3	Brackish water lake, used for fishing and irrigation
Seepage of irrigation canals	235	0.2-3.0	Brackish to saline; with extensive reed marshes
Indus River	6567	5.0-11.5	- -
Sutlej River	3152	3.0-6.0	- -
Bahawal Canal	1935	4.5-6.0	Earlier irrigation reservoir, converted to permanent lake

Table 3. (continued)

Name of the waterbody	Location N.Lat E.Long	Situation
Sindh Province		
28. Sindhi Dhoro Lake	28°09' 69°04'	Jacobabad District; west bank of Indus River
29. Ghauspur (Rup Jheel) Lake	28°08' 69°06'	Jacobabad District
30. Drigh Lake	27°34' 68°02'	Larkana District
31. Hamal Katchri Lake	27°30' 67°55'	Larkana District
32. Pugri Lake	27°18' 68°03'	Jacobabad District
33. Nara Canal Lakes (e.g., Soonhari, Sadhori and Sangharlo)	27°15'- 69°18'- 26°00' 68°47'	Khairpur and Sanghar Districts on both sides of Nara Canal between Sohrab and Sanghar
34. Manchar Lake	26°25' 67°39'	Dadu District
35. Khipro Lakes	25°49'- 69°38'- 25°32' 69°29'	Sanghar District
36. Lakes of Badin District	24°50' 69°00' 24°45' 68°50'	Badin District; east of Indus plain near Tando Bango
37. Kinjhar (Kalri) Lake	24°56' 68°10'	Thatta District, near Chilya
38. Hadero Lake	24°49' 67°52'	Thatta District, 85 km east of Karachi
39. Haleji Lake	24°48' 67°47'	Thatta District, 87 km from Karachi
40. Mahboobshah Lake	24°30' 68°03'	10 km southwest of Sujawal
41. Jafri Lake	24°12' 68°15'	Thatta District
42. Lakes of Nagar Parkar	24°27' 71°00' 24°00' 70°00'	Tharparkar District
Baluchistan Province		
43. Pishin Lora	30°42' 67°01'	Northeast of Karbala near Pishin City; 3000 m above sea level
44. Kushdil Khan Lake	30°36' 67°15'	Quetta District
45. Hanna Lake	30°21' 67°05'	Quetta District, 15 km northeast of Quetta
46. Zangi Nawar Lake	29°27' 65°47'	Chagai District
47. Hamun-i-Lora	29°25' 64°50'	Chagai District
48. Harav Lake	29°02' 69°12'	Dera Bugti, 3000 m above sea level
49. Hamun-i-Mushkel	28°30' 63°10' 20°00' 62°00'	60 km south of Nok-Kundi
50. Harden Lake	27°55' 69°18'	Kalat region, Karan desert; 1550 m above sea level
51. Hamun-i-Murgho	27°45' 63°55'	Kharan District, near Biri Lori town; 500 m abovesea level
52. Hub Lake	25°40' 67°03'	Lasbela District, 35 km north of Karachi
53. Siranda Lake	25°31' 66°37'	Lasbela District, near Karachi to Uthal road
54. Akara Reservoir	25°25' 62°20'	30 km north of Gwadar

Water Source	Area (ha)	Depth (m)	Remarks
Local runoff	660	2.0	- -
Local runoff	-	-	- -
Monsoon rains	182	-	Brackish water lake, earlier connected to Indus River; now a wildlife sanctuary, extensive growth of *Tamarix* and *Typha*
Local runoff	-	-	Brackish water
Local runoff	-	-	Brackish water
Nara canal (from Indus River)	300,000	< 1.0	A group of 200 shllow lakes, upto 200 ha each, scattered over a 150 km stretch; saline, brackish or freshwater; mostly temporary drying out in winter, some permanent; generally surrounded by sand dunes;
Western Nara canal, Rice canal and an inlet at Aral Wah, from Indus River	6,000	2.4-4.9	Estimates of area vary from 60 to 518 km^2 (Hussain 1961, Rao 1989); several islands are present. The inlet at Aral Wah also serves as outlet to Indus River during Nov.-Dec.; used for flood control, fishing, transport and irrigation; high rate of siltation and eutrophication
	30,000	-	A group of 30 permanent and seasonal water bodies, <200 ha each; freshwater, brackish or saline; used for fishing, grazing and waterfowl hunting
Seepage from irrigation canals	2000	-	A cluster of 11 brackish water lakes; e.g., Phoosna, Khanjo (500 ha), Tando Bango and Charwo
Indus River through Kalri Baghar feeder canal and streams	13468	8.0	Formed in 1930 by joining Kinjhar and Sonehri lakes; freshwater highly eutrophic, used for water supply to Karachi, and commercial fishing (see Nazneen 1980)
SLM drain and Jam Branch Canal	1321	1.7	Natural brackishwater lake, used for fishing and waterfowl
Jam Branch Canal from Kinjhar Lake	1704	5-6	Shallow saline lake converted to freshwater reservoir in 1930 for water supply to Karachi; now also a bird sanctuary and a Ramsar site
Seepage water from Indus River	100	-	Privately owned, fresh to brackish water; used for fishing
Seepage water	200	-	brackish to saline water
Seepage water	54	-	Saline playas used as a source of calcium carbonate Area surveyed by Mahar (1991)
Local rainfall	-	-	Temporary saline depression
Local rainfall and seasonal flood	1296	2-3	Old storage reservoir, used for irrigation
Snow melt from Zarghum mountains	-	-	Built by damming a narrow defile in resistant limestones
Rainfall and seasonal flood	2070	-	Temporary lake, dries out in summer (see Rao 1989)
Rainfall and seasonal flood	-	-	Large shallow expanse of water
Seepage from surrounding streams	-	-	Small saline lake
Runoff from Ras Koh Range, Chagai Hills & Iranian mountain ranges	-	-	Brackishwater playa lake
Baddo and Karan Rivers & other streams		-	Saline lake
Local runoff	-	-	Temporary saline lake
Hub River	-	-	Reservoir built in 1981; used for irrigation, fishing, water supply to Karachi; also a wildlife sanctuary
Local runoff, and seepage from sea	-	-	Medium sized temporary brackishwater lake
Akara River (ephemeral)	50		Recent reservoir for drinking water supply

far are summarised in Table 4. The biological data generally refer to only a list of organisms recorded from different water bodies and rarely information is provided on their numbers, seasonal dynamics or relationships with physical and chemical parameters. The studies made on different water bodies are reported here briefly.

Lotic Waters

Although Indus River is one of the largest rivers of South Asia, no planned limnological study has ever been made except for a few preliminary reports. Ibrahim (unpublished, see Arian an Khuhawar 1982) analysed the water quality of Indus River (at Kotri Barrage) from the viewpoint of pollution and agricultural use during 1975-1978. The concentration of sodium chloride was fairly high, followed by that of $Ca(HCO_3)_2 > Mg(HCO_3)_2 > CaSO_4$ and $MgSO_4$. $NaNO_3$, $CaCl_2$, $Ca(NO_3)_2$, $MgCl_2$, Na_2SO_4 and Na_2CO_3 were present less frequently. Iron was present both as carbonate and sulphate. Small amounts of silicates and phosphates were also present. Heavy metals like mercury and cadmium were not found. Arian and Khuhawar (1982) who investigated the annual carbon transport of Indus River during February 1981 to January 1982, observed that the transport of dissolved and particulate carbon by the River Indus increased with increasing discharge due to the drainage of organic rich water into the main channel at the time of flood. Ali et al. (1980) also studied the River Indus and its tributaries near Tarbela Dam (Table 4) for a few water quality parameters and the biota. They reported 42 genera of algae of which the diatoms were most dominant. Among the fauna, 54 species of macroinvertebrates (mostly insects) and 35 species of fishes were recorded. The productivity (both number and weight) of bottom fauna was observed to be high during the summer season. Other studies on the fisheries of River Indus are those of Khan (1946), Bhuiyan (1960), Hussain and Sufi (1962a, 1962b) and Sajid (1962).

The effect of pollution on the water quality and aquatic organisms of Soan River (within Rawalpindi City) and Kabul River were examined by Ali et al. (1976b, 1977a). They reported a decrease in pH and dissolved oxygen, and an increase in the alkalinity, calcium, total hardness and chlorides in the water of Soan River (Table 4). Ali et al. (1977) and Ahmad and Khan (1983) have also reported very low level of dissolved oxygen in Kabul River.

Butt and Shafiq (1987) described some physico-chemical characteristics of water in Sardaryab River, a branch of Kabul River near Charsadda, and observed that the water was suitable for warm water fishing. The algal flora of Swat (Shameel 1980, 1984) and Kabul rivers (Ali 1981 and Hadi et al. 1988) consists of 63 species of which the green algae are the most dominant. The most abundant genera are *Spirogyra* (12 species), *Cosmarium* (5 species) and *Zygnema* (5 species).

The aquatic insects of Indus, Kabul, Haro and Soan rivers were investigated by Akhtar an Ahmad (1975) and Khatoon and Ali (1975a, 1975b, 1977a,b and 1978). These studies recorded 13 species of Coleoptera, 22 Diptera, 14 Hemiptera, one Hymenoptera and Lepidoptera, 3 Odonata, and 7 species Trichoptera. Most of the species are reported new. The fish fauna of Swat, Jhellum, Soan, Haro, Sutlej and Kurrum rivers has been surveyed by Hussain and Shah (1960), Siddiqui (1966), Islam and Siddiqui (1971), Mirza and Ahmad (1987b), Mirza and Kashmiri (1973), Razaq and Mirza (1992),

Mirza and Omer (1974), Qureshi et al. (1968), Bashir and Mirza (1975), Ahmad and Mirza (1964) and Mirza et al. (1973, 1989).

The fishes of the Indus River system can be grouped into four catagories:

(i) species occurring only in the Indus River, such as *Amblyceps mangois, Aila coila, Badis badis, Barilius bagarius, B. bola, Boleophthalmus dussumieri, Botia birdi, Colisa fasciata, Crassius auratus, Gadusia chapra, Labeo boga. L. boggut, L. caeruleus, L. fimbriatus, L. microphthalmus, L. pangusia, Macrura ilisha, Monopterus cuchia, Nandus nandus, Nangra nangra, N. robusta, Mystus aor, M. cavasius, M. gulio, M. horai, Schistura baluchiorum, Schistura, alepidota N. kessleri, N. parashari, Periophthalmus keelreuteri, Pristis microdon, Puntius gelius, P. punjabensis, P. waageni, Rasbora daniconius, Rhinomugi cascasia, Schizopyge curvifrons, S. esocinus, Seruricula gora, Trilophysa gracilis, T. vasinensis*, and *Xenentodon cancila;*

(ii) The species that occur in the main river and in any one tributary, such as *Ailichthys aor, Barilius bendilisis, Catla catla, Clupiosma garua* and *Labeo gonius* which are reported only from Sutlej River;

(iii) *Barbodies sarana, Chanda nama, C. ranga* reported only from Haro River, and

(iv) *Channa baculis* and *Cirrhinus mrigala* reported from Jhelum and Kabul rivers, respectively.

Similarly, the studies on the fish fauna of rivers of Baluchistan Drainage System such as Rivers Bolan, Hub, Porali, Dasht, Rakshan, Hingol and Zhob (Siddiqui 1962, Mirza and Naik 1967, 1972, Nazneen and Iqbal 1986, Nazneen et al. 1989, Mirza and Saboohi 1990, Mirza 1992, 1994, Mirza et al. 1994) show that whereas some fishes (e.g., *Aspidoparia morar, Aphanius dispar, Channa punctatus, Crossocheilus diplocheilus, Cyprinion watsonii, Danio devario, Esomus danrious, Labeo dero, Mastacembelus armatus, Puntius conchonius, P. terio* and *Tor putitora*) occur in most of the rivers of both drainage systems, some species (*Barilius pakistanicus, Labeo dyocheilus, Labeo rohita, Notopterus chitata, N. notopterua, Osteobrama cotio, Racoma labiata, Schizocypris brucei, Schizothorax plagiostomus, Schistura Kessleri, Tilapia mossambica*) occur in only one or two rivers of the two drainage systems, and still others are confined to the rivers of Baluchistan. *Cyprinion microphthalmum, C. milesi, Gadusia rosica, Labeo gedrosium, Schistura kessleri, Schistura baluchiorum, Schistura lindberji* occur in Rakhshan River, *Glossogobius giuris* in Hub and Porali Rivers, *Schistura arifi, S. punjabensis* in Zhob River and *Liza subviridis* in Hub River only. In a study of invertebrate macrofauna, Nazneen et al. (1994) reported four species of gastropods of which *Thiara (Melanoides) tuberculata* was most abundant in Hub River.

The hill streams of Swat, Kaghan, Kohat and Kurram agencies in the North West Frontier region have been studied particularly for their fish fauna (Ahmad and Mirza 1963, Ali 1968a,b, Mirza and Niak 1973, Ali and Khatoon 1979, Mirza et al. 1993).

In Punjab, Wah and Leh streams are among the most investigated. Khalil and Ahmad (1976) enumerated the algae of Wah stream. Qureshi (1979) observed that the maximum growth of algae occurs in summer, moderate in winter and least in spring and autumn seasons. Khatoon and Ali (1975a, b, 1977a, b, 1978) and Akhtar and Ali (1976) investigated the aquatic insect fauna which included several new species of Diptera, Hemiptera, Hymenoptera, Coleoptera, Trichoptera and Lepidoptera. The fishes of these streams were surveyed by Ali (1966). Some preliminary limnological observations have been made by Ali et al. (1976a) and Barlas and Anjum (1990) (Table 4).

Table 4. Physico-chemical characteristics of water (mg L^{-1}) in some freshwater bodies of Pakistan

Name	Water temp. °C	Total alkalinity	Total hardness	pH	Dissolved oxygen	Free CO$_2$	Calcium	Magnesium	Chlorides
Rivers									
Indus River									
(a) Near Tarbela dam	13-33	38-400	280-350	7.2-7.5	5.2-7.1	-	97-123	-	83-122
(b) 160 km from sea	15-31	18-46	16-332	7.4-8.9	7.0-11.4	-	29-66	9-17.5	16-30
Kabul River	19-27	38-320	382	7.3-7.6	5.2-5.5	-	112	-	104
Gilgit River	10	120	230	7.9	-	-	72	-	15
Haro River	11-19	44	280	7.3-7.5	5.4-8.0	-	193	-	172
Hunza River	5	160	130	8.0	-	-	24	-	20
Soan River	12-35	125-330	93-360	7.2-8.6	2.3-14.0	-	28-130	-	25-130
Layari River	22-35	-	19-28	7.0-8.0	0.2-1.5	0.04	25-57	19-35	44-307
Streams									
Kohat stream	20-26	180-230	280-340	7.2-7.6	6.2-7.2	-	72-91	-	40-60
Wah stream	18-25	18-400	280-410	7.0	5.5-	1.0-	76-120	-	20
Springs									
Spring joining Ramli stream	21-27	105-112	120-159	7.2-7.6	3.1-4.9	-	-	-	-
Laki Hot Spring	40-42	-	310-480	6.3-8.1	-	-	64-108	-	280-3800
Lakes									
Rawal lake	14-32	108-274	132-328	7.2-8.0	1.2-12	-	17-62	-	7-29
Kalar Kahar lake	35	140-600	380-695	7.8-8.0	0-8.0	-	40-96	-	170-1260
Kinjhar lake	17-32	-		6.5-8.0	2.2-7.3	2-7.5	8-16	4-8	44-156

Table 4. (continued)

Name	Water temp. °C	Total alkalinity	Total hardness	pH	Dissolved oxygen	Free CO_2	Calcium	Magnesium	Chlorides
Reservoirs									
Warsak Reservoir	10-29	100-300	-	7.0-8.0	5-12	-	-	-	-
Mangla Reservoir	-	62-158	72-110	6.5-7.8	7.2-11.3	-	9-34	-	-
Ponds									
Pond near Hiranpur	14-32	60-200	220-2900	7.4-8.4	5.3-13.0	-	40-360	-	354-4500
Ponds of Fatehjung	20-23	78-103	210-240	7.7-7.8	7.2-9.0	-	56-72	-	50-140
Ponds of Charharpal (Rawalpindi)	21-34	12-206	16-880	8.0-12.6	2.6-8.6	-	-	-	2.3-36

The quantities of chemical constituents, except pH are given in mg L^{-1}.

In Sindh, the Layari and Malir rivers which pass through Karachi, have been investigated most. Both are seasonal rivers lying in the Gadap Basin. The rocks of the synclinal troughs of these rivers belong to the Upper Tertiary period (Muhammad 1995). The studies on the water chemistry, molluscs and fishes of Layari River (Nazneen and Begum 1988, 1994, Nazneen et al. 1990, 1993c, and Begum and Nazneen 1988, 1991, 1992a-e) show that the course of this highly polluted river can be divided into four parts: (i) Hypersaline upstream region, situated beyond Karachi limits, completely devoid of live molluscs but with fish (*Lebistes reticulatus*) surviving in the string of pools present in the river bed, (ii) Less saline and less polluted part where the river enters Karachi. This part is inhabited by molluscs most common of which are those of the families Bithyniidae, Lymnaeidae, Melaniidae, Planorbidae, Physidae and Viviparidae although some dead specimens of family Corbiculidae and Unionidae were also recorded. (iii) Another highly polluted water stretch devoid for living organisms, and (iv) The estuarine region.

Malir River is also heavily polluted with no live molluscs among the macro-invertebrates (Begum and Nazneen 1995) but the Khadeji River, also near Karachi, is not polluted and supports several fish species (Nazneen and Saeed 1987).

Among hot springs of Sindh, only Laki Spring has been studied for its physico-chemical characteristics (Khuhawar et al. 1986) and Cyanophyceae (Leghari and Theobo 1983).

Lentic Waters

The flora and fauna of the lakes and reservoirs of the Upper Indus Plain (Punjab Province) have received much attention (Arora 1931, Majeed 1935, Ali 1968a,b, Ali et al. 1974, Ali et al. 1980-1981, Aziz and Jafri 1975, Sarim and Faridi 1976, Ali and Qureshi 1977, Ali and Khatoon 1978, Bokhari and Rana 1979a,b, Sarim and Ali 1981, Rao 1989, Khwaja et al. 1990, Mirza and Omer 1973, Mirza and Ahmad 1988, Mirza and Mirza 1988, Mirza and Hussain 1988 and Mirza and Khan 1994) whereas very little work has been done on other limnological characteristics (see Table 4). Butt et al. (1986) and Butt and Diyar (1987) studied the seasonal changes in water temperature, depth, inorganic and organic suspended solids and dissolved organic matter in Warsak and Tanda reservoirs from the viewpoint of their suitability for fish culture. Ali (1980-81) reported on the hydrological data of eight lakes and reservoirs of Punjab. Although some reservoirs such as Chasma, Islam Headworks, Mangla, Marala, Qadirabad and Taunsa, were studied under a FAO Project (FC: TCP/4506, December 1985), the data have not yet been published.

The lakes of the lower Indus Plain (Sindh Province) such as Manchar, Haleji and Kinjhar, are all highly eutrophic and filled with aquatic vegetation (Nazneen et al. 1993c). Kinjhar Lake has been studied in some detail by Baqai et al. (1974a,b), Nazneen (1974), Nazneen and Bari (1979), Bari and Nazneen (1984) and Nazneen (1980). The seasonal distribution of phytoplankton species in the lake cannot be described in terms of four definite seasons in the tropical environment because gradual changes occur with the interaction of light and temperature regimes. The nutrient concentration in water remains high throughout the year in spite of their utilization by phytoplankton and aquatic weeds, except that phosphorus and nitrogen become limiting factors for phytoplankton for a short period during May when their concentration is abnormally low. Nazneen and Siddiqui (1976) have recorded higher counts of bacterial population in May than in December in Kinjhar Lake. High nitrate concentration coincided with phytoplankton bloom in Kinjhar Lake indicating the presence of nitrogen-fixing bacteria e.g., *Achromobacter spp., Azobacter agilis*. It has been suggested that a balance of nitrate and dissolved phosphorus is maintained by bacterial activities which in turn control the growth of phytoplankton. Importance of phytoplankton as fish food has been studied under field and laboratory conditions by Bari and Nazneen (1976, 1984), Nazneen (1976, 1977), Nazneen and Bari (1982) and Nazneen and Begum (1985). Leghari and Thebo (1983) have studied the epizoic algae from the molluscs of Kinjhar lake. Iqbal and Baqai (1975) observed a seasonal abundance of Cladocera in Kinjhar Lake, and correlated the peaks of zooplankton with the maximum production of phytoplankton. Further studies have been made on fish (Sufi 1957 and Siddiqui et al. 1973), molluscs (Nazneen and Begum 1992) and prawns (Zuberi 1990).

Several studies have also been made on the Haleji Lake; for example, hydrology (Baqai et al. 1974b), seasonal distribution of phytoplankton (Bari and Nazneen 1984), production of the bottom fauna (Saqib et al. 1991a,b). Water chemistry and biology of Manchar Lake, the largest natural lake in Sindh, have been studied by Baig and Khan (1976), Parashad and Mukerjee (1930), Sufi (1962), Hussain (1961) and Memon (1963). Some preliminary studies have been made also on other lakes; for example, water chemistry and gastropod fauna of Aziz Bhatti Lake, Karachi (Nazneen and Jamal 1987, Nazneen et al. 1992b, 1994), algal flora of Dilyar salt lake (Leghari et al. 1986), and fisheries potential of water bodies associated with Nara Canal (Khan 1962). Mahar (1991) used satellite remote sensing to assess the biomass and water resources in the Nagar Parkar area.

Like the rivers, both freshwater and saline lakes of Baluchistan have also received negligible attention. Some preliminary studies on the water quality characteristics and seasonal distribution of zooplankton of Hub Lake have been made by Iqbal (1986, 1989, 1990) and Iqbal et al. (1990).

Among standing water bodies the least investigated are the ponds. No significant limnological work has been done on any pond except those of Karim and Inglis (1971) on some artificial ponds, Ali et al. (1974, 1977b, 1978) on the effects of water quality on the organisms of ponds of Charharpal in Rawalpindi, ponds near Hiranpur (district Jhelum) and ponds of Fatehjung in Attock. These studies indicate organic pollution in the ponds of Fatehjung and Charharpal due to the presence of *Tubifex*, a number of beetles and *Hydrobaeuus* larvae. However, the pond of Hiranpur was affected by waterlogging and salinity as both the total hardness and chloride contents were high. Algal flora of some ponds has been surveyed by Leghari and Arbani (1984), Zahid and Sultana (1981), Aizaz and Farooqi (1972), Zahid and Farzana (1982) and Zahid (1989). Shameel and Butt (1984a) reported 49 species of Chroococcales and Nostocales from the ponds, ditches and wet soil of Karachi.

Water Pollution

Most of the permanent water bodies are heavily polluted from domestic and industrial wastes. The large lakes of Sindh are biologically polluted due to the luxuriant growth of macrophytes like *Hydrilla verticillata*, *Ceratophyllum*, *Hydrilla verticillata*, *Lemna*, *Myriophyllum*, *Nymphaea lotus*, *Potamogeton* and *Vallisneria spiralis*, etc.

The Malir, Layari and other small rivers are used to discharge the industrial and sewage effluents into the Arabian Sea. Before the expansion of Karachi metropolis, the river water was used for drinking water supply. The studies made on Layari River by Nazneen and Begum (1988, 1992) and Nazneen et al. (1990, 1993) indicate that the high level of pollution has caused serious damage to the biota as indicated by the total absence of bivalves. Similar pollution by industrial effluents has been examined in the streams of Sindh Industrial Trading Estate of Manghopir Area (Beg et al. 1978) and Kabul River (Ali et al. 1977).

In Punjab, the streams and small rivers are mainly polluted due to the agriculture, cattle and domestic wastes (Naik 1968). However, Ali et al. (1976, 1993) have observed a great reduction in the number of species in the Soan River and Leh Streams as compared with the unpolluted parts of these water bodies.

Saleem (1962a, 1980) has measured the relative chemical and biological parameters for the assessment of water pollution and has also observed the great fish mortality in the Soan River due to the severe pollution.

Applied Limnology

Beginning with the early work of Khan (1939, 1942 and 1945) and Malik (1940) in Punjab and N.W.F.P., studies on the culture of fishes has received much attention in Pakistan (Ahmad 1952, 1954a,b,c, 1962, 1977, 1980, H. Hussain 1959, Z. Hussain 1961, 1962, Hussain and Sufi 1962a,b, Saleem 1962b, A.G. Hussain 1965, Khan and Bhatti 1967, Ansari 1968, 1976, Khan 1968, Naveed 1968, 1973, Khan 1969, Naik 1969, 1971, 1972a,b, 1973, 1976, 1978, Islam and Akhtar 1970, Talbot 1970, Bari and Nazneen 1976, Zaman 1979, Nazneen and Begum 1981, Ataur-Rahim 1985, Afzal and Rab 1986, Khan 1987, Mirza and Omer 1987a, Mehboob et al. 1988, 1993, Salam and Janjua 1991, Bhatti et al. 1992, Naik and Mirza 1992, Salam and Khaliq 1992, Salam and Mahmood 1993, Salam et al. 1993, Afzal and Akhtar 1994, Bhutta et al. 1994a,b, Bhutta and Naeem 1994c and Nazneen et al. 1994. Pakistan Agricultural Research Council (PARC) has published a review on "Inland Fisheries and Aquaculture in Pakistan" with the efforts of Lone (1983). Water and Power Development Authority (WAPDA) established a Central Directorate of Fisheries in 1984 at Lahore to manage and develop the big water resources employing the latest technologies for the development of fisheries. This institution, with the collaboration of FAO, prepared a report (FC: TCP/4506 December 1985) for the utilization of big reservoirs for cultivation of fishes. According to this report, these reservoirs are not being utilized due to the lack of information regarding (i) limnological characteristics, (iii) dynamics of physico-chemical factors, (iv) fish food, (v) fisheries statistics, (vi) distribution, biology and ecology of major commercially exploitable fishes.

At the time of independence in 1947 the inland fishery production was based on the fish catch from the natural resources by the traditional methods by a limited number of fishermen. The total annual fish production in 1947 was 7050 MT out of which Sindh accounted 6000 MT. The private fish farming was conducted only by hobbyists. In 1974-75 there were only 10 private fish farms, this number increased to 50 in the year 1977-78 (National Commission on Agriculture Report 1988). However, with the approval of First Aquaculture Development Project in December 1979, the annual fish production increased from 46,320 MT in 1980 to 105,009 MT in 1989. The

Table 5. Number of fish ponds, their area and production (MT yr⁻¹) in various districts of Punjab Province

Table 5. Number of fish ponds, their area and production ($MT\ yr^{-1}$) in various districts of Punjab Province

District	Area of Fish Farms with Fishery Dept	Area of Village Ponds	Fish Culture in Private Sector			
			No. of fish farms	No. of fish ponds	Area	Total Fish Production
Lahore	7.9	6.9	114	164	159.0	1600
Sheikhpura	8.2	8.4	256	406	307.1	1650
Kasur	41.6	25.9	116	85	121.3	1950
Okara	161.8	10.5	117	149	79.7	1500
Gujranwala	40.8	43.3	412	475	352.0	2050
Hafizabad	-	-	106	142	152.0	-
Gujrat	12.1	10.5	148	187	115.7	1450
Sialkot	26.3	0.0	239	297	179.5	-
Narowal	26.3	0.0	85	101	48.5	1650
Rawalpindi	111.1	7.2	68	96	64.2	1450
Attock	661.2	14.5	49	138	226.8	1850
Jhelum	140.8	14.5	45	62	44.1	1200
Chakwal	484.4	0.0	31	32	28.5	700
Sargodha	2.0	10.5	57	67	122.8	1500
Khushab	186.1	0.0	13	13	12.9	1550
Mianwali	145.6	0.0	38	42	16.0	3280
Bhakar	0.0	0.0	22	22	9.8	1250
Faisalabad	3.6	10.9	88	91	62.3	1450
Jang	6.0	12.5	90	99	88.2	2850
Toba Tek sing	6.4	32.3	105	115	32.7	1250
Dera Ghazi Khan	24.6	0.0	106	119	73.3	1600
Muzaffargarh	31.7	0.0	118	144	82.6	3550
Liah	0.0	0.0	25	30	10.7	1500
Rajanpur	0.0	0.0	21	25	14.5	2000
Multan	0.0	3.2	106	120	49.3	1600
Lodharan	0.0	3.2	22	22	9.2	1600
Sahiwal	0.0	18.6	77	78	27.6	1350
Pakpattan	-	-	19	25	19.3	1350
Khanewal	7.6	5.2	80	84	37.0	1300
Vehari	0.0	4.0	80	84	21.3	1400
Bahawalpur	-	-	96	96	27.9	2250
Bahawalnagar	-	-	145	196	110.0	2300
Rahim Yar Khan	-	-	102	125	98.4	2050
Total	2136.1	242.0	3196	4031	2806.3	51000

fish production increased further after the implementation of Second Aquaculture Development Project in 1989 (Report of Sindh Statistics Bureau 1989). The number of fish farms increased greatly both in the public and private sectors. According to the

Inland Fisheries Department of Punjab, presently fish farms covering approximately 2205 hectares area are under the direct management of the Fisheries Department whereas village ponds occupy an area of about 242 hectares. Further, 3196 fish farms and 4031 fish ponds comprising a total area of 2806 ha are under private management (Table 5). In Sind, 1229 fish ponds with an approximate total area of 328,835 ha are managed by the Fisheries Department and 1350 fish ponds are in the private sector (Table 6). These aquaculture projects have also provided job opportunities for full-time fishermen who are engaged in different aspects of fishing. The local consumption of fish and shrimps is also increasing gradually (Handbook of Fisheries Statistics 1990). However, freshwater fish and shell fish are not being exported at present.

Table 6. Number and area of fish ponds utilized for aquaculture in Sindh

District	Managed by Fishery Department		Private Management
	Number	Area (ha)	Number
Hyderabad	84	244	120
Badin	92	3558	246
Thatta	304	3445	380
Sanghar	7	1048	8
Tharparkar	9	957	17
Dadu	208	836	24
Khairpur	36	16209	20
Naushero Feroz	-	-	26
Nawabshah	56	26352	20
Sukkur	77	2104	107
Larkana	284	249348	155
Shikarpur	47	681	79
Jacobabad	25	24013	148
Total	1229	328,835	1350

The programmes of aquaculture in Pakistan are generally managed by fisheries departments under control of Provincial Governments. The first carp hatchery in Pakistan was established in 1961 in Chhenawan (Punjab). Two other hatcheries were built later in 1978 at Faisalabad and Multan and there are seven fish hatcheries now in Punjab. Six of these are carp hatcheries and only one is a trout hatchery at Murree (Figure 4). In addition to these, eight mini hatcheries/nurseries are being developed in each division of the province to provide 15 million (Table 7) fish fry to 5592 fish farms (under the direct management), 592 village ponds and 7050 private fish farms. There are 20 fish nurseries where carp fry are kept after collecting them from natural resources and hatcheries exist to grow the fishes upto a desirable size. Some hatcheries and nurseries are also managed privately. The Fisheries Department in Punjab has also developed a Training Centre at Lahore which offers different long and short-term courses to the local fishermen for the propogation of fish production in the country.

The aquaculture started much later in Sindh compared to Punjab as the first hatchery was initiated here in 1979 at Chilya, Thatta district (Handbook of Fisheries Statistics of Pakistan 1990). The second hatchery was formed in Sukkur (Figure 4). Recently, three more hatcheries have been constructed in Thatta District privately. Presently Thatta and Sukkur fish hatcheries are working on fish propagation (Second Aquaculture Development Project 1989-1994). Inland Fisheries Department Sindh also offers short term courses to local fishermen once a year at Chilya Hatchery.

The Fisheries Department, N.W.F.P., concentrated mainly its efforts on the culture of brown and rainbow trout for sport fishing and established first trout hatchery in 1928 in Kaghan Valley. Four more hatcheries were developed in 1960 in Swat, one in Dir and two in Chitral Valley. The fish collected from these hatcheries are stocked in cold water streams in the mountainous region of the province. The sport fishing is licensed and the licenses are issued by the Provincial Fisheries Department on payment of a fee. Five thousand licenses were issued to trout fishermen in 1977-78 (Lone 1983) but this number must have increased since then.

Table 7. Production of fish in different hatcheries in Pakistan

Hatchery	Fish Production (million tons)
Lahore (Punjab)	5.0
Chhenawan (Punjab)	8.7
Rawalpindi (Punjab)	7.0
Faisalabad (Punjab)	7.1
Mianchannu (Punjab)	8.0
Bahawalpur (Punjab)	6.2
Jang & Kasur districts (Punjab)	4.5
Sukkur (Sindh)	3.1
Chilya (Sindh)	2.0
Hatcheries in N.W.F.P.	0.41 (trout)
	1.08 (carp)

The freshwater aquaculture is almost neglected in Baluchistan compared to other provinces and the traditional methods of fishing are still employed there. A hatchery has recently been developed at Hub Lake and may start operation during 1995.

Presently in Pakistan fish production depends both on the culture fisheries (Table 7) under aquaculture programmes and on the capture fisheries (Table 8) from the natural waterbodies. In hatcheries the artificial methods of breeding are employed to raise the fish and shell fish production. However, in comparison to fish culture shell fish culture is less developed. Some efforts have been made for the culture of prawns by Shakoor (1968) and Yaqoob (1980, 1994). Pakistan has received the technical assistance for the development of both marine and inland fisheries from UNDP, FAO and other bilateral sources. Asian Development Bank has also financed substantial capital to fisheries sector, particularly aquaculture development projects.

Table 8. Contribution (%) of fish species to total production in Punjab and Sindh

Species (common name)	Punjab	Sindh
Labeo rohita (rohu)	37.6	15.0
Catla catla (Theila)	13.8	15.0
Cirhinus mrigala (mori)	11.7	15.0
Ctenopharyngodon idella (Grass carp)	15.2	-
Hypopthalmichthys molitrix (Silver carp)	15.7	-
Hilsa ilisha	-	15.0
Catfish	-	35.0
Others	6.0	5.0

Conservation

The management of all the big water reservoirs is under the control of WAPDA in Pakistan. It is responsible for the storage of water, generation of electricity, fishing and for decreasing the silt load in the rivers to maintain permanent flow in the streams as it helps to increase the life span of reservoirs. Among the big lakes, Kinjhar and Haleji Lakes which are used to pump the drinking water to the people of Karachi, are under the control of KDA (Karachi Development Authority) and Government of Sindh. Fishing and boating are prohibited here under the Sindh Fisheries Ordinance 1980. Fishing is allowed in Kinjhar lake only under official permission. The other small lakes, dhands and lagoons are auctioned for fishing purposes by the Inland Department of Fisheries, Government of Sindh.

The first game sanctuary was formed on Haleji lake in 1971 by Wildlife and Management Board, under Section 15/1 of the West Pakistan Wildlife Protection Ordinance, 1959. Since then, some reservoirs as Chasma, Rasul, Taunsa, Tarbela and lakes as Khabbaki, Karral (Kharar), Namal in Punjab, Bright, Hadero and Haleji in Sindh, Tarbela reservoir in N.W.F.P. and Hub lake in Baluchistan have also been declared as Wildlife Sanctuaris under Section 14 of the Wildlife Protection Ordinance. In a synopsis of waterfowl of Pakistan, Ghalib (1988) has listed 119 wetlands. Out of these, nine wetlands namely, Lakes Drigh, Haleji, Kinjhar, and Khabbaki, Tanda, Kandar and Kheshki Reservoirs, Malugul Dhand, and Thanedar Wala Lagoon were designated as Wetlands of International Importance under the Ramsar Convention (Rao 1989) when Pakistan became a signatory to the Convention in 1976. Some of the important waterfowl which depend on these wetlands are: *Anas acuta, A. crecca, Anser platy-*

rhynchos, A. strepera, Athya ferina, A. fuligula, Fulica atria, Egretta gargella, E. alba, and *Oxyua leucocephala.*

A sanctuary has been developed for Indus Dolphin (*Platanista indica*) near Kashmore, along a 135 km stretch of Indus River from Sukkar Barrage to the Giddu Barrage. Department of Wildlife of Punjab has also proposed to develop another sanctuary for the Dolphins from the Taunsa Reservoir to the Kalabagh region and other wildlife sanctuaries on Qadirabad, Mangla and Rawal reservoirs.

The lakes which are under private control have no conservation status. Some of these like Tando Bogo Lake, Phoosna Lake, Charwo Lake, Khanjo/Kwaja Lake and Mahboobshah Lake are managed by their owners for fishing and waterfowl hunting.

INSTITUTIONAL FRAMEWORK

There are only a few institutions, mostly within the university system, where limnological studies are made and appropriate courses are offered. The most important of these are:

1. Limnology and Freshwater Biology Section, Department of Zoology, University of Karachi, Karachi 75270. Here Limnology is only taught as a special subject of Zoology to the M.Sc. students. During the period of two semester ten courses related to different topics of Limnology are offered. Thesis and short research projects are also provided to the capable students. Two Ph.D. and two M.Phil. teachers are under regular staff, while the services of teachers from Marine Zoology and Wildlife are also obtained to teach various courses. Since 1966, many students have obtained their M.Sc. degrees in Limnology, while three Ph.D. and three M.Phil. degrees have also been awarded from the same specialization.

2. Phycology Section, Department of Botany, University of Karachi, Karachi 75270. Since 1969, this group has been engaged in the study of systematics of freshwater algae, their cultivation and chemical characteristics.

3. Fishery Biology Section, Department of Zoology, Government College, Lahore, Pakistan. This is among the most active centers of fishery research in Pakistan. Systematics, food and feeding habits, and biology of fishes have been studied in detail, resulting in a book on freshwater fishes of Pakistan and many research papers and reports.

4. Department of Zoology, Gordon College, Rawalpindi. This group has concentrated on the systematics of freshwater organisms, food and feeding habits of fishes, and effects of pollution on water quality in the water bodies of Punjab and N.W.F.P. provinces.

5. Department of Freshwater Biology, University of Sindh (Jamshoro), Hyderabad. Freshwater fishes and algae are the focus of studies of this group. A book "An Introduction to Freshwater Fishery Biology" has recently been published (Sabbir 1993).

6. Department of Fisheries, University of Bhawalpur, Bhawalpur.

7. Freshwater Biology unit, Department of Zoology, University of Pesahwar, Peshawar. The studies of this group are mostly related to freshwater algae and water pollution.

8. Department of Inland Fisheries, Pakistan. The Department has established fish nurseries, hatcheries and fish tanks to increase the fish production from the inland water resources in all four Provinces of Pakistan.

9. Zoological Survey of Pakistan, Karachi. They have also published a few reports on freshwater fauna although their work is chiefly related to the marine fauna, avifauna and mammals.

Scientific Societies

Zoological Society of Pakistan
This society was established in 1970. At its zoological congress, papers are presented in all the major areas of Zoology and related disciplines e.g. Biochemistry, Cell Biology, Entomology and Pest Management, Environmental Biology, Fisheries, Freshwater and Marine Biology, Genetics, Microbiology, Molecular Biology, Palaeontology, Parasitology, Physiology, Toxicology and Wildlife. These papers are published in the annual proceedings. The society also publishes a quarterly *Pakistan Journal of Zoology*. The society has about 300 members all over the country. The recommendations of the society, made at the final session of the congress, are submitted to University Grants Commission (UGC), Islamabad, annually.

Scientific Society of Pakistan
The oldest society, founded in 1954, conducts an annual science conference in Urdu language. This conference is held in different cities of Pakistan to propagate science. Papers are presented in various fields of natural sciences. Society also publishes the papers of the conference in the special issue of its annual magazine *The Jadeed Science*. Presently society comprises about 1000 members throughout Pakistan.

Chemical Society of Pakistan
This society arranges annually a conference at different localities in Pakistan. The zoologists generally present their research papers in the environmental section of this conference.

Pakistan Botanical Society
The Botanical Society of Pakistan organizes an annual conference, the "Conference of Plant Scientists" at different places in the country. It publishes a biannual *The Pakistan Journal of Botany*, and comprises nearly 300 members all over the country.

Pakistan Aquatic Science Society (PASS)
It is in its initial stages of formation.

CONCLUSIONS

Pakistan has vast resources of freshwater, brackish water and salt water in the form of its drainage systems, irrigation canals, reservoirs, lakes, dhands, ponds and lagoons, but all these sources are not fully exploited for fishing purposes due to the lack of scientific knowledge and training facilities in Limnology. Some preliminary studies have been done on rivers, reservoirs and lakes. Mostly, systematic studies have been done on fishes, insects, benthic organisms, food and feeding habits of fishes.

Pakistan has a large network of Indus River and its tributaries but very little work has been done on the ecology of flora and fauna.

Pakistan is a tropical country, therefore, most of the lakes particularly in Sindh are infested with aquatic weeds. The growth of weeds is so thick in some areas that no fish can survive. Due to the high temperature and longer sunshine hours per day both algae and weeds grow very rapidly which naturally causes deterioration of water bodies. According to an estimate, 182,118 hectares of waters suffer from this menace. By eradicating water plants, the fish production can be increased manifold. Manchar, the oldest natural lake of Sindh, due to the same reasons is in senescence. No conservation measures have ever been taken to save this lake.

An Institute of Limnology with fully equipped labs and necessary library facilities is greatly needed to achieve the research goals in this field of science in Pakistan. In this part of the world the exchange of limnologists from other countries and short training programmes will also be helpful in promoting limnology.

REFERENCES

Afzal, M. and Rab, A. 1986. Induced spawning of major carps *Labeo rohita*, *Catla catla* and *Cirrhina mrigala*. Progress of Farming in Pakistan 6: 21-25.

Afzal, M. and Akhtar, N. 1994. Fish composition and balance in population of Rawal Dam reservoir of Pakistan. Pakistan Journal of Zoology 26(1): 51-56.

Ahmad, K.S. 1969. A Geography of Pakistan. Oxford University Press, Karachi. 262 pages.

Ahmad, M. 1952. Hilsa fishery in Sindh. Agriculure Pakistan 3: 54-57.

Ahmad, M.F., Khan, S.A. and Mirza, M.R. 1976. A checklist of the freshwater fishes of the Indus plain, Pakistan. Biologia (Pakistan) 22: 229-295.

Ahmad, N. 1952. Fish culture in Pakistan. Proceedings of 3rd Indo-Pacific Fisheries Council Symposium, Madras: 170-172.

Ahmad, N. 1954. Mortality of fish during cultural operations: causes and preservation. Pakistan Journal of Science 6: 102-106.

Ahmad, N. 1962. Tilapia culture in extensive water areas in West Pakistan. Agriculture Pakistan 13: 449-452.

Ahmad, N. 1977. Water hyacinth and fish farming. Pakistan Journal of Science 29: 55-59.

Ahmad, N. 1980. Aquaculture in Pakistan. Proceddings of Pakistan Congress of Zoology 1: 43-58.

Ahmad, N. and Khan, F. 1983. Dissolved oxygen and biochemical demand of Kabul River and industrial waste water of Nowshera Industrial Area. Physical Chemistry (Peshawar University) 3: 87-95.

Ahmad, N.D. and Mirza, M.R. 1963. Hill stream fishes of Kaghan and Swat. Scientist (Karachi) 6: 153-161.

Ahmad, N.D. and Mirza, M.R. 1964. Some fishes from Kurram River near Parachinar. Pakistan

Journal of Scientific Research 16: 44-46.

Ahmad, S. 1951. Climatic Regions of West Pakistan. Oxford University Press, Karachi. 262 pages.

Aizaz, I.R.and Farooqi, P.R. 1972. On the morphology and development of some Chloroococcales from Karachi. Pakistan Journal of Botany 4(1): 171-181.

Akhtar, S. and Ahmad, M. 1975. Productivity of bottom fauna and chemical nature of Haro River. Bulletin of Hydrobiological Research (Gordon College) 1(3): 17-24.

Akhtar, S. and Ali, S.R. 1976. Aquatic Lepidoptera of Pakistan. Bulletin of Hydrobiological Research (Gordon College) 1(11): 136-144.

Ali, S.A. 1993. An Introduction to Freshwater Fishery Biology. University Grants Commission, Islamabad, Pakistan. 269 pages.

Ali, S.R. 1966. Fishes of Wah streams and springs. Agriculture Pakistan 18 (4): 471-476.

Ali, S.R. 1968a. Bottom fauna of the streams and rivers of Hazara District after summer rains. Pakistan Journal of Scientific and Industrial Research 11 (2): 208-211.

Ali, S.R. 1968b. Bottom fauna of the streams of Kohat District and Kurram Agency after winter rains. Pakistan Journal of Scientific and Industrial Research 11 (4): 449-454.

Ali, S.R. 1980-81. Hydrological studies of the lakes of Punjab. Project Report, Pakistan Science Foundation, Islamabad. 16 pages.

Ali, S.R., Ahmad, M. and Akhtar, N. 1974. The productivity and chemical nature of three ponds of Churharpal, Rawalpindi. Bulletin of Hydrological Research (Gordon College) Series 1 (1): 1-4.

Ali, S.R., Ahmad, M. and Khatoon, S. 1978. Effect of pollution on the village ponds of Fatehjung, Attock. Bulletin of Hydrological Research (Gordon College) Series 1 (24-25): 505-510.

Ali, S.R., Ahmad, M. and Khatoon, S. 1993. Effect of pollution on the macrofauna of the Leh stream, Islamabad/Rawalpindi. Proceedings of Pakistan Congress of Zoology 13: 255-263.

Ali, S.R., Ahmad, M. and Qureshi, P.A. 1976a. Hydrological studies of two places in the Leh stream, Rawalpindi. Bulletin of Hydrological Research (Gordon College) Series 1 (12): 136-144.

Ali, S.R., Ahmad, M. and Qureshi, P.A. 1976b. Effects of pollution on physico-chemical nature and aquatic organisms of the Soan River, Rawalpindi, Bulletin of Hydrological Research (Gordon College) Series 1 (12): 161-186.

Ali, S.R., Ahmad, M. and Khalik, Z.U. 1977a. Effect of industrial wastes on water quality and organnisms of the Kabul river. Bulletin of Hydrological Research (Gordon College) Series 1 (14): 255-261.

Ali, S.R., Ahmad, M. and Qureshi, P.A. 1977b. Water quality and organisms in a pond near Hiranpur District, Jhelum. Bulletin of Hydrological Research (Gordon College) Series 1 (16): 308-313.

Ali, S.R., Ahmad, M., Mirza, M.R., Ansari, M.A.S. and Akhtar, N. 1980. Hydrological studies of the Indus River and its tributaries above and below the Tarbela Dam. Pakistan Journal of Scientific Studies 2 (1&2): 15-31.

Ali, S.R. and Khatoon, S. 1979. Hydrological studies of certain streams of Kohat District. Bulletin of Hydrological Research (Gordon College) Series 1 (26-27): 539-544.

Ansari, M.A.S. 1968. Fish culture in Mangla Reservoir. Indus Pakistan 10: 16-22.

Ansari, M.A.S. 1976. Possible effects of altered water regime on fish and fisheries of Tarbela lake, Pakistan. Proceedings of Indo-Pacific Fisheries Council Symposium 19: 1-5.

Arian, R. and Khuhawar, M.Y. 1982. Carbon transport in Indus River. Preliminary Results. Mitteilungen der Geologisch-Paläontologisches Institut, Universität Hamburg, SCOPE/UNEP Sonderband, Heft 52: 449-456.

Arora, G.L. 1931. Entomostraca (water fleas) of Lahore. Bulletin of the Department of Zoology, Punjab University, Lahore, 1: 61-100.

Ata-ur-Rahim, M. 1985. Trout culture in northern areas and Balistan. A Survey. Agriculture Pakistan 7(10): 33-37.

Aziz, K. and Jafri, M.H. 1975. Potamogetonaceae. Flora of West Pakistan 79: 1-11.

Baig, N.A. and Khan, M.Y. 1976. Biological and chemical conditions of Manchar Lake, Dadu (Sindh). Pakistan Journal of Science 28: 23.

Baqai, I.U., Zuberi, V.A. and Iqbal, M. 1974a. Limnological studies of Kalri Lake. Agriculture Pakistan 25(2): 119-135.

Baqai, I.U., Zuberi, V.A. and Iqbal, M. 1974b. Limnological studies of Haleji Lake. Agriculture Pakistan 25(4): 321-344.

Bari, G.A. and Nazneen, S. 1976. Comparison between the growth rate of herbivorous fish (Puntius conchonius Hamilton) and a carnivorous fish (Chanda nama Hamilton). Records of Zoological Survey of Pakistan 8(1&2): 69-72.

Bari, G.A. and Nazneen, S. 1984. Correlation of the elementary canal structures of some fishes of Haleji lake with their herbivorous nature of feeding. Pakistan Journal of Agricultural Research 6(2): 131-133.

Barlas, A. and Anjum, R. 1990. Some limnological studies on a spring joining Ramli stream. Pakistan Journal of Zoology 22(4): 99-400.

Bashir, K.A. and Mirza, M.R. 1975. Fishes of the Sutlej river in Lahore District, Pakistan with the description of a new subspecies. Bulletin of Hydrological Research (Gordon College) Series 1(9): 91-104.

Beg, M.M.A., Mehmood, S.N. and Yusafzai,A.H.K. 1978. Industrial effluents, their nature and disposal in Karachi region. Proceedings of Pakistan Academy of Science 15(1&2): 11-22.

Begum, F. and Nazneen, S. 1987. Biological studies of freshwater of Pakistan. Some freshwater bivalves of Sindh. Biologia (Pakistan) 33(1): 1-14.

Begum, F. and Nazneen, S. 1988. Systematic study of molluscan fauna of Layari River. IV. Neogastropoda (Stenoglossa). Journal of Science and Technology, University of Peshawar 12: 13-17.

Begum, F. and Nazneen, S. 1991. Systematic study of molluscan fauna of Layari River. Mesogastropoda (suborder Taenioglossa). Bangladesh Journal of Zoology 19(1): 107-121.

Begum, F. and Nazneen, S. 1992a. Systematic study of molluscan fauna of Layari River. Part 3. Mesogastropoda (suborder Aglossa). Pakistan Journal of Zoology 24(1): 145-152.

Begum, F. and Nazneen, S. 1992b. Systematic study of Layari River. Part 7. Palaeoheterondonta (Unionida: Bivalvia). Philippine Journal of Science 121(1): 53-64.

Begum, F. and Nazneen, S. 1992c. Systematic study of molluscan fauna of Layari River. Part 1. Archaeogastropoda (Aspidobranchia: Prosobranchia) from the Estuarine region. Pakistan Journal of Agricultural Research 35(10): 401-405.

Begum, F. and Nazneen, S. 1992d. Systematic study of molluscan fauna of Layari River. Part 5. Basommatophora (Pulmonata). Bangladesh Journal of Zoology 20(1): 135-141.

Begum, F. and Nazneen, S. 1992e. New records of bivalves from Pakistan (Layari River). Journal of Conchology 34(4): 258.

Begum, F. and Nazneen, S. 1995. Study of macroinvertebrate fauna of Malir River at Drigh road Region. Project. University Grants Commission. Karachi University, Karachi. Unpublished.

Bhatti, M.Z., Naik, I.U. and Mirza, Z.S. 1992. Induced spawning of grass carp (Ctenopharyngodon idella) using carp pituitary hormogenate and human chroionic gonadotrophin in Punjab. Proceedings of Pakistan Congress of Zoology 12: 429-433.

Bhuiyan, N.I. 1960. Hilsa fishery in River Indus. Agriculture in Pakistan 11: 511-519.

Bhutta, M.S., Salam, A. and Naeem, M. 1994a. Body composition of wild mahseer, Tor putitora in relation to body size and condition factor. Proceeding of Pakistan Congress of Zoology 14: (in Press).

Bhutta, M.S., Bokhari, Z.D. and Naeem, M. 1994b. Induced spawning of bighead carp Aristicthys nobilis at fish hatchery, Islamabad. Proceedings of Pakistan Congress of Zoology 14: (in Press).

Bhutta, M.S. and Naeem, M. 1994c. Breeding of carps with ovarim (LH-RH analogue) at fish hatchery Mian Channu. Proceedings of Pakistan Congress of Zoology 14: (in Press).

Bokhari, M.H. and Rana, M.A. 1979a. Aquatic plants in Iran and Pakistan. I. Potamogetonaceae. Biologia (Pakistan) 25 (1&2): 1-16.

Bokhari, M.H. and Rana, M.A. 1979b. Aquatic angiosperms of Iran and Pakistan. II. Ranunculaceae. Biologia (Pakistan) 25 (1&2): 87-102.

Butt, J.A., Akhunzada, I.R. and Khan, J. 1986. A limnological study of Warsak Dam water, North West Frontier Province. Proceedings of Pakistan Congress of Zoology 6: 169-178.

Butt, J.A. and Diyar, M. 1987. Limnological studyof Tanda Dam, Kohat, North West Frontier Province, Pakistan. Proceedings of Pakistan Congress of Zoology 7: 207-215.

Butt, J.A. and Shafiq, M.M. 1987. A study of the physical features of Sardaryab River near Charsadda, North West Frontier Province, Pakistan. 7th Pakistan Congress Zoology, pp. 199-205.

Day, F. 1875-1878. The Fishes of India; being a natural history of fishes known to inhabit the seas and freshwaters of India, Burma and Ceylon. William Dawson & Sons, London. Text and Atlas in 4 Parts. 20 + 778 pages, and 195 plates.

Faridi, M.A.F. 1971. Genera of freshwater algae of Pakistan and Azad Kashmir. Biologia (Pakistan) 16(2): 123-142.

Gazdar, M.N. 1987. Environmental crisis in Pakistan. The Open Press, Kuala Lumpur. 61 pages.

Ghalib, S.A., Perveen, S. and Hussain, S.A. 1988. Synopsis of the waterfowl of Pakistan. Records, Zoological Survey of Pakistan 12. Zoological Survey Department, Pakistan.

Hadi, S.F., Sarim, S.M. and Akhtar, S. 1988. The freshwater algae of Kabul River. Sarhad Journal of Agriculture 4(5): 671-680.

Handbook of Fisheries Statistics of Pakistan, 1986-89 (Published 1990). Marine Fisheries Department, Government of Pakistan, Fish Harbour, West Wharf, Karachi. 200 pages.

Hussain, A. and Shah, S.Z.A. 1960. Survey report of Swat River (Swat State) with special reference to trout culture. Agriculture in Pakistan 11: 301-310.

Hussain, A.G. 1965. Report on preliminary survey of trout fisheries of Gilgit and Baluchistan. Biologia (Pakistan) 16: 547-550.

Hussain, H. 1959. Desirability of culturing Tilapia mossambica Peters. Agriculture in Pakistan 10: 4-8.

Hussain, Z. 1961. Manchar Lake: how to improve and judiciously exploit it for stepping up for fish production. Agriculture Pakistan 12: 222-237.

Hussain, Z. 1962. Management and utilization of dams for fish production. Proceedings of Conference of Fish Officers, W. Pakistan: 31-38.

Hussain, S. 1973. Fish and fisheries of Lower Indus Basin (1966-67). Agriculture in Pakistan 24(3): 297-322.

Hussain, Z. and Sufi, S.M.K. 1962a. Hilsa fish and fish ladders at Gulam Muhammad Barrage on the River Indus, West Pakistan. Biologia (Pakistan) 13: 335-345.

Hussain, Z. and Sufi, S.M.K. 1962b. Biological and economical effects of barrages on Hilsa ilisha (Ham) and its fisheries in the Indus. Biologia (Pakistan) 13: 346-359.

Iqbal, M. 1986. Preliminary studies on limnology of Hub Lake. Journal of Science, University of Karachi 4(2): 53-61.

Iqbal, M. 1989. Studies on the ecology of some limnetic zooplankton of Hub Lake. Journal of Science, University of Karachi 17 (1&2): 151-159.

Iqbal, M. 1990. Cladocera of Hub Lake with notes on species and size composition. Sarhad Journal of Agriculture 6(1): 85-88.

Iqbal, M. and Baqai, I.U. 1975. Preliminary observations on seasonal abundance of genera in Kinjhar Lake with notes on phytoplankton production. Agriculture Pakistan 26(2): 251-257.

Iqbal, M. and Baqai, I.U. 1976. Seasonal abundance of cladoceran genera in Kinjhar Lake. Journal of Science, University of Karachi 3(1&2): 74-77.

Iqbal, M., Kazmi, A. and Shaukat, S. 1990. Multivariate analysis of seasonal variation of zooplankton composition of Hub Lake. Pakistan Journal of Zoology 22(2): 123-131.

Islam, A. and Akhtar, T. 1970. The effects of chorionic gonadotrophin on reproductive tract of female *Channa punctatus*. Biologia (Pakistan) 16: 59-66.

Islam, A. and Siddiqui, M.N. 1971. Fishes of Jhelum with some new records from Punjab. Biologia (Pakistan) 17: 27-44.

Javed, M.Y., Bhatti, N. and Mirza, M.R. 1993. Inland fisheries research in Pakistan. Fisheries Newsletter, Department of Fisheries, Government of Punjab, Lahore, Pakistan, 51 pages.

Karim, M.A. and Inglis, J.M. 1971. Limnological studies of the artificial ponds. Pakistan Journal Science and Industrial Research 23(1&2): 69-74.

Kawaja, M.A., Shah, J. and Zafrullah. 1990. Monitoring and pollution studies in some areas of Peshawar (N.W.F.P.) Proceedings of National Chemical Society, Pakistan 1: 161-163.

Khalil, Z.U. and Ahmad, M.1976. Algae of Wah streams. Bulletin of Hydrobiological Research (Gordon College) Series 2(4): 13-26.

Khan, A.B. and Bhatti, M.N. 1967. Induced spawning of major carps fishes of Pakistan. Agriculture Pakistan 18(4): 399-418.

Khan, H. 1939. Mortality of fish in tanks and ponds. Seasonal notes. Punjab Agricultural Department, Government of Pakistan 18: 49-50.

Khan, H. 1942. Spawning of carps and their spawning grounds. Seasonal notes. Punjab Agricultural Department, Government of Pakistan 18: 1-13.

Khan, H. 1945. Observations on the spawning behaviour of carp in the Punjab. In: Symposium on the factors influencing the spawning of Indian carps. Proceedings of the National Institute of Sciences, India 11: 315-320.

Khan, H. 1946. A fishery survey of river Indus. Journal of the Bombay Natural History Society 46: 529-535.

Khan, H.N. 1987. A note on the preliminary observation of intensive fish culture of local and exotic species. Bulletin, Fish Department, Government of Punjab, Article 1: 1-21.

Khan, M.A. 1969. Trout culture in Swat. Proceedings of Conference of Fish Officers, West Pakistan: 107-110.

Khan, M.D. and Dastgir, S.G. 1971. On the mollusca - gastropod fauna of Pakistan. Zoological Records of Pakistan: 17-0130.

Khan, M.D. and Dastgir, S.G. 1972. On the mollusca - pelecypoda fauna of Pakistan. Agricultural Research Council of Pakistan, Lahore. 206 pages.

Khan, M.N., Janjua and Naeem, M. 1992. Breeding of carps with ovaprim (LH-RH analogue) at fish hatchery Islamabad. Proceedings of Pakistan Congress of Zoology 12: 545-552.

Khan, M.Y. 1962. Fisheries potential of the Eastern Nara and its connected dhands. Agriculture in Pakistan 13: 410-426.

Khan, M.Y. 1968. Trout culture in Chitral. Proc. Conference Fish Officers. West Pakistan pp 117-129.

Khatoon, S. and Ali, S.R. 1975a. Aquatic Diptera of Pakistan. I. Bulletin of Hydrological Research (Gordon College) Series 1(2): 5-14.

Khatoon, S. and Ali, S.R. 1975b. Aquatic Hymenoptera of Pakistan. Bulletin of Hydrological Research (Gordon College) Series 1(5): 33-39.

Khatoon, S. and Ali, S.R. 1977a. Aquatic Coleoptera of Pakistan. 2. Bulletin of Hydrological Research (Gordon College) Series 1(14): 228-246.

Khatoon, S. and Ali, S.R. 1977b. Tricoptera (Caddis flies) of Pakistan. I. Bulletin of Hydrological Research (Gordon College) Series 1(18): 386-416.

Khatoon, S. and Ali, S.R. 1978. Aquatic Hemiptera of Pakistan. 2. Bulletin of Hydrological Research (Gordon College) Series 1 (22 & 23): 487-494.

Khuhawar, M.Y., Theobow, S.N. and Leghari, S.M. 1986. Physico-chemical investigations of hot Laki springs of Sind, Pakistan. Physical Chemistry (Peshawar University) 5: 43-49.

Leghari, S.M. and Thebo, S.N. 1983. Cyanophyta of hot springs at Laki Shah Sadar, Sindh, Pakistan. Sind University Research Journal (Science Series) 15: 147-150.

Leghari, S.M. and Thebo, S.N. 1984. Epizoic algae from the molluscs of the Kinjhar Lake and adjoining areas of river Indus. Sind University Research Journal (Science Series) 16(1): 89-91.

Leghari, S.M. and Arbani, S.N. 1984. Survey of freshwater algae from ponds and lakes of lower Sindh. Sindhological Studies (Summer): 68-91.

Leghari, S.M., Arbani, S.N. and Khuwar, M.Y. 1986. A preliminary survey of algae flora of Dhilyar salt lake, District Sanghar, Sindh, Pakistan, Sind University Research Journal (Science Series) 18: 179-184.

Lone, K.P. 1983. Inland fisheries and aquaculture in Pakistan. A review. Pakistan Agriculture Res. Council, Islamabad.

Mahar, A.W. 1991. An assessment of biomass, water and natural resources in the Nagar Parkar, test site of Thar region using satellite remote sensing data. Regional Seminar on Application of Remote Sensing Techniques to Landuse Planning and Environmental Surveying. Jointly organised by SUPARCO/ESCAP/UNDP-RRSP at Karachi, 21-27 October. 6 pages.

Mahboob, S., Sheri, A.N., Sial, A.B., Javed, M. and Afza, M. 1988. Seasonal changes in physico-chemical and planktonic life of commercial fish farm. Agriculture in Pakistan 25: 22-27.

Mahboob, S., Sheri, A.N. and Fauzia, T. 1993. Effect of physico-chemical factors on the dry weight of planktonic biomass in the brood stock pond. I. Fish seed hatchery Faisalabad. Pakistan Journal of Zoology 25(1): 15-18.

Majeed, M.A. 1935. The freshwater algae of Punjab. Part 1. Bacillariophyceae (Diatomaceae). Punjab University, Lahore. 44 pages.

Malik, G.M. 1940. The cases of mortality of brown trout Salmo trutto fario Linn. in the hatcheries of Hazara District, N.W.F.P. Journal of Research Society of Bengal 5: 7-18.

Menon, A.G.K. 1963. Manchar Lake, a study of fish industry. Pakistan Geological Review 18: 13-29.

Mirza, M.R. 1992. A note on the fishes of river Rakshan with the record of Garra rossica (Nikolsky) (Pisces, Cyprinidae). Pakistan Journal of Zoology 24 (1): 79.

Mirza, M.R. 1994. A note on the fishes of river Hingol, Pakistan. Pakistan Journal of Zoology 26 (2): 181.

Mirza, M.R., Abubakr, K. and Saeed, T.B. 1989. Fishes of the river Kurram in Afghanistan and Pakistan. Science International (Lahore) 1: 378-379.

Mirza, M.R., Abubakr, K. and Saeed, T.B. 1990. Freshwater Fishes of Pakistan (in Urdu). Urdu Science Board, Lahore. 125 pages.

Mirza, M.R. and Ahmad, I. 1987. Fishes of the river Jhelum in Sargodha District. Biologia (Pakistan) 33: 253-263.

Mirza, M.R. and Ahmad, I. 1988. Fishes of Chasma Lake. Biologia (Pakistan) 34: 45-47.

Mirza, M.R. and Alam, M.K. 1994. A checklist of the freshwater fishes of Pakistan and Azad Kashmir. Science International (Lahore) 6 (2): 187-189.

Mirza, M.R., Ali, I. and Javeed, M.N. 1993. A contribution to the fishes of the Kurram Agency, Pakistan. Punjab University Journal of Zoology 8: 37-40.

Mirza, M.R. and Hussain, S. 1988. Record of trout (Salmo sp.) from Mangla. Pakistan Journal of Zoology 19: 316.

Mirza, M.R. and Hussain, S. 1989. A checklist of the fishes of Mangla Lake, Pakistan. Journal of Scientific Khyber, Islamia College, University of Peshawar, Peshawar 2: 287-292.

Mirza, M.R., Javed, M.N. and Tariq, M.A. 1994. A note on the fish fauna of the river Zhob, Pakistan. Pakistan Journal of Zoology 26(2): 189.

Mirza, M.R. and Khan, A.J. 1994. Fishes of Marala, Sialkot District, Pakistan. Biologia (Pakistan) 34: 151-153.

Mirza, M.R. and Kashmiri, K.M. 1973. Fishes of the river Soan in Rawalpindi District. Biologia (Pakistan) 19: 61-182.

Mirza, M.R. and Mirza, N.A. 1988. A note on the fishes of Khanpur Lake, North West Frontier Province, Pakistan. Pakistan Journal of Zoology 19: 314-315.

Mirza, M.R. and Naik, I.U. 1967. A checklist of fishes from Bolan River. Pakistan Journal of Scientific & Industrial Research 19: 54-56.

Mirza, M.R. and Naik, I.U. 1972. Freshwater fishes of Baluchistan Province, Pakistan. Biologia (Pakistan) 18(2): 152-190.

Mirza, M.R. and Naik, I.U. 1973. Fishes of Kohat and adjoining areas. Pakistan Journal of Science 24: 253-254.

Mirza, Z.S., Naik, I.U., Bhatti, M.Z. 1992. Induced spawning of major carps using carp pituitary and human chorionic gonadotrophin in Punjab (Pakistan). Proceedings of Pakistan Congress of Zoology 12: 423-428.

Mirza, M.R. and Omer, T. 1974. A note on the fisheries of the River Haro with record of *Tor mosal* (Hamilton) from Pakistan. Pakistan Journal of Zoology 6: 193-194.

Mirza, M.R. and Omer, T. 1987. Trout culture in northern areas. Agriculture Pakistan 9: 41-43.

Mirza, M.R. and Saboohi, S.A. 1990. A note on the freshwater fishes of river Dasht with the description of *Tariqi labeo* a new subgenus (Pisces, Cyprinidae). Pakistan Journal of Zoology 22: 405-406.

Muhammad, M.J. 1995. Textural and compositional variations along an ephemeral river, Malir, Sindh. Karachi University Journal of Science 23: (in press).

Naik, I.U. 1968. Fish and water pollution. Pakistan Ind. Fish. Int. 5: 24-29.

Naik, I.U. 1969. Culture of *Tilapia mossambica* Peters in Peshawar. Pakistan Journal of Science 21: 151.

Naik, I.U. 1971. Tilapia and its culture in saline water areas. Agriculture Pakistan 22: 81-91.

Naik, I.U. 1972a. Introducing grass carp *Ctenopharygodon idella* (C. & V.) in Pakistan. Pakistan Journal of Science 24 (1-2): 45-52.

Naik, I.U. 1972b. Water hyacinth and its control in West Pakistan. Pakistan Journal of Science 24 (1-2): 25-28.

Naik, I.U. 1973. Studies of *Tilapia mossambica* Peters in Pakistan. Agriculture Pakistan 4 (1): 47-76.

Naik, I.U. 1976. A review on the induced spawning of major carps in Pakistan. Pakistan Journal of Scientific Research 28: 6-12.

Naik, I.U. 1978. Analysis of induced spawning experiments on *Labeo rohita* and *Cirrhina mrigala* during the year 1976 at fish and seed hatchery, Chhenawan. Agriculture Pakistan 29: 20-23.

Naik, I.U. 1986. Inland fisheries and aquaculture in Pakistan: review of the progress and new activities. Paper presented at FAO/Indo-Pacific Fisheries Council Workshops on strategies for the management of Fisheries and Aquaculture in Mangrove Ecosystems. Bangkok, Thailand, 23-25 June 1986.

Naik, I.U. and Mirza, Z.S. 1992. Use of Ovaprim-C in induced spawning of Indian major carps in Punjab, Pakistan. Proceedings of Pakistan Congress of Zoology 12: 411-416.

Naveed, S.A. 1968. Introduction to trout in Chitral. Pakistan Journal of Science 20: 34-41.

Naveed, S.A. 1973. Trout in North West Frontier Province. Pakistan Journal of Forestry 23: 344-353.

Nazneen, S. 1974. Seasonal distribution of phytoplankton in Kinjhar Lake. Pakistan Journal of Botany 6: 69-82.

Nazneen, S. 1976. Feeding effects of phytoplankton on the growth of fish. Bulletin of Hydrological Research (Gordon College) Series 1(3): 200-203.

Nazneen, S. 1977. Study of phytoplankton composition in the gut contents of some fishes from Kinjhar Lake. Pakistan Journal of Scientific & Industrial Research 20 (6): 359-361.

Nazneen, S. 1980. Influence of hydrological factors on the seasonal abundance of phytoplankton in Kinjhar Lake. Internationale Revue der gesamten Hydrobiologie 65 (2): 269-282.

Nazneen, S., Bano, F. and Begum, F. 1994. Estimation of food consumption rates in *Ziphophorus helleri*. Proceedings of Pakistan Congress of Zoology 14: (in press).

Nazneen, S. and Bari, G.A. 1979. Systematic account of the diatoms of family Epithemaceae. Biologia (Pakistan) 25: 1-5.

Nazneen, S. and Bari, G.A. 1982. Gut contents of Haleji Lake fishes for determination of the importance of phytoplankton as fish food. Pakistan Journal of Agricultural Research 13 (3): 156-169.

Nazneen, S. and Bari, G.A. 1984. Seasonal distribution of phytoplankton in Haleji Lake. Agriculture Pakistan 5 (3): 183-189.

Nazneen, S., Basit, M.A. and Begum, F. 1990. Chemical analysis of Layari river water by titrimetric method and atomic absorption spectrometry. Proceedings, National Chemical Conference, Chemical Society of Pakistan, Karachi 2: 166-168.

Nazneen, S. and Begum, F. 1981. Salinity tolerance in some freshwater fishes. Biologia (Pakistan) 27 (1): 33-38.

Nazneen, S. and Begum, F. 1985. Effects of various diets on the growth of *Tilapia* fish. Pakistan Journal of Agricultural Research 6 (2): 131-133.

Nazneen, S. and Begum, F. 1988. Hydrological study of Layari River. Pakistan Journal of Scientific & Industrial Research 31(1): 26-29.

Nazneen, S. and Begum, F. 1992. Seasonal distribution of molluscan fauna of Kinjhar Lake. Pakistan Journal of Zoology 24(2): 1111175-177.

Nazneen, S. and Begum, F. 1993a. A bibliography of the limnological studies in Pakistan. University Day Special Publication, Zoology Department, Karachi. 27 pages.

Nazneen, S. and Begum, F. 1993b. A study of the food habits of fishes of the Hub River, Baluchistan. Phillipine Journal of Science 122(2): 179-191.

Nazneen, S. and Begum, F. 1994. Distribution of molluscs in Layari River (Sindh), Pakistan. Hydrobiologia 273(2): 95-100.

Nazneen, S., Begum, F. and Erum, N. 1994. Seasonal abundance and feeding habit of gastropods of Hub River. Journal of Scientific Khyber, Islamia College, University of Peshawar 7: 93-97.

Nazneen, S., Begum, F., Erum, N. and Jahan, N. 1992. Study of jaws and radula of some freshwater gastropods in relation to their feeding habits. Proceedings of Pakistan Congress of Zoology 12: 589-598.

Nazneen, S., Begum, F., Hasan, S.K. and Basit, M.A. 1993. Chemical constituents as pollution indicators in Kinjhar Lake and Layari River. Proceedings of Pakistan Congress of Zoology 13: 565-571.

Nazneen, S., Begum, F. and Jahan, N. 1994c. A survey of gastropods of Aziz Bhatti Lake and their feeding habits. Journal of Agriculture, N.W.F.P., Peshawar 10(1): 87-90.

Nazneen, S. and Iqbal, M.A. 1986. Systematic studies of the fishes of Hub river Baluchistan. Journal of Pure and Applied Science 5 (2): 73-78.

Nazneen, S. and Jamal, G. 1987. Physico-chemical study of Aziz Bhatti Lake. Pakistan Journal of Scientific & Industrial Research 30 (2): 901-904.

Nazneen, S., Khan, M.S.A. and Iqbal, M.A.1989. A note on the fishes of Porali river (Baluchistan). Pakistan Journal of Science International, Lahore 1 (5): 325-326.

Nazneen, S. and Saeed, B.1987. A note on the fishes of Khadeji river. Journal of Pure and Applied Science 6 (1): 55.

Nazneen, S. and Siddiqui, P.A. 1976. Seasonal abundance of bacterial isolates and their influence on the phytoplankton distribution in Kinjhar Lake. Karachi University Journal of Science 4 (1-2): 40-45.

Niamatullah, M.A., Farooqi, M.A. and Mohsin, S.I. 1992. Preliminary structural studies around Hanna Lake area, Quetta. Karachi University of Journal of Science 20 (1-2): 85-90.

Parashad, B. and Mukherjee, D.D. 1930. On the fishes of Manchar Lake (Sindh). Journal of the Bombay Natural History Society 34: 164-169.

Pithawala, M. 1959. A Physical and Economic Geography of Sindh. Sindhi Adabi Board, Sindh. 389 pages.

Qureshi, M.R. 1965. Common Freshwater Fishes of Pakistan. Report FACRP 19. Food and Agricultural Research Council, Government of Pakistan, Islamabad. 61 pages.

Qureshi, P.A. 1979. Seasonal fluctuations of algal flora in Wah streams. Bulletin of Hydrological Research (Gordon College) Series 2 (5): 34-41.

Qureshi, M.A., Rafiq, M., Awan, F.A. and Mirza, M.R. 1988. Fishes of the Haro River, Pakistan. Biologia (Pakistan) 34: 179-191.

Rao, A.L. 1989. Pakistan. pp. 295-265, In: Scott, D.A. (Compiler) Directory of Asian Wetlands. World Conservation Union (IUCN), Gland, Switzerland.

Razaq, A. and Mirza, M.R. 1992. Some new records of fishes from the river Soan. Proceedings of Pakistan Congress of Zoology 12: 291-293.

Report of the National Commission on Agriculture. 1988. Ministry of Food and Agriculture, Government of Pakistan, Islamabad.

Report of the Sindh Statistics Bureau, 1989. Karachi. 112 pages.

Sajid, A.S. 1962. Occurrence of the fish Pristis microdon Latham in River Indus near Hyderabad, West Pakistan. Agriculture in Pakistan 13: 547-548.

Salam, A. and Janjuia, M.Y. 1991. Morphometric studies in relation to body size of Farmed rohu, Labeo rohita: A culturable major carp from Multan. Journal of Research Science B.Z. University Multan, Pakistan 3: 59-63.

Salam, A. and Khaliq, R. 1992. Weight-length and condition factor relationship of a farmed mrigal, Cirrhinus mrigala. Journal of Research Science, Bahauddin Zakaria University, Multan, Pakistan 4: 39-43.

Salam, A. and Mohamood, J.A. 1993. Weight-length and condition factor relationship of a freshwater under yearling wild, Catla catla (Hamilton), From River Chenab (Multan), Pakistan Journal of Zoology 25: 127-130.

Salam, A., Mahmood, J.A. and Butt, A.N. 1993. Studies on the biology of freshwater catfishes of Multan: Weight-length relationship of Wallago attu (Schneider) from River Chenab. Pakistan Journal of Zoology 25: 195-199.

Saleem, A. 1962a. Preliminary study on the pollution and causes of mortality of fish in the Soan river. Pakistan Journal of Zoology 13: 551-556.

Saleem, A. 1962b. Water quality criteria for fish culture. Agriculture Pakistan 13: 575-581.

Saleem, A. 1980. The relative chemical parameters and relative biological parameters (RCP+RBP) in the assessment of water pollution. Bulletin of Hydrological Research (Gordon College) Series 28-29: 563-569.

Saqib, T.A., Siddiqui, P.A. and Qureshi, W.M. 1991a. Studies on the productivity of bottom fauna in Kinjhar Lake: an index of eutrophy. Zoologica Pakistan 2(1): 39-42.

Saqib, T.A., Siddiqui, P.A. and Qureshi, W.M. 1991b. Studies on the productivity of bottom fauna in Haleji Lake, Sindh, Pakistan. Zoologica Pakistan 2(1): 51-58.

Sarim, F.M. and Faridi, M.A. 1976. Closterium in Peshawar valley. Pakistan Journal of Botany 8(2): 121-189.

Sarim, F.M. and Ali, Q. 1981. Some algae from the Kabul river. Biologia (Pakistan) 27: 199-201.

Shakoor, A. 1968. Investigation report II. Freshwater prawns of West Pakistan. Directorate of Fisheries, West Pakistan, Lahore. 9 pages.

Shameel, M. 1980. Contributions to Ulothrix (Chlorophyceae) from Swat, Pakistan. Nova Hedwigia 30 (4): 377-384.

Shameel, S. and Butt, N.I. 1984a. On the occurrence of Cyanophyta from Karachi, Pakistan. Pakistan Journal of Botany 16(1): 75-79.

Shameel, S. and Butt, N.I. 1984b. Observations on Ulothrix shameelii Faridi (Chlorophyta). Pakistan Journal of Botany 16(2): 275-277.

Shamim, A. and Ahmad, M. 1975. Productivity of bottom fauna and chemical natural of Haro River. Bulletin of Hydrological Research (Gordon College) Series 1 (3): 17-24.

Shamshad, K.M. 1980. The Meteorology of Pakistan. Royal Book Company, Lahore.

Siddiqui, N.M. 1966. A list of fishes found in river Jhelum. Pakistan Journal of Science 18: 216.

Siddiqui, P.A., Bagai, I.U. and Iqbal, M. 1973. A checklist of fishes of Kinjhar Lake with notes on environmental conditions and fisheries potential. Agriculture Pakistan 24 (2): 201-220.

Siddiqui, S.A. 1962. River Bolan. Agriculture Pakistan 13 (2): 306-312.

Snelgrov, A.K. 1967. Geohydrology of the Indus River. Sindh University Press, Sindh.

Sufi, S.M.K. 1957. Fish fauna of Kinjhar Lake (West Pakistan) with an account of major fishing implement employed by the local fishermen. Agriculture Pakistan 8: 208-229.

Sufi, S.M.K. 1962. Checklist of the fishes of Manchar Lake (West Pakistan) with a note on the effect of the Sukkar Barrage and canalization of the feeding channels of the fish fauna of the Lake. Agriculture Pakistan 13 (20): 499-503.

Talbot, g.B. 1970. Report to the Government of Pakistant on Hilsa fishery and fish passes. FAO Report No.1008: 1-12.

Thomas, R.H. 1855. Manchar Lake, Memoirs of Sindh. pp. 391-393, In: Siddiqui, M.H. (Editor). 1979. The Discovery of Sindh. Karim Sons, Karachi.

Yaqoob, M. 1980. Reasons of an economic freshwater prawn *Macrobrachium lamarrei* H.M. Edwards under laboratory conditions (research note). Pakistan Journal of Agricultural Research 1 (2): 139-141.

Yaqoob, M. 1994). Pond culture of freshwater prawn, *Macrobrachium malcolomsonii* (Milne-Edwards, 1844) in Pakistan. Pakistan Journal of Zoology 26 (3): 243-247.

Zahid, P.B. and Sultana, T. 1981. Survey of Phytoplankton and selection of resistant varieties around Sindh area. Pakistan Journal of Scientific & Industrial Research 24 (3): 109-110.

Zahid, P.B. and Farzana, A. 1982. Culture collection of freshwater algae at the Department of Botany, University of Karachi. Biologia (Pakistan) 27 (1): 61-74.

Zahid, P.B. 1989. Studies of thermophilic algae at Karachi. Journal of Scientific Khyber, Islamia College, University of Peshawar 2 (2): 157-159.

Zaman, M.S.U. 1979. Culture of common carp (*Cyprinus carpio* Linnaeus) in the Punjab. Pakistan Journal of Science 31 (1-2): 60-63.

Zuberi, V.V. 1990. Kinjhar lake and its prawns (In Urdu). National Language Authority, Islamabad, Pakistan. 118 pages.